THE IMPOSSIBLE MOCK ORANGE TRIAL

ISBN   (Paperback)   978-1-7357825-1-5
ISBN (Hardback)   978-1-7357825-2-2

Table of Contents

PREFACE   5

CHAPTER ONE   7

CHAPTER TWO   25

CHAPTER THREE   35

CHAPTER FOUR   53

CHAPTER FIVE   67

CHAPTER SIX   79

CHAPTER SEVEN   91

CHAPTER EIGHT   101

CHAPTER NINE   117

CHAPTER TEN   135

CHAPTER ELEVEN   147

CHAPTER TWELVE   159

CHAPTER THIRTEEN   171

CHAPTER FOURTEEN   185

CHAPTER FIFTEEN   193

CHAPTER SIXTEEN   207

CHAPTER SEVENTEEN   227

CHAPTER EIGHTEEN	241
CHAPTER NINETEEN	247
CHAPTER TWENTY	263
CHAPTER TWENTY-ONE	277
CHAPTER TWENTY-TWO	289
CHAPTER TWENTY-THREE	299
CHAPTER TWENTY-FOUR	325
CHAPTER TWENTY-FIVE	339
CHAPTER TWENTY-SIX	355
CHAPTER TWENTY-SEVEN	371
CHAPTER TWENTY-EIGHT	397
CHAPTER TWENTY-NINE	421
CHAPTER THIRTY	441
CHAPTER THIRTY-ONE	461
CHAPTER THIRTY-TWO	491
CHAPTER THIRTY-THREE	503
CHAPTER THIRTY-FOUR	521
CHAPTER THIRTY-FIVE	535
CHAPTER THIRTY-SIX	555
CHAPTER THIRTY-SEVEN	565
CHAPTER THIRTY-EIGHT	579
CHAPTER THIRTY-NINE	601

PREFACE

Ted Born and a young untested associate were called upon to defend a tough - seemingly impossible lawsuit in one of the most challenging county courts in the United States. The facts looked bad: the client was a tire manufacturer of a tire that blew out, followed by a vehicular crash resulting in a child's death, a brain injury for another child and other serious injuries. The dead and injured were all African American residents of a county where juries were all or mostly African Americans, with a history of rendering verdicts in generally millions of dollars in favor of local residents against big out-of-state corporations, even in minor cases. The case leads them through a labyrinth of mystery and intrigue they could not have imagined, with a conclusion rocking all precedents.

This is a work of fiction exploring the actions and imagined mental processes of fictional characters whose minds and interactions are laid bare as the story unfolds.

The result is tense and high-octane drama, reason enough to offer it in these pages. But there is more. The story explosively confronts the meaning of justice in the context of right-and-wrong, corporate and personal responsibilities, sympathy and objectivity, racial relations, and our judicial system as a means of resolving countervailing positions with their heavy emotional baggage.

It also dissects the moral character of jurors thrust, through no choice of their own, into a web of competing angels and demons that vie to influence their verdict - where ultimate neutrality is not an option. This work of fiction does not purport to reflect any real case, although it draws upon elements of a lifetime of actual litigation experience. None of the characters represent any particular persons, living or dead. It is written to entertain and engage the reader, while illuminating issues critical to justice in our courts, and what civil justice really means.

CHAPTER ONE

THE DAY TRIP

The children screamed, and Bess Johnson's eyes were disks of uncomprehending glass, her fists clenched ineffectively about a steerless wheel in a van careening leftward across the country road. Doretta Anchrum, buckled in the front passenger seat, gasped as a powerful inertial force threw her to the side, while behind her young Katyna Johnson desperately reached forward and grabbed at Anchrum's seat, hugging it and peering with helpless horror around the side. Sarena Miller, behind the driver, dropped a new pink dress from the fingers of her small hands and screamed all the more, her face the dark shadow of a child's terrifying nightmare, as though her four-year-old eyes had fixed upon a life-snatching demon. Jimason Anchrum, in rear center, shrieked and flung one

7

hand wildly in search of something more substantial than the corded piping of the seat cover he grabbed with the other. The van seemed drawn swiftly and almost magnetically to a large tree off the shoulder on the opposite side of the road.

A thunderous sound and a seismic shock reverberated in the van as Bess Johnson's face and body slammed against the steering wheel, bounced back against her seat, hit the steering wheel again, then crumpled onto the floor-board area, and Sarena became a small human missile launched head-on into an impossibly small wedge of space between front door and front seat, a space from which she did not bounce back. Jimason found daylight between the two front seats but struck the center console with massive force as his young body hurtled frontward and fell limp. Katyna took a compression jolt against the front seat she clung to, and she was then thrown backward. It had all happened in a matter of six fate determinative seconds in the rural countryside of South Carolina.

The day had dawned peacefully that morning, the early light shining faintly with an amber glow through Bess Johnson's shaded window. The glow brightened, fill-ing the room with the certainty of a new day only partly restrained by the muting of a translucent shade, causing Bess to open defensively blinking eyes that instinctively looked at the bedside clock.

She did not immediately stir from her iron-posted bed with its cheap box springs and thin, sagging mattress. This was Saturday, a break from work at Whitesell

Packing Company, the slaughterhouse, and Bess Johnson could indulge herself a little longer than usual, lying in bed quietly, half awake, half dreaming. At rare times when she could claim a few quiet moments, as now, Bess sometimes liked to imagine her small, grim house magically transformed into a Hollywood star's mansion, with canopied mahogany beds and gorgeous rugs and curtains, chandeliers and silk covered furniture. Servants would bring her breakfast in bed, and she could spend the morning at the beauty parlor getting the full hair and beauty treatment.

She smiled as she thought fleetingly of this fantasy, this narcotic dose so vital to her defenses against a real world. Then the smile faded with the reverie as her eyes, her logic, overcame her imagination. "No, ain't meant for me, just a dream, hard enough to survive, no matter what. Somebody, somewhere'll hit the lottery, but not me."

Bess Johnson's house, a rectangular raised cottage, crowned with laterally slanting wings of a tin roof, was set some fifty yards back from the road and rested on irregularly leaning intermittent brick pillars joined by broken latticework. An open porch commanded the front, sheltered by an overhang supported by spindle posts. Eaves were rotting, porch boards much patched and squeaky, where they were in place at all, and traces of bilious green paint, of a type popular some seventy years earlier in tenant farmhouses, could be detected on the gray-weathered woodwork.

Bess thought of the day before her, and remembered her ten o'clock appointment with Dr. Elias Jones, a dentist who saw patients until noon on Saturdays. *This* was reality, a dreaded dentist's chair, not a pleasant morning at a beauty shop, she thought. She had no car since her last one hit a cow crossing the road and, while Bess had regular rides into work weekdays, it was a hassle to get around on weekends.

Maybe, she thought, she could borrow a car today from her cousin Dash, who had nice ones; really, they were too nice. He did not trust Bess with his cars, and actually Bess did not trust herself with them either, and besides, Dash was a big-shot drug dealer. It would be just her luck to be stopped by the cops in Columbia and have them find some of Dash's cocaine or crack in the car.

No, better her uncle Sam, Sheriff of Phoenix County, South Carolina, and a very important person, tall, muscular and handsome, a rising star, generous and hard-working, even having a part-time job making deliveries for a pharmacy. The whole family was proud of Sam, they looked up to him, almost everybody in Phoenix County looked up to him.

Sam had always been good to Bess, had never refused her, and in fact, Bess was getting her dental work done on Sam's Sheriff Department insurance. She simply told the dentist her name was Cornelia Johnson, Sam's wife, and showed them Sam's insurance card, readily accommodating her ethics to the advantage of the insurance that was not hers, all perfectly natural and reasonable, the pragmatic ethics of coping in a harsh and unforgiving world.

She rose from the bed and raised the shade at her solitary window, pausing to observe how the sun had fought past gray early morning clouds on the horizon, contending now with schools of white cumulus clouds swimming through a fluid blue March sky. A nice day, she said to herself, a day to do something more than go to the dentist, *especially* something to do to reward herself as compensation for having to endure stainless steel tools in her mouth.

The children had not yet roused themselves, Bess mentally noted as she went to the bathroom mirror and began removing the curlers from her jet hair, combing out a gentle curl. As she combed, Bess surveyed her face, frowning with regret and resignation at the leathery texture of her brown skin, beginning to show the lines of lost youth among the contours of her face. She parted her lips to see her inside hollow cheeks, halfway dreaming in her early wakefulness that she might see a miraculous restoration of a full set of once pearly teeth. She had five yellowed hulls left on top, two of which would be pulled today, and nine on the bottom. Soon there would be a full plate on top, a partial plate below, a prospect she dreaded without conscious regret for the lack of care which caused it. This is the way things are, that's all.

Bess dressed and walked to the room where the children still slept. All three children - two boys and their younger sister - shared the only other bedroom in the home. "Katyna," she said to the girl gently, "start waking up, now. I want you to go to town with me. I gotta see the dentist. Come on now and wake up, Katyna. Let your brothers sleep some more. I'm go'n be fixing a little breakfast. You go on and get up now, 'cause Easter's coming. I'm go'n get you some Easter clothes. How'd you like that?"

Katyna was mostly unmoved until the words "Easter clothes" were mentioned. Then she raised herself, reached out her arms and hugged her mother who leaned toward her: "I love you, mama."

They held the embrace as Bess whispered, "And I might call up Coz'n Agnes and see if Sarena can come with us. How's that? That child won't get no Easter clothes 'less I get 'em for her."

"Yeah, mama, let's do." Bess gently pulled her up. "But you go'n get me some'n nicer'n Sarena, ain't you, mama?"

"Why, sure, honey," her mother smiled warmly, "you my own, but you both go'n look real nice. Now get yourself ready, and I'll fix us some breakfast. Not sure I'll eat much. Nothin' tastes good to me anymore. Better enjoy good food while you're still young."

Bess called Sam Johnson about the car and got Cornelia on the telephone: "Cornelia, I've got this dentist appointment this morning, don't you know, Dr. Jones. I'm wond'rin if you got a car I could borrow. I thought maybe Sam'd be using his Sheriff's car...."

Cornelia interrupted, "Let me ask Sam, Bess. - Hey, Sam, can you hear me? Bess needs to borrow a car -"

CHAPTER ONE

Sam was in the back of the house, shaving. "What's that?" he said, stepping out of the bathroom, razor in hand. Cornelia repeated. "Well," said Sam, "tell her I reckon she can use the van - the Logos. What's she need it for?"

"She's got to go see the dentist," Cornelia answered.

"On Saturday? Well, anyway, tell her she can have it, but be careful. And she'll have to come get it. I gotta get to the Sheriff's office."

"Okay, Bess, he says you can use the van. You mind walkin' over here?" Cornelia asked.

"No. I walk all the time. That ain't far."

With transportation secured, Bess got out the skillet, began cooking bacon, cracked some eggs to scramble in the bacon grease, and boiled some water for the instant grits. The telephone rang. It was her friend Doretta Anchrum, calling for no reason at all, except she knew this was Saturday and Bess was off work. "Doretta, I really can't talk much right now. I'm fixing breakfast for me and Katyna. Boys can get what they want when they get up. I gotta go to Columbia to the dentist, maybe do a little shoppin'." Then it occurred to her that Doretta might like to go to Columbia for the day, as Doretta also had no car and had never learned to drive. "How'd you like to go with me? We've got Sam's car. I might be taking Sarena - you know, my little niece Sarena Miller - but I think there's plenty of room."

The delighted Doretta had no job and no husband, but somehow she endured. "Sure, Bess, I'd love to go.

13

But could I bring Jimason with me? I need to get him some things." Jimason Anchrum was Doretta's eleven-year-old son.

"Yeah, that's fine, Doretta. Bring him, too. I'm about to burn this bacon. Gotta go, but I'll be by to pick you up in about, say, forty-five minutes." To herself she was thinking, "I like Doretta, she's good company, just to talk to. Not sure she knows how busy I stay, her not having no job or nothin'."

Bess removed the well-cooked bacon from the skillet, dropped the eggs into hot bacon grease, and began scrambling. Katyna appeared and casually mentioned that her brother Will was getting out of bed. "Well, he'll have to fix his own. Oh, well, maybe I'll put in some more eggs and grits, but I gotta hurry. I ain't never called Agnes yet." She began helping a plate for Katyna. "Get yourself some butter for the grits. There's salt and pepper on the table. Go ahead and eat, and I'll come in a minute. Gotta call Agnes."

Bess called Agnes and reminded her Bess had promised to outfit Sarena in Easter clothes. "I'm gonna make this day trip to Columbia, Agnes. Yeah, gotta see the dentist... . Yeah, he sees patients on Saturday mornings. Shouldn't take me too long... . Yeah, I prob'ly won't be feelin so good, but it'll cheer me up to see Sarena in her Easter outfit.... Well, I'd like for you to come along too, but, see, Doretta called and she wants to come, and I've got Sam's van, but I don't think it'll hold three grownups and the chil'ren. Just trust me, she'll be beautiful in her outfit."

After breakfast, Bess Johnson and Katyna began to walk to Sam Johnson's house, the mother bidding son Will to watch after the younger boy while she and Katyna were away. Bess looked back at her house when she reached the road. "Almost too bad I own that house, it ties me here, cain't never seem to ever pay it off and nobody'd ever buy it from me. 'Course, I really couldn't move, with the chil'ren and my friends and all that. I don't know as I'd fit somewhere else, 'less I had a lot of money. With money, I could do lotsa things, uproot the chil'ren, make new friends, buy a new house, move to California." Then the mother and daughter turned their faces toward the uphill rise leading to Sam Johnson's house near the intersection of Highway 53 and the Mimosa Springs Road and trudged on.

Bess Johnson lived on an unpaved road just south of Groveton, connecting Groveton with the tiny community of Mimosa Springs. The land on all sides had once been under cultivation, but much of it had now gone back to natural forest as rich and poor, young and old, black and white had left the rural south for urban areas. Here and there, small plots with houses, yards and family gardens interrupted the mingled pines and hardwoods. It was sometimes hard to tell the inhabited houses from those long abandoned, judging by maintenance and repair.

"Mama, why don't we get a car like other people?" Katyna asked her mother as they walked.

"Costs too much, Katyna. I just lost my last car in a wreck, you know. It'd cost more'n our house, maybe, to buy another one - can you believe that? Then on top of that, there'd be gas to buy and oil changes and tires and repairs, and with a late-model car I'd have to have insurance, too. Cars don't hold their value good. One of these days, we'll get another one, but right now I'm doin' my best and you and the boys have the school bus and your bicycles."

"What would you get, mama, if you could buy a car right now?" Katyna asked.

"I don't know, girl, I don't keep up much with cars, you know. Don't mean lots to me. Other folks go crazy about 'em. Just a way to get around, for me. 'Course, I do like cars. They give you freedom and power. Sometimes you feel like the wind. Maybe one day I'll get a car, wouldn't be a new 1993 model, but at least it'd be transportation."

They had come to the highway and could see Sheriff Sam Johnson's imposing house across the road, once the home of a well-to-do planter, now owned by Sam. It was set on a hill, a two-story white frame house with an old-fashioned veranda surrounding it on three sides. They crossed the highway, went to the front door and knocked, then entered without waiting for an answer. "Hello, Cornelia? You home?"

Cornelia appeared. "Just a minute, Bess, I'll get the keys." Cornelia came with the car keys and said "We're gon' let you take the Logos today. It might be low on gas.

Better check it. It's been parked for a week or two, but it oughta run."

Bess looked apprehensive, "The Logos? I've never drove a Logos. Does it drive like a car?"

"Oh, yes," Cornelia reassured her, "it's automatic and everything. Only thing is, you're sittin' a little higher. Take it easy and you'll be fine. Come on out and I'll show you."

Cornelia took her to the Logos parked in the side yard. "Really, this is better, Bess. You can carry more stuff in it. If you want to buy groceries and stuff, you know, you've got lots more room than in a car. It rides real good too."

Bess Johnson surveyed the Logos, still hesitant, but coming around. After all, Sam and Cornelia were *lending* it, and Bess could hardly be picky. "All right, Cornelia. I'll try it. And I sure do appreciate y'all lettin' me borrow it. I'll take real good care of it. Might do a few errands in Columbia before I comes back, so don't worry if I don't see you 'til sometime around three or four o'clock. Sure do thank you."

Bess and Katyna stepped up into the Logos, a blue and white model, turned the ignition, and Bess seemed pleasantly surprised to find that it started just like any car. "What's this, Cornelia?" Bess asked, pointing to the four-wheel drive control.

"Oh, that's if you want four-wheel drive. You won't want to use that to drive to Columbia - just if you were goin' off-road or somethin'. Sam took it off-road last time he drove it, ended up pulling another guy out of a ditch, but he re-set it in two-wheel. Just leave it there." Bess nodded and drove off with Katyna. Cornelia watched her for a moment, wondering to herself if this had been a good idea after all to let Bess take the Logos, but Bess seemed to be coping all right as the van disappeared.

"Mama, a van! I ain't never been in a van like this. I feel so high, I can see everything down the road! Mama, please get a van like this one when you get a car, please, mama!" Katyna pleaded.

"Oh, I don't think so, Katyna. This thing does feel kind of good in a way, settin' high up and all that, but I think I want me a car. Watch out, Katyna, you kind of scared me with that bubble gum popping in my ears. Be careful with that," Bess Johnson said.

Passengers gathered, Bess and Doretta Anchrum sat up front with the three children behind them, then headed toward Columbia. They drove past the Groveton Courthouse Square, north on State Highway 53. Groveton had a population of exactly 713 souls as of the last census and, if anything, had probably shrunk since then. Its "downtown" area had the trappings of a rural hamlet, a few stores and service stations, one restaurant on the outskirts (the in-town restaurant had not survived), a scattering of houses, no motels or hotels. Groveton's one distinction, really its only raison d'être, was its status as county seat, the place where the Courthouse, the county offices and the Sheriff's Department of Phoenix County were located.

The Courthouse in Groveton had seen all-white juries in years past sit in judgment on racially tinged cases with

unfortunately predictable results. With voter enfran-
chisement after the historic Voting Rights Act, African
Americans had gradually taken control of most county
offices in Phoenix County where they held a three-to-one
advantage in the voting rolls.

More recently, the Courthouse had seen a series of all-
black juries render huge punitive damage verdicts, large
even by standards of states notorious for huge verdicts
in products liability, personal injury and fraud litigation.
The Courthouse had definitely changed its character,
from one extreme to another.

Memories associated with the Phoenix County
Courthouse were a part of the character of older residents, though scarcely more than civics lore for three
not-yet-teenaged children in the Logos. Perhaps it was
the sign of liberation that black and white residents had
worked through much of the past racial antagonisms and
were at least superficially at peace, where the past for
adults was relegated to the back of the mind's bus, and
where children of both races seemed little consumed by
its dark shadows. Yet change was fragile, and the cancer
of the past could rise again to infect the future - mutated
in form, perhaps, but strong and virulent.

On this Saturday in March, it was the present rather
than the past that concerned Bess and Doretta as they
spoke of plans for the day, of dentists and grocery stores
and Easter clothes. Bess looked at the gas gauge and saw
it was near the empty mark. She pulled over for a fill
up - the least she could do, she thought, in appreciation

for the loan of the car. It was a self-service station and she pumped her own gas, not taking time to check the oil or water or air pressure in the tires, as she was in a hurry. She paid for the fill-up, got back in the vehicle and drove on. Bess was running a little late, not of great concern to her because the dentist scheduled loosely, and sometimes she had to wait a long time to see him.

However, today there was no wait for Bess Johnson, Dr. Jones barely suppressing his irritation at her tardiness. The dentist gave Bess a shot of Novocaine, waited for it to take effect, and proceeded to extract two upper teeth. "That's about all we should do today, Cornelia, but we certainly need to get the other three uppers and maybe the lowers as well," he told her. Bess made an ap-pointment to return in two weeks. "Be careful driving. You should be okay to drive, but I was a little heavy on the shot because I know it can be painful to have teeth pulled," he advised.

"Well, my mouth is dead," Bess managed to say with uncooperative upper lips, "but I think I can drive all right." Bess paid the co-pay on her relative's insurance, and then she went through the swinging door back into the waiting room where she rejoined Doretta and the children, who were restless and ready to go.

As they returned to the car, Bess noted that it was about eleven-thirty, a little too early for lunch, and actually she did not feel much like eating, the way her mouth felt, especially with cotton absorbent pads in place where the teeth had been earlier that morning. She cranked up the van, put it in reverse and quickly spun backward until the van was jolted. "What was that!" Bess said with annoyance.

"You've hit the corner of one of them concrete slabs at the edge of the parking lot," Doretta told her.

"Well, it's okay, ain't it? The van's not hurt, I don't think. I just didn't see it, 'cause it was there in my blind spot on my left. I mean, I knew they had slabs here, but I didn't think I'd backed that far. Anyway, nothin's hurt," Bess reassured herself.

They went shopping for clothes, first to K-Mart, where Bess found shoes for Katyna, and Doretta a pair for Jimason, who proudly wore them out of the store. It did Bess and Doretta good to see the children happy. They were all nice-looking children with good dispositions. By then the children wanted lunch, and Bess stopped at a nondescript fast food restaurant. Bess removed the cotton pads from her mouth but still was uninterested in food. However, the others had no such problem with their appetites.

Several stores later the Easter clothes had been bought and laid in the back of the van. Sarena's was a pink dress with a white pinafore edged in eyelet, Katyna's a silky blue with lace on the collar and a broad sash. Then off to the grocery store they drove to undertake some serious shopping, as both carless women seized the opportunity to stock up. Altogether, Bess and Doretta bought fifteen sacks of groceries, nearly four hundred dollars' worth in combinations of food stamps and cash.

It was now after three o'clock that Saturday afternoon and, all missions accomplished, Bess and Doretta loaded themselves and the children into the Logos to return to Groveton. Bess never bothered with seat belts, and Doretta was not always careful to use them, but this time she did. As Doretta buckled, she thought of the children and their seatbelts but mentally waved it off, "No, they've got all that energy and they need room to squirm around, if they want to. They'll be okay." They turned on U. S. Highway 195, which would take them to State Highway 53 and on to Groveton. It was a nice drive on a nice day. By this time, the blue of the sky was unchallenged, save for crows and jay birds, and clearly spring had come ahead of its appointed season. Jonquils and forsythia painted the roadside in brilliant splotches of yellow, while pale green leaf buds competed with snowy peach blossoms to confirm a glorious new season.

Bess felt the exhilaration of the season and of the road, tempered by small talk with Doretta and the sounds of children behind her. As she turned south onto Highway 53 to drive the last few miles back to Groveton, Bess somehow felt the urge to accelerate to 65 mph on this two-laned, mostly straight-as-an-arrow road with small undulations in the ribbon that traversed the forests and rich farmland. Not that she was in a special hurry to get home, although her mouth made her painfully aware of the tooth extractions, and the occasional outbursts of the children were beginning to get on her nerves. She knew speed was pointless so near her destination, but on a beautiful clear day, on a familiar straight road leading home, in light traffic, who could resist feeling the power of the Logos taking charge of the road?

Four-year-old Sarena was the quiet one in the back, humming unrecognizable fragments of songs, mainly withdrawn into her own private world. She had reached back to find and hold her new Easter dress, which she alternately hugged up to herself and viewed it admiringly. Jimason teased the girls about pro basketball, quizzing them about his basketball heroes, confident he could impress them with his knowledge, oblivious to their indifference. Katyna popped bubble gum, sometimes loudly, talked to Jimason, at one point urging Jimason to swap seats. Jimason did not mind giving up his window seat to Katyna, as he could still see well over the low console between the two front seats.

The Logos came over a low rise and, in the distance, on the right side of the road at the top of the next small rise, Mrs. Driscoll's house came into view - one of the finest homes in Phoenix County. "That Miz Driscoll, she's really got the money," Bess was saying to Doretta. "That lawsuit. Must've been somethin'."

At that moment it happened. Bess would say later that she heard a loud pop. The Logos lurched down the sloping road, first to the right, then zigzagging to the left, passed over a bridge spanning a small stream, then veered off to the left, crossing the yellow center line and rushing down a six-foot embankment off the far shoulder. Down into the marshy low area the van raced, homing in on a large mock orange tree. The sound of crashing, bending metal and shattering glass thundered with ghastly dissonance in the rural stillness.

CHAPTER TWO

JAWS OF LIFE

Sam Johnson was returning to the Sheriff's office from a call in south Phoenix County, when he heard on his car radio there had been a bad accident on Highway 53 just north of Groveton near the Driscoll house. He headed for the area, having no idea who or what was involved in the accident. It was just another accident, like hundreds he had investigated before, maybe this time worse than most. Sam did not think of Bess at first, nor of his Logos.

As he approached the scene, he saw through a small crowd a blue-and-white Logos crumpled against a tree, and his mind instantly processed that it was his Logos. "Damn! My Logos! Never should have let that Bess have it, never could drive worth a damn!" His first feeling was pure anger, the anger of betrayal and disgust, not at first

25

aware of the human loss. But then he was overwhelmed with the sight and with the thought of Bess, his niece, and Katyna still confined in the wreckage, not knowing their conditions. Was Bess alive? And Katyna? He walked over to the van and winced at what he saw. The grille and hood had a giant "V" engraved in it by the head-on impact with the tree. The body of the van was crumpled downward in the center so that it almost touched the ground there. Glass was shattered. The rear seat had folded forward. Expecting to find only Bess Johnson and Katyna, he saw several women and children in horrible conditions inside the van, five rather than two, making a terrible situation hideously worse. He had no idea Bess had taken four others with her into Columbia. Sam put his hand to his eyes, momentarily overcome. "My God! Tell me this ain't happened," he said aloud to himself, trying to will away the unspeakable tragedy. He tried to open the front passenger door, but it would not budge. He recognized Doretta Anchrum inside, dazed but apparently alive, which gave him hope. Someone was yelling that no doors would open.

The crowd was swelling as vehicles lined the shoulders of the road on both sides and people poured out of them to view the wreckage and stand by helplessly, some of them passersby, some the idle curious who had heard about the accident. The state troopers had been called but had not yet arrived. Sam, helpless as the rest to aid the injured, instinctively reassumed his law enforcement role, going out to the street and directing traffic.

State trooper Jake Milsap arrived, blue lights flashing. He quickly looked at the wreck, tried the car doors unsuccessfully, and returned to the trooper car to call for the jaws of life. The rescue squads were beginning to arrive, but they too could do nothing until the victims could be gotten out of the van.

Officer Milsap picked up an accident report form from the seat of his car and looked at this watch. It was three fifty-four p.m., and he estimated the accident occurred twenty minutes earlier. He began interviewing bystanders. Had anyone seen the accident? One person claimed he had seen it. Lonnie Gresham said he had been driving a couple of hundred yards behind the Logos which seemed to be going about the same speed he has going. How fast was that? Gresham thought a second, reflecting on the fact he was confessing his speed to a state trooper, and estimated fifty-five. Did he see a brake light come on when the van went out of control? No, he didn't.

"Must've hit the accelerator instead of the brake," mused the trooper. "Would've sped up, say, another five mph." He wrote down sixty as the Logos's estimated speed.

Milsap observed Sam Johnson directing traffic, saw the rescue squads getting stretchers in place and hovering helplessly around the van where five passengers were trapped, then decided to do some accident reconstruction while waiting. He followed back up the embankment the faint path of the Logos, then noted one clearly visible yaw mark on the pavement and another fainter mark which crossed the first - all tracing a path north across the bridge and toward the southbound lane of traffic. He took some photographs of the marks, and some also of the van.

The jaws of life arrived, and the growing swarms of persons at the scene moved back to make way for it to come in. With ferocious power it cut through the entire top of the van and set it down. Then someone tried the doors and found one or two could now be opened, the tension on the doors being relaxed by the giant jaws. Members of the rescue squad entered cautiously. They found loaves of bread and canned goods and vegetables and milk and food and clothes thrown randomly forward in the van, covering passengers, floorboards and odd corners of the interior. The paramedics quickly began clearing the groceries, tossing them onto the ground, and anywhere else, to get to the passengers and retrieve them. Doretta Anchrum was the first to emerge. Her seatbelt had served her well, and she could walk, unsteadily, out of the van assisted by paramedics who quickly settled her into a rescue ambulance.

The paramedics found Bess crunched down onto the floorboard, her face bruised and lacerated, a large gash in one knee, and probably other unseen injuries. When they got her into the rescue car, she spat up broken enamel bits - most of her remaining teeth - cracked off as her face crashed into the steering wheel. Bess was dazed but conscious, largely incoherent. The first of the rescue cars sped off to Columbia to the

Kessler Hospital with Doretta and Bess on board.

The situation with the children in the back seat looked grim, and it showed on the faces of the rescue workers. First came Katyna who had been sitting on the far right. She was unconscious, pulse normal, though. A lot of bruises and at least a broken thigh. This was the good news from the back seat.

The last two to be removed were Jimason and Sarena. Jimason was obviously in critical condition. He had been thrown onto the console between the two front seats, and at first the paramedics thought he was dead, but then detected a faint pulse. The paramedics brought him out, laid him on the ground, and noticed the danger signs of posturing, his legs becoming rigid, then shifting to fetal position. "CPR quick!" someone shouted, and paramedics responded immediately. It was clear Jimason at least had a broken skull with severe cranial depression. As soon as Jimason's condition seemed stable enough, he and Katyna were put into a second vehicle and rushed to the hospital.

Meanwhile, extricating Sarena was proving to be extremely difficult. She was on the floorboard of the back seat, with her head wedged between the driver's seat and the side panel and door on the driver's side. It seemed impossible that a person's head, even a child's head, could fit into that narrow space. There was no apparent pulse, but still the rescue workers continued, finally getting her out with crowbars widening the space between seat and side. Immediately, CPR was administered to her as she lay on a stretcher on the ground, with no positive results. Sarena strangely had no cuts to speak of, nor any obvious bruises, which might mean there was still a chance. Hurriedly, the paramedics got her into a third rescue ambulance and sped toward the hospital.

The crowds had grown larger at the scene, now numbering around two hundred or more. Among them were several lawyers making their pitches to anyone and everyone who had any connection with any of the passengers. Some worked on Sam Johnson, while he directed traffic. Others worked on Sarena's parents, Ben and Agnes Miller, who had come to the accident. For the moment, Sam kept them at arm's length from himself. He needed to go to the hospital and discontinued his traffic control.

"Hey, Sam," called Officer Milsap, "What do you want to do with the Logos? Got a garage you want us to call?"

"Well, call Ridley, I reckon. But I'm sure it's gon' have to be junked," Sam Johnson answered. "Gotta go to the hospital now." Johnson observed that the state troopers were doing measurements and writing their report, but he felt he needed to be with the injured and was off. The milling crowd began to thin.

Milsap waited until the wrecker came. For the first time during all the commotion, Milsap noticed that the left rear tire was flat. "So that's what happened," he said to himself, "tire blew out, driver lost control, single vehicle collision with a tree. Yeah, that's just what happened." He took a photograph of the tire and some additional photographs of the van, from several angles. When the wrecker arrived, the rear end was raised, and a spare was put on the left rear so the van could be towed. Milsap took a look at the now removed ruptured tire. "Well, it ain't totally bald. Not the greatest shape but, would I've put it on my car? Maybe. Must have been a helluva blowout. Look at that hole, clear across the tread from sidewall-to-sidewall, and all those wires pulled out!"

The wrecker pulled the remains of the Logos through the mud at the base of the embankment and lumbered off toward the garage. Milsap looked at the tree, with its unmistakable signs of the impact, the fence wire attached to it decimated on one side. He glanced at the groceries strewn on the ground. The looting had already started, some of the looters eyeing Milsap warily, but Milsap did not care. No one but the looters seemed to care about the remains of what had once been fifteen sacks of groceries.

Officer Milsap left as dusk was setting in to go to the hospital himself, to get the rest of the information for the accident report. He knew Sam Johnson well, through the Sheriff's Department with which he regularly coordinated in his job, but he knew none of the passengers in the van - only that it was Johnson's Logos, and some of Johnson's relatives had been in the van. A bad day, a horrible day, for Sam, he thought.

When Milsap arrived at the hospital, Jimason was in emergency surgery, which would continue for some time. He saw Johnson in the waiting room. The depth of the tragedy was confirmed; Sarena had been pronounced dead on arrival, as he had feared. Milsap had already gotten the essential information on Sarena from her parents at the accident scene when they had held back their emotions out of hope for Sarena, so he was glad he did not have to press them for information now that the dammed up emotions of grief had broken through, the worst possible grief, grief for a lost child and for a childhood that was left unfinished. Sam Johnson accompanied Milsap to see Doretta first and then Bess, both of whom were conscious and able to supply some needed information. Actually, Doretta was in pretty fair condition, no broken bones or bad lacerations, and the doctors were saying she might be discharged in the morning.

Family and friends had assembled in the waiting room, in mourning and fear. Ben and Agnes Miller waited there too, not knowing why. With the young girl dead, no doctor would be emerging to tell the Millers how Sarena was doing. No doctor could know that, none could see into the world beyond.

A hospital chaplain came somberly to comfort the Millers and pray with them. "Why did she have to die?" wailed the distraught mother, tears bathing her cheeks.

"My faith doesn't answer that question, Mrs. Miller," said the chaplain. "I can only tell you that this is not the end for Sarena. There is still life, a different life from what we know, but an even better life. Your faith will help you face it."

"Say the twenty-third Psalm to me, preacher, I need to hear it," Agnes Miller asked.

When the chaplain got to the part about walking

through the valley of the shadow of death and fearing no evil, Ben Miller interrupted and said, with an emotion cracking voice, "Preacher, Sarena's walked through the valley, and I feel like I've walked it with her. Did God protect her? Is he gon' protect us or anybody?"

"Hush, Ben, and let the preacher finish," Agnes said.

The chaplain stopped, though, and said, "That's the point, Mr. Miller, Mrs. Miller. God is with us in life and in death. And we don't have to be afraid, whatever might happen."

"I'm not afraid, preacher," said Ben Miller. "I'm mad. I've always been a religious man, and I know just what you're sayin', but now I want vengeance. I might can accept it someday, but it wasn't no time for her to go. I never even got to say goodbye to her. I never got to say to her, 'Baby girl, I love you!'"

The big brawny man, so stoic and glassy-eyed a few minutes ago, was crying uncontrollably, inconsolably, as was Agnes Miller. "I tucked her in last night and gave her a kiss this morning when she woke up," sobbed Agnes, "and tonight she won't be there. Why did God give her to us so short a time and then take her away?" The chaplain put one hand on Ben's shoulder and one on Agnes and prayed for healing, and for answers he did not have.

There were some present in the waiting room who had clear answers not based on a theology of the spirit nor of the hereafter. Theirs was the gospel of greenbacks which could wipe away all tears. They were waiting with the expectations of handling a lawsuit against big, rich corporations. This could be a BIG CASE, hard to say how big, but definitely BIG.

CHAPTER THREE

FEATHERS FLY

"Damn it, Jack, you're not hearing me. They've already filed the friggin' lawsuit! Yeah, Jeff Tokers and his crowd. Don't understand how in God's holy name this could've happened. I called you just as soon as I got the word from Mrs. Driscoll the day of the wreck and told you to get out there and get'em signed up. Now looks like we've blown it. Maybe - just maybe - the best lawsuit that's ever come down the pike in these parts!" Fred Bates was livid at his law partner Jack Ripps.

"You live a lot closer to Phoenix County than I do, and I thought you could get the job done, but you got outmaneuvered by Tokers! Now, damn it, Sam owes us one. I defended him twice on police brutality charges. Got'im off and didn't charge him a red cent. Didn't he tell you he would deliver? Now we gotta go talk with him. Let's both go together. Damned it's a competitive world out there!"

Fred Bates was beginning to cool down a bit as he and Jack Ripps debated their problem. Fred was about six-ty-five years old, would have liked to go into retirement mode but was not quite ready. Maybe one more big hit would do it for him. He had spent most of his law career in the hog wallow of small-town mediocrity and anonymity. He had started out practicing in Garfield, South Carolina, but eventually got himself installed as Phoenix County district attorney. He had prosecuted criminal cases of all sorts, not necessarily the most glamorous job and certainly not a blue-ribbon job, but - as they say - you get a lot of trial experience with it. Then followed a short stint as a small claims and petty criminal offense judge, but he found he couldn't survive on the salary and quit.

After that, he went back to Garfield in private practice again, this time defending mostly criminal cases, picking up a few civil suits and divorce cases. Bates got some notoriety, and some credit from civil rights groups, when he undertook the representation of a black man accused of raping a white woman. His defense was that the relationship was consensual. That was a tough defense in those days in the mid-sixties in South Carolina, when most white South Carolinians were not ready to believe any white woman would consent to sexual intercourse with a black man. Bates got his client acquitted by an all-white jury. He liked to tell this story, and he was a pretty fair storyteller. He always ended by saying, "And as soon as that 'Not Guilty' verdict came in, that fella left the courthouse, got in his car and kept going. And as far as I know, he's still moving. 'Course, I had already got my fee up front." His ending always drew chuckles, especially from those who knew how jealously Bates guarded his fees.

Bates had begun to notice what was happening in the rural counties of the low country and other parts of the old plantation belt. The juries in those counties were becoming predominantly African American, often entirely so, and some big plaintiff verdicts were coming out of those counties. The wisdom among lawyers up to that time had always been that small rural counties were usually not good for plaintiffs, because rural juries were conservative and not accustomed to dealing with big numbers plaintiff lawyers wanted in verdicts. All of that was changing.

It was not something one would find neatly analyzed in the newspapers or discussed on radio or TV talk shows, but legal eyebrows lifted a notch all over the state when the big verdicts began to come in from those unlikely venues. Fred Bates' figurative eyebrows were raised higher than most. All those years in Phoenix County, his career bogged down in an invisible county few knew anything about, a county from which he had tried so hard to escape, THIS was precisely the background needed to tap into the new fertility of the belt's legal fields. Bates was fond of boasting that he knew every person in Phoenix County, probably a bit of a stretch, and he now began touting it louder than ever. He had looked himself in the mirror and saw a few more years of practice despite his sixty-five years. There was a likable Santa Claus build hanging from his frame, a glistening, polished look to his crown and a coal black monk's fringe with a too-dark bottled hue.

So five years earlier, Bates had decided to move his law offices to the City of Columbia. It appeared that other plaintiff lawyers were having success operating out of centrally located Columbia, a much bigger city than Garfield, and furthermore the capital of the state, with the possibility of handling cases in multiple rural counties within easy driving distance. Bates knew Jack Ripps, a struggling younger lawyer with Phoenix County roots, but with a stable practice in Columbia. They struck up a law partnership together in the capital city, firm of Bates & Ripps. Two years later, they were joined by Alton Fox, a lawyer who had a lot of special experience with tire cases, but not a lot of good tire cases had come along and the name of the firm remained Bates & Ripps even after Fox joined them.

Jack Ripps was pragmatic and understood the same thing Fred Bates understood, that there was money to be made on plantation belt juries, and maybe only a narrow window of time when white lawyers could tap into it, before black lawyers took it over. Ripps was not as experienced a trial lawyer as Bates, but he was willing to do leg work and otherwise do his part.

The first big case for Bates and Ripps had been the *Driscoll* case. Mrs. Driscoll (everybody called her "Mrs. Driscoll" now) hired Bates and Ripps to represent her in a consumer fraud case where she claimed a used car salesman sold her credit life insurance for more coverage than she was ever likely to need.

Mrs. Driscoll acknowledged that she had taken out the credit life policy and that she had duly signed the credit life application. However, she claimed the coverage was excessive, based on the full amount financed, whereas that amount would be reduced each month as payments were made. She said she did not realize she had more coverage than she needed until much later. When she was unable to make payments and the finance company was about to repossess the car, Mrs. Driscoll went to Fred Bates and he conceived counterclaiming for fraud against the used car dealer, the finance company, and the credit life company. This was more of a defensive stratagem in the beginning, but it became the central issue in the case.

It paid off, too. Bates took the case to the jury in Phoenix County, and the jury found all three defendants had tried to defraud Mrs. Driscoll, awarding the plaintiff more than eight million dollars in punitive damages.

This was the first really big plaintiff verdict in Phoenix County, right in line with the trend that had begun in other plantation belt counties. Something in the range of one thousand dollars was in issue in actual damages, even if the plaintiff's case was meritorious. But Bates and Ripps and Mrs. Driscoll hit the jackpot with millions in damages, ostensibly to punish the used car dealer and the finance and credit life companies for their wrongdoing.

Fred Bates was proud of the *Driscoll* case. When he

received the check in satisfaction of the judgment, he framed and displayed a copy of it on the desk in his office, turned outward so as to face potential clients who would look at that check as Bates negotiated contingent fee contracts to represent them. No longer was Fred Bates a small-time operator in an obscure part of the state. He had won a BIG ONE, and his notoriety spread quickly.

As for Mrs. Driscoll, she instantly became the wealthiest person in Phoenix County, with more wealth than several highly compensated executives or professionals could amass in a lifetime of hard work. Mrs. Driscoll also became instantly the most famous resident of Phoenix County. She built herself a large Mount Vernon style two-story house on a rise (locals called it a hill) just north of Groveton on Highway 53, made of dark red brick and white columns and rambling expansively over the crest of the high ground.

It was in fact across the street from the lower reaches of Mrs. Driscoll's estate that the accident with the Logos took place that Saturday afternoon in March. Mrs. Driscoll's young son, Lattus Driscoll, had been playing outside the Driscoll house in the yard when the accident occurred. He had not actually seen the accident, but he heard the crash and then looked and saw the wreck. He went into the house and told his mother, who immediately made two telephone calls, first to the Sheriff's Department, second to Fred Bates. "Attorney Bates," she said, "there's a bad accident right down here below me. Yeah, Highway 53. Somebody liable to've got killed.

They might need a lawyer if they ain't dead already. I cain't never thank you enough for what you did for me and I just want you to know 'bout this accident. They might need you. You're the best."

"Thank you, Mrs. Driscoll. We'll get right on it. Really appreciate you thinkin' of me. We'll let you know how it comes out."

It was then that Bates had called Ripps to dispatch him to the scene. When Ripps got there and found out it was Sam Johnson's Logos with some of Johnson's relatives in the car, Ripps felt he had a good chance to get this case, because he and Bates had helped out Sam Johnson a lot. Ripps tended to concentrate his efforts on Sam Johnson, but a rival firm was working some of the other potential plaintiffs and signed some up. For all the sense of obligation Sam Johnson felt to Bates, he was in no hurry to sign the paperwork. He did assure Ripps that the plaintiffs would employ whomever he decided, that he had the influence to deliver the case.

But then there was the shock when Bates found out the *other* firm had beaten him to the courthouse and had filed suit purporting to representing all the occupants of the car, naming Universal Tire Company and Tergano Motor Corporation as defendants, along with a local automobile dealership in Columbia. Bates was beside himself with anger. Phoenix County, he felt, was his proprietary territory, perhaps not his exclusive hunting grounds, but this case, at least should be his. He and Ripps went immediately to see Sam Johnson.

Johnson up to now had been reluctant to push too hard too fast with the potential plaintiffs. He realized well that it was his Logos that went out of control and that it was his tire that had blown out. He suspected that some of the others probably blamed him for the accident, though nobody had said it.

Indeed, the others had been doing a lot of reflecting. Sarena Miller had been buried after a short delay for the Coroner's autopsy. The Coroner found her small neck had literally been snapped by the jolt of the collision of her small frame with the narrow opening into which it had been rocketed. She had apparently died almost instantly.

There was much praying and mourning for Sarena. Ben and Agnes Miller continued grief stricken and were bitter at this wrong, this totally irrational end of their daughter's young life. Bess had asked Sam Johnson from her hospital bed to go back to the wreckage of the Logos, to see if he could find Sarena's Easter dress. She wondered if Ben and Agnes would like for Sarena to be buried in that dress. Sam did find the dress, still in the van at Ridley's Garage, where he encountered the spoiled stench of some of the groceries that had still remained in the van. "Gotta get those groceries cleared out," he said to himself. Broken bottles of ketchup were lying around, some of it on Sarena's Easter dress. At least Sam hoped it was ketchup; it was sometimes hard to tell the ketchup from the blood.

At first the Millers rejected the idea of burying Sarena in that Easter dress she had seen only briefly that afternoon. But they reconsidered, got the dress all cleaned up, and Sarena finally wore it. The Millers had come to envision little Sarena looking down from the pearly gates watching with pride as she saw herself in the dress that she loved.

It would take a lot of comforting from preachers and friends to heal the Millers, more comfort than can be given, more than can exist. As with an amputation, the Millers would limp along with such emotional crutches as they could find. They would become resigned to Sarena's death, because there was no choice, because time and the pressure of coping would crowd out the very opportunity for grief.

Money cannot heal either, but money can help with coping, and money can give security as a surrogate for comfort. Some lawyers, vying for representation of the plaintiffs, were promising the Millers a good prospect for lots of money, and the Millers had been listening.

"Who we gon' sue?" Ben asked. "How about Bess? I know she could've done somethin. I think she was prob'ly speedin'. And what about Sam Johnson? I hear tell another deputy warned him to get the tires changed out."

The lawyers had a ready message, wrapped and tied in visions of dollar bills, lots of them. And the lawyers were always available and solicitous for prospects. They told the Millers, "Naw. Don't bother with Bess and Sam. They haven't got any money anyway. What you folks need to do is to stick together. Don't go fightin' with each other. What you need to do is sue the hell out of the big boys, the big corporations. They got plenty of money - millions! And who's going to be deciding how many millions you'll get? Why, it's your very own friends and neighbors right here in Phoenix County. You'd probably know most of the jurors, and they'd give you whatever we ask. How much was Sarena's life worth? One million? Two million? Ten million? A hundred million? Why, those jurors couldn't look you in the eye unless they gave you millions. We can do a good job whipping up the sympathy - and the anger - for a big verdict."

The Millers signed up with the Tokers group, and later Doretta Anchrum did also. It was a straight 40% contingent fee arrangement, all expense advancements to be made by the lawyers. It was on this basis that the first complaint was filed in court in the race to the Courthouse to see which attorneys would stake out their claims to this case.

Meanwhile, Sam Johnson had been talking to both Doretta and Bess. Doretta had in fact been released from the hospital the morning after the accident. But hospitals and doctors would remain a preoccupation with her for months ahead, for Jimason was in very serious condition.

The report from the brain surgery advised that some crushed and splintered skull, together with fluid build-up, had been surgically removed from Jimason's right frontal lobe in the twelve-hour operation, that there had been shock and probable damage to the left frontal lobe, with pressure on the hypothalamus and pituitary glands.

The surgeons in Columbia recommended Jimason be transferred to St. Joseph's Hospital in Louisville, Kentucky where there were more specialists and better equipment to evaluate and monitor his progress. Jimason was helicoptered to Louisville with his mother Doretta. She stayed with him for the first week, watching him as he would drift in and out of consciousness, and getting reports on his progress. A broken arm and some cracked ribs would mend fine, assuming he survived the brain damage. But there was further buildup of air and fluids on the brain which had to be relieved. Massive doses of antibiotics were given to counter possible infection. By the end of the first week, it appeared Jimason would likely survive, but the long-term prognosis was guarded at best, maybe "bleak" would be more accurate. For the time, Doretta had stayed as long as she could, and returned to Groveton to re-collect her other children who had been parceled out to friends and relatives.

Doretta was a woman of few words and limited understanding. She had become a good friend of Bess Johnson in part because Bess was dominant and somewhat domineering with the need to be a leader, and Doretta was the classic complementary follower. Bess knew something about the workaday world, but Doretta had never had a job for more than a few months and was totally dependent on welfare. Doretta, though not seriously injured in the accident, was overwhelmed by it and the events which followed. Her primary emotional response was resignation and bewilderment. She never really blamed anyone for the accident, not Bess, not Sam Johnson, not the tire-maker nor vehicle manufacturer. She did understand that there might be money that could be gotten out of some kind of lawsuit, but beyond that she understood little.

When Doretta returned to Groveton, it was the Millers who first contacted her about filing a lawsuit. They went to her with their lawyers - the Tokers group - and she readily signed the contract, hardly asking a question in the process.

Afterwards, Doretta and Bess Johnson talked, and Bess told her she had not signed yet, that she was looking to her uncle Sam Johnson for advice. Bess said she thought Sam was in favor of the Bates and Ripps group. Bess had told the Millers she wasn't ready yet to sign a contract. In one sense Bess was not quite as important to the lawsuit as the Anchrums and Millers, because her injuries and those of her daughter Katyna were not nearly as serious as those of the brain-damaged Jimason, nor as tragically final as the death of Sarena. However, she was critical to the case in one sense, for only she could support the theory that the accident was not caused by her own driving but solely by manufacturing or design defects in the tire and van. This was especially true since Doretta, the only other adult in the van, did not drive and knew little or nothing about cars and car handling.

Bess wondered about the condition of the tire and whether Sam Johnson was at fault in not having replaced it with a new tire, maybe new tires all the way around. But Bess certainly could not seriously think of suing her uncle, nor would she likely even find lawyers willing to sue the popular Sheriff, who in any event had no deep pocket. Then, too, Sam had been nice to lend her the van. After all, *she* had asked *him* to lend it.

Bess pondered her own injuries, the loss of all her remaining teeth, the gash in her forehead, another on her right knee, plus a broken right arm and a lot of sore and painful bruises. There were significant permanent injuries as well as the healable bruises and transient pain, but the gash in the forehead would be mostly concealed by her hair, and her dress would cover the bad scar on her knee. She had already embarked on a plan of tooth extraction anyway, and while she would not have chosen to remove the remainder of her teeth by steering wheel impact, the result was what she had intended all along. She wondered whether her broken right arm might be weakened so as to make it hard for her to lift things as she sometimes had to do at work. But a lot of people seem to work at hard manual labor after a broken arm. Maybe she would not be all that much worse, in the long run.

As for Katyna, she miraculously suffered only a broken leg and some healable bruises. The doctors had put a steel rod in her leg, but this would be manageable without a lot of long-term effect.

The consensus had jelled to sue the deep pocket manufacturers where there was a possible basis for doing so, but as yet there had been no consensus as to who the plaintiff lawyers would be. Nevertheless, a lawsuit had been filed by lawyers who had contracts only with the Millers and Doretta Anchrum, apparently in the hope that such filing would be a preemptive strike to squeeze out other lawyers pursuing contracts with the plaintiffs.

However, Fred Bates and Jack Ripps were not deterred by this apparent *fait accompli* and, to the contrary, were energized into action. They had called ahead to the Sheriff's Office and had asked that Sam Johnson be radioed to alert him Bates and Ripps were en route to see him. As the two lawyers turned into Courthouse Square in Groveton, they could see Sam Johnson's Sheriff car pulling into its customary parking space on the street at the far side of the courthouse. Although head of the Sheriff's department, Johnson did patrol work right along with his three deputies, as customary in small counties. As Johnson got out of his car, he saw Bates and Ripps approaching, and he waited for them. It was nearly noon on a spring-like day in the third week of March, and Johnson summoned the two lawyers to sit with him on a bench on the courthouse grounds. The trio walked toward the bench but did not in fact sit down.

Bates tried to be diplomatic but firm with righteous indignation: "Sam, what is this crap about a lawsuit being filed by that other crowd? Know anything about it?"

"I just heard it myself this morning. I called Bess. She says she ain't signed no papers and I sure as hell ain't signed none. I got a copy in the Clerk's Office, and it don't even show me as a plaintiff. You know I'm not goin' to stand for that," Johnson responded.

"Well, Sam, here's the thing. We're your friends and friends of your family. I'd do anything I can to help you, and I really want to handle this case because I think I can do you and your family - and the Millers and Anchrums, too - the best job. You know what I did for Mrs. Driscoll, don't you? I'm the one who changed the whole climate around here to make these big verdicts possible. I've lived here in Phoenix, and I've practiced here, and I know everybody in the County, and I can do what it takes. Those other guys don't know Phoenix like I do," Bates reasoned.

"Yeah, I know, Attorney Bates, I know all that. And you know I appreciate what you've done for me. This is just one of them things that's got to be handled. I can do it. Just leave it to me," Johnson said.

"Well, Sam, that's fine. No problem, but I hear the Millers and maybe Doretta Anchrum have already signed contracts. That's serious, and if we're goin' to turn things around, we need to do it quick. Now a client always has the right to switch lawyers. It won't be a happy situation, but it can be done. This means a lot to me and Jack, not just because we'd make some money out of it, but because I think we'd do a better job for you on the case," Bates said.

"How 'bout if I get 'em together right now? I might not can get Ben, 'cause he'll be at work, but I can get Bess and Doretta, and maybe I'll pick 'em up in my Sheriff's car and carry 'em to my house. That'll mean somethin' to 'em," Johnson suggested.

"That's great, Sam. I'll have our contract with me." Ripps had let Bates do the talking, as he usually did when the two of them met with others on serious business.

Sam Johnson went to his office in the Courthouse to make some telephone calls. Bates and Ripps paced in front of the bench. Then Bates nervously sat down. "Tell you what, Fred," Ripps spoke, still standing, hands in pockets, "I think we ought to offer a clincher to close this deal. I think we ought to offer to do it for a one-third contingency, you know, shave some off Tokers' forty percent contingency. Sure, I know we might be giving up a million dollars or more, but what the hell.... we'd get the case, and if it does turn out to be as big as it *could* be, what's a million dollars in a big case?"

"Well," said Bates, "we could have some heavy expenses in this one, with expert witnesses and all that. But I don't disagree with you, with one condition: that they sign the contract now - today - and all of 'em sign. I'd only do it to put this baby to bed." Ripps nodded.

Sam Johnson emerged from the Courthouse. "Well, everybody's in today, even Ben. Didn't need him today on the construction job. He and Agnes gon' meet us at my house. I'll pick up Bess and Doretta. You know where I live? Okay, see you in a few minutes."

Bates knew it would take him roughly forty-five seconds to drive four blocks to Sam Johnson's house, and he didn't want to get there before Johnson. He and Ripps waited a few minutes by the bench. Bates looked up at the Courthouse. "That's been a good Courthouse for me, Jack. And these Phoenix people, they've been good to both of us. Not exactly my kind of people, you understand, but on the other hand maybe they're just exactly my kind of people."

"Yeah," said Ripps smiling, "I know just what you mean. Whoever pays for my retirement, they're my kinda people. We can make a living and, ha!, 'help our fellowman' all at the same time. Why, I feel like a crusadin' saint gettin' all this justice for these poor folks and making a little livin' all at the same time."

Bates and Ripps sauntered over to the car and drove away to the big meeting at Sam Johnson's house.

CHAPTER FOUR

TO BURN TO ASHES IN PHOENIX

Universal was served with a Summons and Complaint at its home office in Pittsburgh, which the legal department forwarded to case manager Bert Sayre. Sayre was specially designated to handle cases involving light truck tires, and the accident described in this complaint involved a Logos van which used that type tire. The lawsuit papers concerned a single vehicle collision in some place in South Carolina Sayre had never heard of, Phoenix County, allegedly caused by a blowout of a Universal tire. Though the papers gave minimal information, it was clear this was a serious case, with a death and some other severe injuries.

Sayre had worked as an assistant to George Orel for several years in the Universal organization, but now Orel had taken early retirement and Sayre had been promoted to do one aspect of Orel's old job, which had been divided into several parts and added to the workloads of existing staff. He looked at the complaint and mused, "South Carolina. H'mn. Who did George usually refer cases to in South Carolina?" He looked through the company's card file of approved counsel and found the name "Ted Born" with a list of cases Born had handled, all with apparently fine results. The problem was, Sayre thought to himself, "I don't see any tire blowout cases on the list. But George wrote some pretty darn strong things about this guy. I'll give him a call."

"Ted Born? This is Bert Sayre with Universal. Wanted to talk with you about a new case we got in the office here. Don't know much about it, you know the complaint never tells you anything much, but apparently it's a tire blowout, and it's serious. Ever handled any tire blowout cases?"

"Bert, I've been handling cases for Universal for probably ten years. But let me think. There was the pyranol spill, then several fraud cases, a wrongful death case we settled, I remember, for less than a thousand dollars, some personal injury and products liability cases. I think probably there have been some tire blowouts, but I can't remember any serious injuries or any case where the blowout was the central issue. But Bert, I'm confident we can handle this case, and I assure you it will get our priority attention. We don't overstaff cases, but we also don't cut corners, and we won't make any important moves without talking it out with you in depth," Born explained.

"Well, I don't have any doubt you're a competent lawyer, from what George has written about you. The only thing I was wondering about was your experience with tire cases. But I'm inclined to see what you can do with this one. I'll overnight the complaint to you with Universal's standard instructions for handling cases of this type. Give me a call when you get it and have had a chance to look it over." If Born had known at the time what would lie ahead, he might have immediately delegated the case to someone else, justifying it somehow to the client. At the time, he assumed rather casually that he would handle it himself, with some sort of staffing assistance from a younger lawyer.

"What court was the case filed in?" Born asked.

"It's the Phoenix County Circuit Court. Where is Phoenix County, near Greenville?" Sayre inquired.

"Phoenix is in the central part of the state. I'll get you some information on it," Born promised, hoping Sayre would not press him for more information he did not have at hand. "Thanks for thinking of us. I'm looking forward to working with you on the case. We'll do a good job."

When the call was over, Born went immediately to his library to check out Phoenix County and its demographics. Born was a twenty-five-year lawyer in a medium-sized firm, Grant, Ogletree & Bailey. He had sandy hair, graying at the temples, and he had broad shoulders on his lanky frame.

Born's litigation record was solid: lead counsel in

more than twenty reported cases in the last ten years, written up in the official published reports of court opinions, winning every single one of them. Some victories had been quite remarkable, even landmark cases. Besides that, Born had gotten good results in numerous cases which never got to trial.

Still, Ted Born was not a name that had become synonymous with "leading litigator." It had to do with the fact that Born was a renaissance-type lawyer in an era of growing specialization in the bar. Born was a registered patent lawyer, an adjunct professor of law, a business litigator, and did his share of paper-shuffling corporate law. His partners had two main criticisms of Born: first, he spread himself too thin on too many areas of the law, "general practice just doesn't work anymore"; and second, he did not delegate enough of his work to junior lawyers, doing a lot of things himself that his contemporaries contended should be delegated.

The truth was, Born always had wanted to be a lawyer, not an intellectual property lawyer nor an antitrust lawyer nor a litigator nor corporate lawyer. He just wanted to be a lawyer, someone who could help people with whatever problems they had. His idealized image of a lawyer harkened back to a simpler time when it was possible for a lawyer to be all things to all people. For better or for worse, Ted Born would do whatever he had to do to hold on to his concept of what a lawyer should be, bringing the breadth of modern legal expertise to his own embodiment of an old-fashioned and perhaps outdated ideal.

A second truth was that his clients loved him, and many were insistent that he personally do their work because they had never found any other lawyer who pleased them. He did in fact delegate a good deal of work, but he also continued to stay in the middle of the fight as a lawyer, resisting the trend of becoming more of an administrator, a client jockey, and less a lawyer, as he climbed the seniority ladder.

It was this strange anomaly of a modern lawyer, who strode quickly into his library and headed straight for the commercial and business atlas, where he knew he would find the core demographic information he needed. Born, of course, knew generally where Phoenix County was; in fact, he had grown up not far from Phoenix County in an area culturally akin to it. He just did not know the statistical particulars, nor was he specifically aware of the recent dramatic changes in the litigation climate in Phoenix County.

Total population according to the most recent federal decennial census was about 10,500 comprising roughly 3500 households. About seventy-five per cent were African American, the rest Caucasian, virtually no Hispanics, Asian-Americans, nor Native Americans. Unemployment was among the highest in the state, and per capita income was among the lowest. There were few industries, and per capita retail sales were even lower than the other data would have suggested. Residents obviously did their major shopping in surrounding counties, not in Phoenix.

Born's younger partner Tom Jenkins passed by the

library table where the big atlas was sprawled out. "What have you got going in Phoenix County?" Jenkins asked.

"A new lawsuit, tire blowout. I just got a phone call about it, haven't seen the complaint yet," Born answered.

"Ted, you've got my sympathy. Do you know about my experience in Ware County, in that same area?" No, Born really did not know.

"I had this case where we were about to go to trial. We actually struck a jury, Jess Robinson and I did. And we found out the plaintiffs were bribing a witness."

"No kidding!" Born reacted.

"Sure did," Jenkins said. "See, we had gotten a statement from the witness first, and we thought we knew what he was going to say, and then the other side filed an affidavit signed by the witness which was 180° different from what he had told us. We went back to the witness and asked him why he changed his story and, without batting an eye, he said, 'Cause they paid me more money, but I'll change it back if you'll top what they did for me.' Ted, Jess and I were both there and heard him say it and, of course, Jess is a highly regarded black civil rights lawyer, and there's no doubt the witness said it."

"What'd you do?" asked Born incredulously.

"Jess and I went to the other side, and we told them we knew there was bribery and asked them to dismiss us from the case, but they wouldn't do it. We finally got the plaintiffs to come down to a million dollars from their ten-million-dollar settlement demand, and I thought it was outrageous to pay that kind of money to people who had engaged in deliberate bribery. But, you know what? It was money well spent. Our co-defendant refused to settle, and they got hit for twenty-two million dollars! Can you believe that? Twenty-two million in a case that ought not to be worth more than ten thousand at the outside, and there was bribery to boot on the other side." Jenkins related this tale with feeling and emotion.

"Did the co-defendant get a new trial?" Born asked.

"Hell, no!" Jenkins answered.

"What'd you think about the jury?" Born asked.

"The jury pool was awful. It was as though they were all trying to get on the jury, saying things in answer to voir dire questions they thought the defendants would want to hear, so they wouldn't get struck, but Jess told me that jury was bad news. And he was sure right. I tell you what, Jess is well respected in that whole area. He practices all over. I have a good relationship with him. Would you like me to see if I can get him to commit to work with you on your new case?"

"I think probably that would be a great idea, Tom, but I'll need to get authorization from the client. Let me get the complaint and read it. I should have it by tomorrow morning, and then I'll get with you. Seems to me with your expertise you'd be ideal to work on this case with me."

"I'll tell you, Ted," Tom said, "I'll do what I can but I'm pretty busy right now, and I can't really get too involved. Best thing I can do is to get Jess to work with you." Tom obviously was backpedaling away from another plantation belt case. Any help from him would definitely be at a distance.

The next day the complaint arrived, but it was as vague as Sayre had indicated, and Born knew little more than he had known the day before. Born called Sayre to acknowledge receipt, to give him some vital statistics on Phoenix County, and to relate Tom Jenkins' experience in neighboring Ware County. Sayre was inclined to accept the recommendation to get Jess Robinson aboard, but wanted to pass it by some of his superiors. A few days later he called back and gave the necessary approval. Born and Jenkins then got on the telephone and tried to reach Jess Robinson. Robinson was not available, but Jenkins spoke with his secretary who said she felt like Robinson would be glad to work with them but of course she could not speak for him. Jenkins promised Born he would continue trying to get Robinson aboard as local counsel.

A few days later Sayre called Born and said, "Ted, this is the damndest thing I ever heard of. Help me figure it out. We've been served with another complaint in that Phoenix County case, and this one's by a different set of lawyers, a firm of Bates & Ripps in Columbia. What do you make of it?"

"Beats me," said Born. "Maybe these new lawyers have been associated on the case by the first set, and they've all redrafted and amended the complaint."

"Doesn't quite look that way, but I'll send it to you, and you can try to figure it out," Sayre said. "By the way, I notice one thing different about this complaint, right off the bat. This one has a Sam Johnson as a plaintiff in addition to the others. Says he owned the van."

"That's interesting," Born observed. "I guess he's suing for the value of the van only, no personal injuries or punitives."

"Yeah, I presume so, but the complaint isn't very clear," Sayre responded.

Within a couple of days, the puzzle of the two complaints was resolved by a "Motion to Withdraw as Counsel," filed in court by the Tokers firm. The motion simply stated: "Although we had a valid contract to represent the plaintiffs, the parties now apparently want someone else to represent them. Accordingly, counsel request leave of the Court to withdraw."

It immediately became clear. Two sets of plaintiff lawyers had locked talons over the property rights to this lawsuit, mauling each other in aerial assaults, but with Bates & Ripps winning out. Born reacted to this turn of events on two levels, deploring the image suggested by two vultures fighting over carrion, unseemly and unprofessional, but on a second level chuckling at the self-destruction of plaintiff lawyers fighting among themselves, a spectacle more suggestive of Orwellian pigs than of eagles.

In any event, the lawsuit was a fact, aside from the particular lawyers handling it. The parties would now embark on a long process of preparing the case for trial. They would assemble or complete the assembling of their legal teams and their expert witnesses. They would take depositions of witnesses on oral examination and propound and answer written questions called interrogatories. They would plan their respective strategies, and, in time, the case would go to the jury, if not settled out of court before that time.

As for the possibility of settlement, it would depend - from the tiremaker's standpoint - on whether Universal would conclude that the tire was defective after examining it, settling only if convinced the tire was defective. The company had a strong policy of defending tires it believed were well made and nondefective, and in such case settlement for any amount, even a nominal amount, would be out of the question.

Of course, Universal had not yet seen the tire which allegedly blew out. The complaint identified the ruptured tire by serial number, but the serial number obviously was incorrect because it did not fit the standard format for Universal tires. Born tried to get custody of the tire for Universal so it could be analyzed and subjected to testing, but it was out of pocket at the moment, being examined by one of plaintiffs' own experts. So, during the first few months after the complaint was filed, Universal knew essentially nothing about the tire or its condition.

An unusual feature of the lawsuit was that it had been filed so quickly after the accident occurred, partly as a consequence of the fight among plaintiff lawyers for representation rights. What this suggested to Born was that an investigator needed to start locating and interviewing witnesses and helping make some sense of what had happened, while events were still fresh in the minds of witnesses. He called his usual investigator, Chaz Christopher, gave him the basic facts and asked Chaz to get the accident report and go forward from there.

Meanwhile, Born talked with Sayre about a future date when the two of them could go down and look at the accident scene while it was still fresh. They settled on a date about two weeks later to give Chaz some time to gather basic facts. "I'm stymied at the moment, Bert," Born advised, "because I don't have the tire, I have almost none of the facts, and I don't want to take depositions of the key witnesses or of the plaintiffs until I know enough about the case to do a good job. You know, you have to be in control in order to take an effective deposition, and knowledge is the tool for control. You have to be able to ask leading questions if you want to channel the deposition in the direction you want it to go. Sometimes you can get away with going into a depo cold turkey, knowing nothing about the case, and get yourself educated in the process. But there're going to be high stakes in this one and discovery is critical. So, until Chaz completes his investigation and until we get to see the tire, we can't do much. But at least in a few days we can see the accident scene while it's still relatively fresh."

A few days later, Born learned that the lawyer for co-defendant Tergano Motors and co-defendant Citizens Tergano was Trip Gillespy who worked with a small litigation firm in Columbia. Born and Gillespy had never before represented co-defendants in a common lawsuit, but they immediately established a good and fairly open relationship. Both immediately recognized it would be extremely important to share information and ideas and to avoid any finger-pointing at each other's clients. Gillespy mentioned that he was merely local counsel, reporting to Tergano's regional counsel, and he was not sure at this time whether he would be taking a lead role or a supporting role in the litigation.

Gillespy said he had had several cases in Phoenix County, the judge was good but the litigation climate terrible. "My God! Do you know who Sam Johnson is? He is just about the worst opposition we could have, in one of the worst defense counties in the state. He runs the Sheriff's Department and has the power in Phoenix County to make his friends happy and his enemies miserable. Besides that, we've got a death and terrible injuries to black plaintiffs and we'll probably have an all-black jury. Let me tell you, Phoenix County has nothing in common with the phoenix bird of Egyptian mythology. When you burn in Phoenix County, as all defendants do, you definitely do not rise from your ashes," Gillespy mused ruefully, enveloped by a sense of resignation.

"Trip, if it turns out we've got a good case for summary judgment, will this good judge in Phoenix grant the motion and save us from the jury?" Born asked.

"Probably not, Ted, realistically, unless it's more compelling than I think it's going to be. He reads the Supreme Court opinions and knows he'll probably be reversed if he does that. You know our state Supreme Court does not look kindly on summary judgments."

"How about removal? Can we hope to remove the case to federal court?" Born asked. "I know the plaintiff lawyers aren't really interested in Citizens, it's just a sham inserted in the complaint so there would be a South Carolina-based company among the defendants, thus preventing removal by destroying diversity of citizenship jurisdiction of the federal courts. But do you think we can get Citizens struck as a sham defendant so it would then become removable?"

Trip's response was discouraging: "Unfortunately, Ted, Citizens has virtually zero records covering the time period. The plaintiffs seem to be saying Citizens sold the bad tire that blew out, or something like that, and maybe serviced the Logos and could have some responsibility for the accident. We'll be hard pressed to refute those charges because Citizens was involved in a different unrelated lawsuit last year where a lot of its key records got lost. Not only that, but none of the employees have any specific recollection about work done on this particular Logos. I've already checked it out."

Born frowned, "You're not helping my feelings much about this case."

"Oh, yeah," Gillespy said, seeming to remember something, "it was a mock orange tree the Logos hit."

Born was puzzled, "So?"

"So, a mock orange tree is a tree black folks hate, even today, around here. It's a reminder of slavery. You might've never heard this, but mock orange trees were planted in pre-Civil War days on plantations as a kind of line of demarcation. They are usually planted as bushes, and they spread and can make a kind of hedge. In the spring and early summer, they have white blossoms and have a wonderful smell like orange blossoms. They grow well in this climate. The field hands, as opposed to the more privileged house servants, were forbidden to cross the line of mock orange bushes or hedge, could not get any closer than that to the plantation house. It was a barrier back then, and now the plaintiffs' van has run into this barrier again when it hit that mock orange. Most of them are gone now, but along the outer property lines, some have survived and have grown into the size of trees, because they have been around for a long, long time. But to African Americans, and especially the older generations who know the history, big corporations with their mostly white management are the modern equivalent of the plantation owner. Don't think for a minute that Bates won't use this in his closing argument. Before the case is over, the whole issue will be race, race, race. The mock orange is a natural symbolic bridge paving the way for race to be the decisive issue."

Born was stunned. "I never heard that before. Never knew this random accident would somehow strike racial nerves. Just a big tree, minding its own business. Gee, I've got to think it out. I wonder if Bates or Ripps has any idea about this – might never know 'til the closing arguments in court."

CHAPTER FIVE

THE TOUR

Chaz Christopher had been giving Ted Born daily briefings of his investigation, and within a week Born had in hand a written report of interviews, accompanied by glossy photographs. Born could not resist looking at the photos before reading the reports, arranged in a photograph album with captions. Most of the pictures had been taken by Christopher, but there was a group of twelve which had been made by the state trooper, and another single made by the Coroner of Sarena Miller seemingly asleep on white satin, taken at the time of her autopsy. Born looked at that photograph for as many seconds as he could bear, closed his eyes and covered them with his left hand, shook his head and blinked his eyes open again, turning the page of the album to other pictures.

There were images of the crumpled Logos viewed from several different angles. Born was most interested in a photograph of the left rear tire of the Logos, but it was a poor shot which was dark in the area where the tread rested on the ground. "Too bad," he thought, "I seem bound to be kept in the dark about that tire." The other photographs showed the roadway, precision straight, rising toward each horizon and with the small bridge at the dip in the middle. On two or three photos yaw marks could be seen on the pavement, which Born had difficulty interpreting immediately. There were some shots of the mock orange tree with the Logos grille crushed around it, and a couple of shots of the tree after the vehicle had been pulled back. There were marks on the tree memorializing the impact, but otherwise it was just a stout, hefty tree, unremarkable.

The written reports included interviews with the state troopers, the wrecker driver, some rescue squad personnel and the eyewitness, Lonnie Gresham. The Logos had only stayed a few weeks at Ridley's Garage where it had first been taken. It had then been relocated to Farley's Garage in Columbia secured in an inside, weather-protected area. Basically, there was a blowout, the van went out of control and hit a tree, and death and injury followed, but for Born, nothing would shed light on the cause of the accident until he could get the tire. He directed Christopher to continue his investigation, though it could not include any of those who knew the most about the accident, the plaintiffs themselves, as they could not ethically be contacted without arranging it through their lawyers, something Born was not yet ready to do.

A few days later, Bert Sayre arrived to go with Born to inspect the accident scene. It was the first time the two of them had met in person. Sayre sized up Born, and liked him, but he was still a little apprehensive about Born's handling such a major piece of products liability litigation with so little experience in exploding tire cases.

On the long drive to Groveton, Born sensed Sayre's unspoken reservations and sought to reassure him. "Bert, I minored in mechanical engineering, majored in philosophy - if you can believe that combination - before getting my law degree. In fact, I am a registered patent lawyer. You might ask, 'Is this supposed to be good? Am I supposed to be reassured by that?' Well, you should be, strange though it may seem, because I think you're much better off in a products liability case with a lawyer who has a technical background and can understand the technology of the products in litigation, like tires here. I wouldn't be surprised if you have this notion of patent lawyers as green-eyeshade introverted types who can't deal with people. Well, I admit to being a little introverted, but I'm basically a litigator and I think I can relate to people. I know I have a good record winning lawsuits."

"Interesting. I've never worked with anybody with that kind of background, but I can see possibilities there. Coincidentally, I went to a products liability conference a few months back, and some of the people there had used patent lawyers. Seemed strange when I first heard it, but they had all had good experiences. It runs counter to most of what you hear today, that specialization is the name of the legal game," Sayre commented.

"That's the worst fraud ever perpetuated on the American public, or at least on those who hire lawyers. Specialization means tunnel vision; it robs lawyers of their imagination and resourcefulness. You need the cross-pollination of different areas of the law. What you are really paying for when you hire a lawyer is ten percent legal knowledge and ninety percent judgment, and judgment doesn't get honed very well in the sterile environment of specialization. It's a cop out for lawyers who can't handle real law, to sell themselves to the public as 'specialists' and convince an awful lot of people they should pay more money for worse lawyers."

They were now on Highway 53 on their way to the accident scene. It was the third week in April, and the accident had taken place about six weeks earlier. The two were silent, almost reverentially silent, as they approached the scene. When they saw it a few hundred yards ahead, they had no difficulty identifying it: straight road, two rises and a dip with bridge, and the Driscoll house at the top of the rise to the south ahead. They parked the car, took photographs and measurements, wondered how much of the present debris came from the accident, and paced up and down the highway, picking up odd bits of tire tread, thinking some of the bits might fit into the tire like a jigsaw puzzle. But of course, neither Sayre nor Born had any idea how much tread, if any, had been lost during the blowout, since they had not yet seen the tire. The yaw marks had long since disappeared. The two men thought they could detect parallel tire tracks going down the embankment, really just slight depressions and somewhat stunted vegetation. But was it the path the Logos took en route to the tree, or was it the exit tracks of the van being pulled out by the wrecker, or were they merely imagining they saw something which really had no relationship to the accident?

They stood and looked it over again, visually searching for something they might have missed that would yield a special insight. Sayre thought out loud, "I think we need an accident reconstruction expert to help us make sense out of this. It doesn't add up. Why would she lose control on a straight road? You just don't normally lose control when a blowout occurs on a straight road. Now if she had been rounding a curve, that's different. But here we've essentially got a flat tire, and instead of the van slowly stopping, she loses control. Why?" Sayre's engineering and tire background came to the fore.

They got back in the car and Born drove on into Groveton, arriving at Courthouse Square almost as soon as they had entered the small town. Sayre had seen few rural southern towns, and never one like this. It was as though the twentieth century had bypassed Groveton, except for the unhurried progress of occasional automobiles, an auto parts/service station combo, obtrusive power lines and roof top TV antennas. The Courthouse, an edifice of style and character, was a whitewashed structure of roughly 1880 vintage with imposing curved marble staircases on each side of its facade, leading up to a front balcony outside the upstairs courtroom, all topped by a lovely cupola. However, it was in a surprising state of disrepair for a public building: gutters rusted through, paint peeled off, mildewed and rotting eaves, splotches of rust stains, windows which did not fit square in their casings. The upper level of the Courthouse consisted of only the courtroom, no other rooms of any kind, not even Judge's chambers. The ground level, originally designed for various county offices, had long been inadequate for the purpose, so the solution had been to build a similarly whitewashed rectangular boxy two-story Annex behind the Courthouse. The Annex was connected at ground level to the Courthouse by means of concrete walkways through a small grassy and weedy courtyard, and the upper level, with its own pair of functional metal stairs, was connected to the courtroom via a bridge. "Here in the plantation belt, even the speech and dialect hasn't changed much. Right out of the nineteenth century," Born mused, adding, "I grew up on the edge of the plantation country, and I sound a little like that myself, at least with the slow drawl and accent."

Born and Sayre stopped their car on a side street of the square to view the Courthouse and Annex, but somehow felt conspicuous and did not leave the car. They drove around the Courthouse itself to look at it from all angles, realizing they would be inexorably drawn to that Courthouse, which they would see on many later occasions, and that one day a group of twelve Phoenix County residents would assemble there and make a decision in this case, *their* case.

The three other sides of Courthouse Square featured rows of small one-story buildings, mostly adjoining each other but interrupted by a rather narrow parking lot and alley on two of the streets. It appeared that at least a third, and perhaps as much as half, of the buildings were vacant. In the center of the Square was a grassy square area with sidewalks dividing it into four smaller square quadrants, the sidewalks all converging to a round paved area in the center where stood a rusty fountain, green with slime, actually an old watering trough for horses that had not seen any water for a couple of generations, except for rain.

Born and Sayre explored a few streets in Groveton leading away from the square but quickly ran out of anything resembling a municipality. It was obvious that a tour of Groveton was at most a ten-minute proposition. "How would you like to take a drive around the county to get a feel for the place, see what it's like?" Born asked. Sayre had been fascinated by the sight of Groveton and needed no persuasion.

As anticipated, the county was agricultural, but there were fewer recognizable farms than Sayre had expected. It was obvious that many former farms had returned to nature and wilderness. Most of the plantings visible from the roadside appeared to be individual subsistence farming. To the extent there was serious commercial farming, it tended to be tree farming for lumber or for the pulp and paper industry, with some exceptions.

The housing was of two extremes. In a few areas, there were beautiful antebellum homes, but mostly the housing was modest single-family dwellings, with a fair number of modular and mobile home units.

"Frankly, I don't like mobile homes, which I think are a blight on the land, but I don't know what a lot of people would do if they had not come along. Traditional homes are not affordable for an awful lot of people," Born lamented.

"You know," observed Sayre, "you can see there is real poverty, but I haven't seen any slums or signs of starvation or destitution. Just how bad is it, Ted?"

"Bad," Ted answered. "One of the very poorest counties in the state, and its depressed condition causes a lot of resentment which manifests itself, among other things, in big jury verdicts. It's a way of striking back at 'the system'. But you are right that there's really no such thing as a slum around here. The reason is that per capita income figures don't tell the whole story."

"How so?" Sayre asked.

"For example, they don't tell how low land prices are and how low taxes are. Also, people around here cut out things like car insurance and life insurance, not a real good idea, of course, but they find they can get by. They often depend on Medicaid or Medicare for health coverage. There's a hidden under-the-table economy at work also, and a lot of earnings never get reported and don't make it into those per capita income figures. There are food stamps. Lots of them grow a fair amount of their own food, fresh vegetables right out of the little family garden plot, and the value of those personal consumption crops - like the under-the-table economy - don't make it into the per capita income figures either. Then, too, people here still help each other. If Joe has a problem with his car, John may be able to help him fix it. If John has a problem affording a barn, Joe and others may pitch in and help. And, of course, there's a lot of government assistance. They are good at coping. But still, there's something missing. Coping ought not to be an end, but in Phoenix County all most of them can ever hope for is to endure and survive - and there's where the frustration is, the red-hot, seething resentment that sometimes boils over."

"Hey, you're a psychologist, a social worker and a philosopher all rolled into one - as well as an engineer!" Sayre commented with a smile.

Born laughed. "No, probably none of the above. But I find an effective trial lawyer has to be able to feel things, to empathize, to understand. Being genuine and relating to the jurors, not quite on an intellectual level, not quite on an emotional level, but on, well, a personal level, is what it takes. You don't get that by being a 'specialist'," Born said with disdain.

"You feel pretty strong about that specialization bit, don't you?" grinned Sayre.

"I guess you could say I do," Born acknowledged.

The two men had made a loop through the county and now they had rejoined Highway 53 and headed back to Greenville, "What kind of luck are you having, firming up Jess Robinson to work with us?" Sayre inquired.

"Frankly, Bert, I'm getting kind of discouraged. He keeps saying he'll `see about it' and that he's having problems with his law partners. They're telling him he's on the wrong side, ought to be suing big companies, not defending them. They're saying the money to be made is on the plaintiffs' side, not the defense side, and Robinson's representation of corporations just creates the potential for conflicts of interest in the future. And then there's the trump card: 'Jess, you ought to be helping your African American brothers, not working against them.' He's playing with us, without committing.

"Just the other day I got a letter from him," Born continued, "which is a good example of what I'm talking about. Now remember that I never met the man before in my life, just talked with him on the telephone, though Tom Jenkins apparently knows him pretty well through that lawsuit in Ware County. Well, in this letter, he solic-its a contribution from me for some local school project in his area. Of course, I sent the contribution, and it was probably for a good cause, but he knew - and I know - that there are a lot of good causes and needy schools closer to my home where I'd more naturally be inclined to make a contribution. This is unusual, to say the least, to solicit a contribution from a fellow lawyer who lives more than a hundred miles away, whom he's never met. But I accept it because we need him. He's trying to keep us on the string. I wish he'd just say yes or no."

"Maybe we need to start looking for another local lawyer," Sayre thought out loud.

"Easier said than done," responded Born, "there's nobody else in the area with his stature, except maybe his law partners, who wouldn't even give us the time of day. In fact, there just aren't that many local defense lawyers who could be very helpful."

"You mean *black* defense lawyers?" asked Sayre.

Born winced because the frank question forced him to confront what he was trying so hard to suppress, the conflict between his idealism and his pragmatism. "Okay, I'll try to be honest. Yes, I think it is possible for a white lawyer to be effective with a black person, with a black jury. I just think most of them aren't. The gulf is too wide, and most white lawyers just can't relate to the inner feelings of black people. They can't walk down that road of black experience, talk to them soul-to-soul. I'd rather answer your question, 'yeah, I'm looking for *anyone* - white, black, yellow, red or purple - who can talk to a Phoenix County jury.' But then I have to admit that not many whites can do that, so I'm afraid I have to say I'm really honestly looking for a good black lawyer."

"This is maybe an unfair question, Ted," Sayre eased into his most searching inquiry, "but how about you? Can you do it?"

"Good question, Bert, good question," Born answered pensively. "It's one I've been asking myself. Let's see if I can restate it: Can I, an Ivy-League graduate, southern white male from the 'big city' of Greenville relate to a rural black man or black woman on a jury? Good question, Bert. I can only say to you that I know something about personal suffering, personal pain, and once you know and have felt that - I mean really know and feel it - you join in a kind of fraternity that makes you a brother to all the other suffering people out there. It makes for a bond that overrides other differences. Is this enough? And am I really a part of that fraternity? Can a white man *ever* be, regardless of his background? Maybe I can't. Maybe I have no idea what they've been through, or how they feel. At least I've looked in that window. I have suffered and fought from my own childhood poverty, trying to survive and to improve. Or maybe the point is not to try to be a part of their fraternity but instead to draw them spiritually, intellectually and emotionally into a brotherhood and sisterhood of all mankind. I don't know. I just know that, although I am Ivy, I don't *feel* Ivy."

"Damn!" said Sayre aloud, almost surprising himself. Staring absently into the distance, he said, "Mine eyes have seen the glory..." Then he grinned at Born.

CHAPTER SIX

THE DIAGNOSIS

"Bert, I've got the tires right here in my office. Yeah, all four of them. They've already been examined, as you know, by plaintiff's expert, whoever he is, and he's made marks on the rims and the tires," Born told Sayre via speakerphone so he would have his hands free.

"How do they look?" asked Sayre.

"They're all pretty well worn, but particularly the left rear and right rear. All are the same type tire, Universal's Surefoot brand. I don't know much about reading serial numbers, but they look like they probably were bought as a set of four."

"Let's start with the blown-out tire. What does it look like?" Sayre inquired.

"Well, it's the left rear, you may remember, and it's

split from sidewall to sidewall, and there's a whole tangle of shiny looking wires sticking out of the rubber where the rupture is. It's badly worn, though strangely enough, not as badly worn as the right rear which didn't blow out. One thing I can see is a nail still in the tire. It's flush with the tread on the outside and the head is nearly worn off. Beyond that, I can't tell a lot."

"Any rim damage?" asked Sayre.

"Not much, if any," Born answered.

"What about the other tires?" Sayre asked.

"Two of them have air, seem underinflated. The other is deflated. All the tires, by the way, are still on their rims. Except for the fact that they're worn pretty badly, there's nothing to my untrained eye that looks very remarkable."

"Why don't you ship them all to our lab and we'll take a look at them," Sayre suggested. Born complied.

A few weeks later, Sayre was in the lab with Bob Tegrit, a tire expert who had retired from a competitor tiremaker some four years earlier, having been head of quality assurance for that company. Now he had his own consulting business. "Looks like a pretty good tire," Tegrit observed as he turned it, "Let's remove the tire from the rim and look at it on the inside." They separated the tire from the rim and placed the tire on a bright red multi-pronged wheel so it could be easily turned and viewed from all angles, inside and out. A portable spotlight illuminated the inside. "Yeah, you can see the nail very clearly from the inside and it's bent and lying along the inner liner at the point where it penetrated the tire.

And I see something else. There's a plug in here at another position. It has the characteristic knot appearance, obviously an improper type of repair but it's the way most people do it. And you can see here on the outside there is excessive wear in the two tread areas surrounding the nail hole and also the plug hole."

Sayre observed, "There is also excessive wear on the inside and outside edges all the way around the tire. Would you agree that means chronic underinflation?"

"No doubt in my mind," Tegrit replied, "This tire's been leaking air for a long time. Let me see something. Aha! Flash that light in here on the inner liner. See that? That's the gummy residue of the aerosol gunk some people spray in through the valve to stop a leak - meaning, the owner of this tire knew he had a chronic leak and, instead of getting it repaired properly, he used this `home remedy' to try to seal the leak. Might have helped some, but this tire needed more help than that."

"I've checked the age of the tires from the serial numbers," Sayre told Tegrit. "All four tires were made at the same plant in the same month - six years ago. Undoubtedly left the warehouse together and were sold together as a set of four. With six years of age on them, there must have been some pretty good mileage built up."

"Wish we knew just how many miles," Tegrit commented, "but we know it had to be a lot of miles over a six-year life."

"Well, doctor, the real question is what caused that blowout. I've got my opinion, but you're the expert. How would you size this one up?" Sayre asked.

"Oh, it's classic. It was impact with a road hazard. I could tell that when I saw the tire across the room when I came in here. Absolutely classic."

"I agree, but let me hear your reasons."

"First, you notice this 'X' pattern in the crown. That's where the impact occurred, somewhere in that general area. This was an already weakened area of the crown and did the tire in," Tegrit pronounced professorially. "Little or no loss of tread rubber from the blowout which caused almost instantaneous deflation, causing the rupture to extend from sidewall to sidewall in an almost perfectly straight line."

"How do you explain the clean, polished look of the wires, Bob? Would you expect to see more rubber sticking to them? That bothers me." Sayre looked puzzled.

"What that says to me," Tegrit said thoughtfully, "is that there was probably already some belt edge separation, not too unusual in a six-year-old tire, and then, on top of that, some polishing occurred after the impact. See, the rupture likely did not occur simultaneously with the impact. The impact could have occurred up to two hundred miles, maybe more, before the rupture. It probably broke enough critical wires to weaken the structure and cause nearby wires to begin pulling loose from the rubber. Once that happened, the loose wires were rubbed by the rubber and they got 'polished' by the rubber, rubbing off whatever rubber was still sticking on them."

"It's like a chain reaction," Tegrit continued. "More

and more wires separated from the rubber internally in the tire, and you ended up with just a rubber balloon at the point of impact. There was probably a small bulge in the rubber that wore quickly, tire no longer had integrity. Heat built up in the rapidly wearing rubber, and finally - bang! The rupture occurred, and the tire split wide open, following the lines of the nylon tire cords in a straight line."

Sayre still looked troubled. "Makes sense. That's got to be it, but the belt edge separation bothers me. Doesn't it leave us vulnerable to an argument that the wires began separating at the edge of the belt, *as a result of a manufacturing defect,* and finally the wires worked loose all the way across and the same mechanism you described then operated to cause the rupture?"

"Oh, I'm sure the other side will say just that. But they are going to have one little problem."

Sayre interrupted him before he could say the words: "Tensile fractures?"

"You've got it. Tensile fractures. Let's look right here in the general area where we think the impact occurred. We should find a cluster of tensile fractures caused by the impact, if I'm right. Hand me those tongs over there. Okay, I'm pulling back some of the rubber so we can get a better look. Now, I need a magnifying glass. Yes! Here they are, tensile fractures, just as I expected. QED." Tegrit beamed triumphantly.

"You're totally confident the tensile fractures could be caused only by an impact, I mean, there's no other explanation?" Sayre pressed for reassurance.

"I'm absolutely positive. Of course, you understand I am not a professional metallurgist, but I've been in this tire analysis business for a long time, and it's an article of faith that tensile fractures mean impact. Just look at this cluster right here, through the magnifying glass. You see the rubber is still sticking quite well to those wire filaments, almost right up to the point of the breaks, showing those wires were solidly embedded in the rubber before the break. Now, using the magnifying glass, can you see that cup-and-cone pattern on the ends of the wires where they broke? The diameter of the filaments has attenuated or `necked down' right in the vicinity of the break, and the ends of the wires show either a cone shape or a crater-like cup shape at the actual point of break. If we looked across to the opposite side of the rupture, we would find the matching cup to fit right into each cone at the point of the break, and those matching wires would show the same narrowing `necking' that we see here, like pulling a piece of taffy from both ends which causes a narrowing of the diameter before the taffy separates in the middle - only in wires it happens very suddenly. This pattern can only occur when the wire is being held rigidly in tension in the rubber belting and is then subjected to a powerful and shocking impact, like a massive karate chop. In a tire, I know of no reasonable explanation which would cause such tensile fractures except impact with a road hazard."

"What if we find a mixture? What if we find some fatigue fractures and maybe some shear fractures right along with the tensile fractures?" Sayre probed.

"Well, I off-hand do not see any fatigue fractures. That would be where flexing of the wire from prolonged usage caused them to break. This would be supportive of a probable theory the plaintiffs might expound, if we found fatigue fractures, because it could suggest the wires worked loose through worsening belt edge separation subjecting them to greater fatigue stresses. But in that case, there would be substantially a 90° break angle, and there would be no necking down of the wires at the breaking point. I might see some of that before I finish my detailed examination. Sometimes you do see fatigue breaks in combination with tensile fractures where the rupture is preceded by fatigue, but the tire holds together until it suffers ultimate failure from impact. But I don't immediately see that."

Sayre asked about shear fractures. "Well, we could find some shearing. I've never quite understood the mechanism, but you do sometimes see shears in conjunction with tensile fractures. Of course, I'm talking about shear fractures occurring somewhere between the ends of the wires. Obviously, the two ends of each wire spanning the width of the tire are going to show machine shearing where they were cut to proper length as the belting was being made, and that tells you nothing. No, you can sometimes find shearing between the two machine-cut ends, running at a roughly 45° angle, which can go hand in hand with tensile fractures. This would not detract from the tensile fracture evidence proving an impact origin of rupture, but I can only say shear fractures also occur a good deal of the time, along with tensile fractures. I've never heard a good scientific explanation for it,"

"Bob, if an impact caused the rupture, would you expect to get damage to the rim?" Sayre asked.

"Not necessarily," Tegrit explained. "If it is a sidewall impact, you usually would, or if the road hazard was extremely large or the pothole deep and sharp, you can find damage to the rim. But if the impact is in the crown area and the hazard or object is no larger than, say, eight inches or so, you would not likely see any damage to the rim."

"See anything else?" Sayre asked.

"I do see, now that I look at the rim, signs of the tire bead wearing against the rim and causing this roughness, these abrasions, and you can see the corresponding wear on the bead itself. This is just more proof of the chronic underinflation and abuse this tire has taken," Tegrit said.

"Let's call Ted Born and tell him. Keep in mind that he doesn't know much about tires," Sayre advised.

Sayre and Tegrit went back to Sayre's office and put in a call to Born. "Hey, Ted. Bob Tegrit and I have been looking at those tires. I'm going to let Bob tell you about them."

"Hi, Ted. This is Bob Tegrit. I look forward to meeting you. Bert and I have been looking mainly at the ruptured tire, but we've also eyeballed all four of them. I still have work to do, so this is preliminary, but I don't expect it to change much. Bottom line is, the blown-out tire hit something in the road, or off-road, that did it in, and I can prove it. Some sort of impact with a road hazard. This was an old tire, six years old, undoubtedly heavy mileage on it, and it had been pretty badly abused. You know, chronic underinflation, an unrepaired nail hole - probably leaked air - and an improper plug repair. The tread was thin, less than 2/32 of an inch in lots of places, especially severe wear along the inside and outer edges. A well-made tire, but it was abused and worn out, and in this condition it was an accident waiting to happen. When it hit the road hazard, the internal wires were broken which gave the tire its integrity, and some miles after that, it gave up the ghost, blew out, ruptured. That's it in a nutshell. I've got some more work and then I'll send you a written report, if you want one."

"Looks like the tire was okay, Ted, from a manufacturing standpoint. It was just abused by the owner and then succumbed to the impact. We'll defend this one." Bert Sayre was obviously elated at the preliminary findings.

"I'm glad to hear the tire was a good one. No manufacturing defects, I take it, as far as you can tell?" Born asked.

"I don't see any," Tegrit responded.

"What can the other side say?" asked Born.

"I can't answer that. We know they'll come up with something," Tegrit answered.

"Suppose you were on the other side, Bob. What would *you* say?" Sayre asked.

"I'd tell the truth. But, you mean, what if I was on the other side and was willing to prostitute myself? Then I'd probably say that birdcage mass of shiny wire was the result of belt edge separation which got out of control. But then I'd have to deal somehow with the tensile fracture. Maybe I'd say the tensile fractures were just the final blow to an already dead tire. I dunno. Probably say something like that."

"Would x-rays help?" asked Born.

"Probably not. I'm not inclined to do any. I'm sure x-rays would probably show a good deal of belt edge separation. That would be a red herring, you understand, would have nothing to do with the accident or the rupture, just a matter of age and usage. But it wouldn't necessarily be pretty and might raise doubts in the jury's mind. I know we'd probably find that, and if it's properly understood, it is irrelevant. But I think I'd rather just say I don't know about any belt edge separation except right around the area of the blowout."

Born really did not understand about this "belt edge separation" business, but he figured now was not a good time to get into that kind of detail. "Well, I look forward to talking with you some more after you've finished your work. However, I think I would rather you not send me a written report, at least not just yet. I find you always see something new or different whenever you take another look at anything, tires or whatever, and I'd rather you not set your observations and thoughts in concrete quite yet. Take lots of pictures of course, because I'm going to have to return the tire to the plaintiffs. After all, it *is* Sam Johnson's personal property. So, we need to have good pictures. You are the expert, Bob. Just do what you need to be certain about the cause of the blowout and any misuse and abuse."

"What do you think, Ted? Have we got a case?" Sayre asked, seeking reassurance.

"Bert, I'm not quite sure how I ought to say this, but, yeah, of course I'm glad we feel we're on solid ground on the facts of the blowout. But I'm also hearing Bob say the other side can tell a different story, maybe a full-of-holes story, but one that they can get into evidence. I'm still pretty apprehensive because I know that a jury which wants to find for the plaintiffs can find a way to do it, and the true facts may end up on the garbage heap of irrelevancies. Unless our case is so strong we can get a summary judgment by the judge and avoid a jury decision, I'm not sure the truth makes much difference. We're trying this case, a case with a death and other very serious injuries, in front of a jury of the plaintiffs' friends and neighbors in a county fast becoming notorious for huge and outlandish verdicts, even over trivial things. And if they do that when the issues are trivial and when the plaintiffs are not so well known, what do you think they may do when the injuries are horrible, and our opposition is one of the best-known families in the county?"

"All right, Ted, you've brought me down to earth. You're reminding me of what we're up against, but, damn it, this was a good tire, and unless we have a change of philosophy at the top of the corporation, we are going to defend this tire. The truth may be irrelevant to the jury, but it isn't to us. If we've got a good tire, we'll defend it. Here we do have one, and we will. Better get ready for mortal combat." Sayre was obviously sobered but still determined.

"Speaking of preparation," Ted remarked, "I think I've satisfied myself about staffing this case within our office. I think I'd like to have a young lawyer work with me. He's been with us less than a year, hasn't had much trial experience, but he's bright and would go over well with the jury. His name is Dave Thompson."

CHAPTER SEVEN

MEMBER OF THE TEAM

Dave Thompson was staring out the window of his office. "I'm not sure I can do this," he thought. "I wanted to be a defense lawyer, but this tests me." He had just opened the file of *Johnson v. Universal and Tergano,* and the first thing he had seen was the Coroner's picture of a little girl named Sarena, whose skin tone contrasted sharply with the soft white satin on which she lay. How could he oppose this little girl whose spirit must reside somewhere in the high heaven? How could he oppose her family who must be beside themselves with anguish and grief?

Ted Born had asked him to help on the case, but they had not yet talked much about it. Born's suggestion had been for Thompson to read the file first and then they would talk. About all Thompson knew was that Born thought the client Universal had a good defense, that it was a good tire. But what was the worth of a good defense when a beautiful little girl, who had probably played with dolls and skipped rope and laughed, what good was it when that young child would never play again? Had it all come to this, that all Thompson's years of education and all of his achievements - Order of the Coif and everything - simply brought him to a place where his job was to fight his fellow African Americans in their courtroom aspirations?

Thompson thought back to conversations he had had with other African-American lawyers during the period when he was trying to decide where to practice law and what kind of law he should practice. "Dave, if you go with an 'establishment firm,' race will always either be positive or negative, never neutral," one friend had told him. "They'll put you on cases where your race will help, like when you're in a mostly black venue or there are black plaintiffs, or your company representative is black. They'll keep you clear of cases where there're racist clients or mostly white players. You'll never get a chance to be just another good lawyer." Was he seeing the prophecy come true in this very case? He could not help feeling the resentment for the role his race obviously played in this case assignment.

Was he prostituting himself? Was he being used? Who was this Ted Born anyway? A senior partner he barely knew. Could he work with Born? Would he discover that Born was at heart a racist, and he Dave Thompson would be stuck working with him, hating Born and hating the case? He already hated it. Oh Lord, take this cup from me, he thought.

No, this was wrong thinking, or at least partly wrong, he told himself, giving his head a shake as if to rid it of thoughts he had rejected over the years. "Maybe a black person never shakes those thoughts after all we've suffered, all the pain we know. But here I am as a lawyer. I'm not just a black lawyer, I'm a lawyer. Do I believe corporations, even lily-white corporations, should get fair trials? Of course I do. Do I believe they ought to win or lose based on the evidence, based on the truth? Of course I do, he thought. And should African Americans lose if they don't have a good case, even when they have been injured badly? I guess I do, no, I know I believe they should lose if they've got a bad case. All lawyers, to some extent, are assigned to cases based on their abilities *and* on how well they could relate to clients, jurors, judges, opposing counsel," he thought. He was a new lawyer and he was not afraid to prove himself, at least this once.

"I always wanted to be a lawyer, then I decided to be a defense lawyer. That's what I am, and that's what this case is about," he told himself. "Better get with the program. If it's bad, I can change horses later, but let's give this one a fair shot." He turned away from his window back to his desk and began going through the file.

Thompson knew nothing about Phoenix County. In fact, Thompson had been recruited from North Carolina where he grew up. He soon surmised that Phoenix was a majority African-American county. "Does this make a difference to me?" he thought. "The shoe is on the other foot, *we're* the majority and *they're* the minority. No, that's not relevant" he told himself, "except it may be relevant if all they want me for is to sit at the table and be black."

When he had finished reviewing the file, he went up and knocked on Born's door. "Come in," he heard. "Hi, Dave."

"Hi," Thompson replied, not quite sure whether he should use Born's first name, whether this would be taken as too "familiar" for a young black associate to address a white senior partner, twice as old, by his first name. There was no real precedent to guide either man, as Thompson was the firm's first African-American lawyer.

Born noted mentally the slight uneasiness of Thompson but realized their relationship would have to grow and evolve naturally based on trust and respect. He decided to resist the temptation to go overboard with folksiness, knowing that obsequious behavior would simply convey the message, "I AM ACUTELY AWARE THAT YOU AND I ARE OF DIFFERENT RACES, AND I HAVE TO MAKE YOU COMFORTABLE, PART OF THE WHITE MAN'S BURDEN, YOU UNDERSTAND." No, the only way to deal with the situation was to ignore race, and ignore any recognition of race, just deal with the case at hand. In time, Thompson would be totally relaxed around him. Born was sure of it.

They talked about the facts of the accident, as much as they knew them, and Born passed on the expert's preliminary report on the tire. He then reviewed with Thompson the efforts to get Jess Robinson on the team, and lack of apparent success. "We need good local counsel, and I'm not sure where we're going to find them."

"Are you looking just for a black lawyer?" Thompson thought, but said nothing.

"I want someone a Phoenix County jury can trust," Born continued, "someone the jury can relate to, or if we can't find someone like that, then we need someone who knows the local situation in Phoenix County. In that scenario, you and I would mostly be trying the case, and we'd just depend on local counsel for logistical support and jury selection."

"How about in Phoenix County, are there any lawyers there you could get?" asked Thompson.

"I need to get into that in more depth, but I have the impression the choices are pretty limited, with only two or three lawyers with offices in that county. Most of the cases seem to be tried by lawyers from nearby counties. We need to do something about that, but we've got a little time to ask around and think about it.

"The important thing right now is to get on with the discovery of the evidence. Now that we've seen the tires, we need to schedule the depositions of Sam Johnson and Bess Johnson and Doretta Anchrum. After that, we'll need to depose the troopers and the people with the rescue squads. Eventually, we'll need to take depositions of the medical people who treated the injured plaintiffs, and the opposing expert witnesses," Born stated.

"Meanwhile, I'm sure they'll want a lot of discovery from us," Born continued. "Incidentally, I don't relish defending against their discovery, because Universal is very protective of its technical and proprietary information and won't want to turn it over to the plaintiff lawyers. I guess we'll cross that bridge when we get there. Oh, there's one more thing. See if you can make arrangements for us to inspect the Logos itself; be sure to get a date that's good for Bert Sayre, as I'm sure he'll want to come down for the inspection. The van's more the concern of Tergano Motors, I suppose, but still we might pick up something useful. Which reminds me, we need to co-ordinate with Tergano on the depositions. Their local counsel in Columbia, Trip Gillespy, seems like a nice guy, and apparently is very competent." Born was matter-of-fact about what needed to be done.

Thompson left Born's office and placed his first telephone call in the case. It was to Alton Fox, the lawyer with Bates & Ripps dealing mainly with the tire aspects of the case. Ripps was concentrating on the van, and Bates was overseeing the whole effort. Thompson got Fox's secretary on the line who advised that Fox was not in the office.

Born telephoned Bert Sayre. "Bert, I've just met with Dave Thompson, and I'm calling just to say I'm feeling good about Dave's involvement. I think you'll like him when you meet him. Hard to imagine anyone not liking Dave. He's super! By the way, we are trying to schedule a time for you to see the van. Why don't you look at your calendar and give me some free dates and I'll pass them to Dave to finalize arrangements."

"Okay, I'll give you dates, but first, Ted, tell me a little more about Dave. I didn't want to ask too many questions the other day when you mentioned him to me. You know, Bob Tegrit was on the phone with me and it wasn't a good time. Of course, I'm basically going to respect your staffing of the case, but this is an important one and I'm interested."

"I think he's outstanding," Born replied. "Heavily courted and recruited by law firms all over. I think he came with us because he had a good experience working with us as a summer associate after his first and second years of law school. He's from North Carolina, went to college and law school there, Phi Beta Kappa and Order of the Coif. He has no family in South Carolina, or maybe I should say he has family everywhere, because he's never met a stranger. He's married and has a young daughter eighteen months old. He told me it really touched him when he saw the photograph of Sarena. Oh, yeah, I think he can relate to black jurors. He is black, but really he's Dave. You'll like him instantly."

"One thing is an absolute must, though," Born warned. "He's got to fully participate in the trial of the case, and I do mean *fully*. It's a little risky, no, it's extremely risky to do that with a young associate with so little trial experience. But Bert, this case requires risk. And I think he'll rise to the occasion. It would be a horrible thing, and dangerous, to have him serve as an ornamental fixture at counsel's table. I just wouldn't ask him to do that."

"Ted, how good is your relationship with Dave? Can you relate to him?" Sayre inquired.

"Not as well as I'd like," Born confessed. "As we were talking about the case, I was trying to read his body language. His shoes were turned away from me, and when we would be standing, he would move to the side rather than stay facing me. I'd say there's a little latent, subconscious tension there. But I'm going to work on it."

"I'll have to tell you something, Ted, I've never worked with a black lawyer. I don't have a problem with it, but he needs to be good, really good, because there are no second chances on this case. You've already done a good job convincing me this case is bad news and just about impossible to win. If you use an inexperienced lawyer, black or white, on this case and then lose it, all hell's going to break loose. You need to be damn sure you're right about him." Sayre minced no words.

"There's no way to be sure, Bert. But this is my judgment, and my judgment is the main thing you're buying from me. I want to win this case for you, and I'm going to do everything in my power to win it. I wouldn't suggest Dave otherwise. Remember, Bert, I'm on your side, I'm not the enemy, and what I'm telling you is that Dave has tremendous talent and I'm going to work with him to bring that talent out in this case. I know he's a winner. But I had to be honest and tell you he's new at this." Born was a bit defensive, but firm in his judgment.

"Well, I'll be meeting him soon. Let's defer it for the

moment," Sayre said in a tentative tone of voice.

"No doubt," said Born, "you'll be coming down soon to see the van and also for depositions we have coming up."

CHAPTER EIGHT

TO TELL THE TRUTH

"Now, Bess, I know you're still in shock. I know you're confused. I know it all happened real fast. And maybe the children in the back did distract you, and you can't tell about outside noises because of the children's commotion and Katyna's bubble gum popping, but you've got to try harder to remember. Now we're lawyers. We're gonna ask you questions, but you're the one who's got to answer them. The words have to come out of your mouth. There's a lot of money waitin' out there for you, and I mean millions, and we're trying to help you get that so you can buy anything you want to buy. You want a beautiful house up on a hill like Mrs. Driscoll? You can have it! You want a trip around the world? It's yours. Diamonds, furs, anything you want! You'll never have to do another day's work the rest of your life. The rest of your life! Do you hear? But you gotta help me. We can't do it all by ourselves." Fred Bates and Jack Ripps were in conference with Bess Johnson, explaining about the legal system from their perspective.

"Attorney Ripps," Johnson said, "I want to help. I really do. I just don't remember much about that accident."

"That's not too unusual, Bess. Lots of people are like that. It's what we call a traumatic event. Some people suffer a kind of amnesia. But I usually find that we can help you think back and pull all that information out of your subconscious. It's there, you know. We just have to bring it out. We've had some experience with this, and we have already been studying this case and the van and the tires and the accident scene, and we think we know pretty much what happened. Just follow along, and we'll see if we cain't bring it out."

"All right, Attorney Ripps, I'll do what I can," Bess Johnson said, a little bewildered but beginning to get the picture.

"First of all, you were driving along, coming back from Columbia, and you were traveling between 50 and 55 miles an hour, weren't you?" Ripps led.

"I'm afraid I was goin' a little faster than that, Attorney Ripps," she responded.

Bates couldn't sit still any longer, interjecting, "Now listen to Mr. Ripps, Bess. Maybe you had been going faster earlier, but you must have slowed down because you were going home, and you weren't more than a mile from home. You know good and well you must have slowed down, didn't you?"

"Maybe a little, yeah, maybe I did."

"And you slowed down to the range of 50 to 55, didn't you, Bess?"

"If you say so, Attorney Bates, I guess maybe I did."

"Okay, Jack, sorry to interrupt. This is your deal. Just go ahead now," Bates said.

Ripps continued: "And while you were going along at 50 to 55 miles an hour, headed home, the children had all fallen to sleep in the back seat, hadn't they?"

"I don't know about that, Attorney Ripps, they had been wide awake... ."

"Now, Bess, they had been wide awake earlier, but it had been a long day, they were exhausted, and they had been riding in the van for thirty minutes or more. Don't you think they had fallen asleep by the time of the accident?"

Bates could see his partner was having some difficulty with this client, and he stepped in once more, "Think of it this way, Bess. Just imagine you're in that Phoenix County Courthouse, and just imagine I'm making the closing argument on your behalf. I'd a whole lot rather say something like this: 'And while two mothers in the front seat drove quietly and carefully home, three precious children were sleeping peacefully in the back, with pleasant dreams in their little heads. Little did they know their bed was a death trap and that one of them would never awaken from that slumber, and the other two would have their waking hours radically changed by what was about to happen.' See what this does for us, Bess? First, by saying those children were asleep, it eliminates any suggestion that you lost control because of distractions from the children, and it also helps me paint a more sympathetic picture and get the jury angry at these big corporations that did this terrible thing to these children. Think back, now, don't you remember they were sleeping? Of course, we don't want you to say that unless it's the truth."

"Maybe Sarena was, I don't know," Bess Johnson struggled.

"Try harder, Bess, see if you can't remember they were all sleeping. It's logical."

"Maybe so. But what if Doretta don't remember it that way? Or Jimason or Katyna?" asked Johnson.

"One thing's for sure," Ripps said pointedly, "Sarena's not gonna say anything. Then Jimason, if he ever recovers enough to come to trial, he won't be able to remember anything, or if he contradicts it, we'll just say he was confused after all that brain injury and brain surgery. You oughta be able to lead your daughter Katyna in the right direction. And Doretta? We'll be meeting with her right after you. If her recollection is different on this point, we'll let you know," Ripps advised.

"Don't misunderstand us, Bess. We want you to tell the truth. We never in the world would tell you to do anything other than tell the truth, it's our duty as lawyers. But truth is a hard thing to get a handle on. Different people remember things in different ways, more often than not. And after all you've been through, it's understandable you don't remember everything exactly like it happened, and that's where we come in to help you," Bates explained.

"I appreciate your help. I really do, 'cause you know about these things and I don't. You're attorneys."

"Where were we Bess? Let's see. You were returning home, going about 50 to 55, and the children were in the back seat sleeping quietly. Are you with me so far?"

"I guess so."

"Now," Ripps continued, "you heard a loud popping sound. Do you remember that?"

"My daughter Katyna was poppin' bubble gum."

"For God's sake, I thought you just told us Katyna was asleep. You did hear a loud popping sound, though, didn't you?" Ripps asked.

"Okay, I did," Bess confirmed.

"Okay, you heard a loud popping noise, and that's when the tire blew out, Bess. You with me?"

"I think so," she answered.

"Let me hear you say that, Bess, say, `I heard a loud popping sound.'" Bess Johnson dutifully repeated it.

"Next what did you do?" Ripps asked rhetorically. Johnson, thinking he really wanted to know, answered, "I don't know. I just couldn't seem to control it. I was turning, but nothin' worked."

"Here's what you did, Bess, as we've reconstructed it," Ripps continued, "you tried your best to turn the steering wheel to the right, but no matter what you did, the van veered off to the left. Got that?"

"I tried to turn to the left and the car went to the left?" she ventured.

"No. No. No. No. You tried to turn right, and the van went left. Just think, right-left, right-left, right-left. You right-handed, Bess?"

"Yes, sir."

"Then it should be easy. Think of your right hand first. That's what you tried to do. But then it went to the left. Try that again."

Bess Johnson said triumphantly, as if mastering a new skill, "I tried to turn it to the right, but it went left."

"Yeah! Yeah! You've got it, Bess. That'll help us nail the van maker. Can you smell that money now, Bess?"

"I'm beginning to, I think."

"Another question: Did you apply the brakes, Bess? Did you hit the brakes?"

"I don't think I did. But maybe I did," Bess answered. "Is that right?"

"It's not how I want you to answer, Bess, it's what's the truth, and we're just trying to help you bring out the truth. But the witness in the car behind you, Lonnie Gresham, said he didn't see brake lights and that happens to be helpful, so that's consistent with what you just said. You can stick with that, all right?" Ripps advised.

"When you go in for your deposition they might ask you if you noticed whether the tire was low on air. There was a nail in it, and so it's logical they might ask you if you noticed whether it was low on air. I take it you didn't notice, did you? Good! Next thing - wait a minute. Fred, do you think we should go into that impact thing, where this so-called expert of ours says the tire hit something? Yeah, I think so, too. Bess, you didn't run into any potholes or bricks or pieces of lumber in the road or anything did you?"

"No, sure didn't. Well, now, let me see. Yeah, seems like I did back into one of them concrete things leaving the dentist office, you know, one of them slabs they put to mark parkin' spaces." Bess offered.

"Bess, you know that couldn't have hurt anything. I'm sure that was a small thing that made no difference. You probably ran over an acorn somewhere too, but you wouldn't get into that, would you? Say what you have to, but don't muddy the water with little things that don't matter."

"All right, then," Bess Johnson said.

"Now about your teeth. When they start asking you about your injuries, don't go volunteering to 'em that you had already lost most of your teeth. Just tell them all your teeth were broken when your mouth hit the steering wheel. That's the truth, isn't it? Every single one of the teeth you had in your mouth was knocked out. Now they might find out from the dentist, but then, again, they might never take that dentist's deposition. And if they do, you can just say, `all I meant was I lost all the teeth I still had in my mouth'. Understand?"

"Yes, sir," answered the client.

"What else do we need to cover with you, Bess?"

"Well, I do have a question or two. First, I used my Aunt Cornelia's insurance card for my dentist work, you know, I told the dentist I was Cornelia. Are they gon' find out about that and will it get me or Cornelia into any trouble?" Bess asked.

"Hell, I don't know, Bess, maybe they won't find out. But I'm sure lots of people use other people's insurance. Anyhow, I think the jury will understand and won't hold it against you if it does come out. Any other questions you have?"

"Yeah, got one more. What about my job? I need to do somethin' about it, 'cause if I want to keep it I gotta do somethin' soon. I'm pretty good right now, except my teeth ain't fixed yet. And I know you say I'm gon' get lots of money, but I ain't seen none yet. Went by the packin' company the other day and saw my friends and my boss. I told 'em I thought I was gon' come into a lota money one of these days. I was gon' give myself a retirement party and invite all of 'em to come. And *then* maybe I'll hire my boss to do my yardwork! Ha! Course I didn't say that out loud to him. Truth is, though, I kinda miss the place. Old Henry Holman says he'll keep on givin' me my ride - someday I'm gon' do somethin' nice for him when I get my money. What should I do?"

"Bess, I can answer that," said Bates. "You just can't go back to work while this case is going on. Now I know you want to, but it won't look good. For every dollar you earn if you go back to work, if you can physically do the work, it'll cost you a thousand dollars or more with the jury on your case. You don't want 'em to think you've recovered and weren't hurt real bad. Just take yourself a rest; you deserve it. Maybe we can even get you covered under your Uncle's Sheriff's policy, pay your salary while you're out. Then, like you say, after the trial, you can afford to hire them to work for you! Meanwhile, stay away from that packing company."

"All right, Bess," said Ripps, "if that's all we can do for you, why don't you go on home and prop your feet up and just take it real easy, and as you leave, send Doretta in so we can help her get ready."

Bess Johnson went out into the reception room and saw Doretta. "Looks like it's your turn, Doretta," an-nounced Johnson. "Well, go on in there. They're ready for you, but I don't know whether you're ready for them! I'll talk to you later. Sam's 'sposed to pick us up in for-ty-five minutes. But you go on in and I'll wait here."

Bess Johnson waited in the lawyers' reception room, looking out the windows. She looked at her watch, think-ing and remembering that her uncle was usually fairly punctual unless an emergency should come up in the Sheriff's Department.

She wondered what it would be like, spending all that time at home, instead of working. It used to be she didn't have the time she'd like for her boyfriend, with work and the children. Or she often would be tired and not in a ro-mantic mood. But Louis Goodlett was an on-and-off type fellow who would camp out at her house for periods and then disappear for days at the time. Bess Johnson never asked questions about where he was or what he was doing, though he usually said he had gone to see his mama. On the one hand she was glad he was there a lot, because he could help some with the children, and he always had plenty of flexibility because he had no regular job. On the other hand, she was usually glad to get a break from him when he went away. So, it had worked out pretty well, her arrangement with Louis. Since the accident, her relationship with Louis had been rocky. He was turned off by her toothless mouth, and their love life was fragile. Yet Bess now saw that she would be spending most of her time at home, where he also would be when not working odd jobs. Ironically, they were being thrown together more than ever, at a time their physical and emotional relationship had been cooling. It had not al-ways been cool, she thought, remembering the grasping, the kissing, the laughing, the playful tenderness, the raw and raucous lust they had shared as man and woman. She wondered if he would be there today. Would his hopes for her expected lawsuit winnings be the tie that would bind them hereafter, a substitute for the attraction which had first brought them together?

In the conference room down the hall, Bates and Ripps were preparing Doretta Anchrum for her deposition. It was not going smoothly, as Anchrum was having trouble remembering about Bess Johnson's actions when the van went out of control. After several starts, Anchrum seemed to be getting it together - if only she could remember it the right way. The lawyers were not at all sure she would get it straight: was it that Bess turned left and the van went right, or was it... ?

They tried to help her on some other points but rolled their eyes as Anchrum would get tangled up on what she was to say. "I just don't remember. I don't remember," Anchrum pleaded, almost crying.

Fred Bates frowned at his partner, "Look, Jack, we've just got two main points where she absolutely has to give some testimony, come hell or high water. First, she's gotta support Bess on steering right and the van going left, 'cause Bess is vulnerable without a witness. Obviously, Bess' memory isn't gon' be worth a damn standing by itself. We need Doretta to corroborate that point to stick it to Tergano. Second, she's gon' have to testify about Jimason. She's the kid's mama and there's no way on God's green earth she can avoid testifying about his condition. But as far as the rest of it goes, we can forget it. I mean *forget* it. The lady says she don't remember, doesn't she? Well, let's let her say that." Turning to Anchrum, he continued, "Doretta, if those lawyers for Universal and Tergano ask you about anything other than those two points, you just tell 'em you don't remember, you hear me? Don't go and get all mixed up trying to answer. Just tell them it's all been hard on you, with Jimason's situation and all that, and you just don't remember. How's that?"

"Yes, sir, I can sure say that 'cause I don't remember hardly nothin'," Anchrum answered.

Ripps picked up the dialogue at that point, "Doretta, let's talk about Jimason. He's really just a vegetable, isn't he?"

"Really, he's doin' better'n I ever thought," Anchrum answered. "Jimason, he's back home and he's coming along some ways but he's diff'rent. He's gone back to school, but he don't always stay. I got all that medicine he's 'sposed to take, and he don't take it reg'lar, and, I cain't always remember it. Got so much on my mind. He just goes to the bathroom all the time, though, ain't never seen nothin' like it. Seems like he goes a quart ev'ry time, and often."

"Have you talked with the doctor about that, Doretta?" Ripps asked.

"Yeah, I talked with two or three of 'em, but I cain't tell what they're sayin', somethin' 'bout some glands or somethin' like that. His teachers, they're nice to him, but you know what? He done tried to feel out one of his teachers, yeah, and she called the principal and they all called me, and I don' know what."

"How old is Jimason?" Ripps asked.

"Why, let's see. I think he turned twelve, yeah, sure is twelve," Anchrum answered.

"Is he sexually active, Doretta? Do you know?"

"I cain't swear about that, but I think maybe he's tried. The girls, they all scaired of him, don't want nothin' to do with him, but he keeps on comin' at 'em. I cain't do nothing with that boy. Just try to keep a little peace, all I can do."

CHAPTER EIGHT

"Can he take care of himself; I mean, can he bathe himself and dress himself and go to the bathroom by himself?" Ripps asked.

"Yeah, some he can. Sometimes I helps bathe him," Anchrum replied, "I think he's lots better, but he still ain't right, you know."

"Anything in particular you notice about Jimason you want to tell us?" Bates interjected.

"He don't walk right yet, and one of his arms kinda hangs a little. 'Course, he's tryin' to bounce - what you call it, dribble? - a basketball, but he cain't really do no good at it."

"Which arm is it he's having trouble with?" Ripps asked.

"Lord, I don't know. I knows he's got troubles with his arm, but which one is it, I just don't know."

"How about his leg, which leg is giving him problems?"

"You not gon' believe this, but I just cain't remember. I'll try to notice and maybe I can tell you next time."

Ripps said, "Sure, Doretta, tell me next time. Now let me tell you what I hear you saying. Jimason is nearly lame, you have to bathe him and take him to the potty and dress him, and he's got bladder problems and his mind is gone and he's emotionally like an animal. And, adding all that up, Doretta, he's gon' have to have custodial care. You really need nurses around the clock with him, don't you, Doretta?"

"Well, I sure could use some help sometimes," Anchrum said wistfully.

"Furthermore, he's going to need custodial care around the clock *the rest of his life* and, Doretta, one of these days you're not going to be around to take care of him or do anything for him. When that time comes, Jimason's going to need even more help, isn't he?"

"Maybe so," Anchrum agreed blankly, "but what we gon' say about school? He's goin' to school and takin' care of hisself there."

Bates took that one: "I'm not sure how we handle that, Doretta. I can't bring myself to tell you to keep him home. He needs some schooling, and I'll bet he'd drive you stark screaming mad if he was home all the time. We'll explain it somehow. We'll say they were really just glorified babysitters at school. It's not really school for Jimason, see. Has he got any grades?"

"He ain't got no report card yet, but he's been bringin' home A's and B's and a few C's," Doretta Anchrum said, throwing up her hands.

"We'll have to look into that, get all the medical records, get him psychologically examined. I'd be willing to bet they're just babying him along, giving him 'social grades', knowing he'll never be able to do anything. You know he'll never be able to hold down a job, don't you, Doretta?"

"Me and him both!" Doretta grinned.

Bates' face was flushed, "That's not funny, Doretta. We're serious here, and you know that," Bates scolded.

"Let's go back over all this one more time, Doretta…"
There was a knock on the door, and Sam Johnson
stood there.

"Sorry, Sam, it's taking us a little longer with Doretta
than we thought. We'd be happy to have you stay with
us, but then the other side could ask you what we said to
Doretta. Would you mind waiting out in the lobby with
Bess? I guess Bess is out there, isn't she?" Bates said.

Yes, Bess Johnson was there. "Sam, have you got anything you want to say to Doretta?" Ripps asked, winking.

"Woman, you just do just like these attorneys say.
They're just like doctors. You do what the doctors tell
you, and you do what these lawyers tell you. They win
cases like this," Johnson advised authoritatively.

"You better believe it," Bates preened, "we do win
cases like this."

CHAPTER NINE

THE DEPOSITIONS

The telephone rang in Ted Born's office. It was the receptionist telling him a Mr. Albert Sayre was in the reception room to see him. Born looked at his watch and noted that it was eight forty-five a.m. and Sayre was fifteen minutes early. "No problem," he said to himself, "I'm ready - I hope."

Born walked out of his office on his way to the reception room but paused at his secretary's desk, "Mrs. Shelby, Bert Sayre from Universal is here. We'll be in conference this morning and then we're going out to look at the van this afternoon. Have you met him? I'll bring him by for a minute later. Would you please call Dave Thompson and tell him Bert is here and to please meet us in the north conference room. He knows we have the appointment." Mrs. Shelby lifted the phone to make the call to Thompson as Born moved on toward the reception room. "It's great to have a secretary like Mrs. Shelby," he thought. He always addressed her as "Mrs." Shelby, although a creeping informality in the firm saw lawyers and secretaries increasingly use first names. "It's not professional," Born had always said, though he found himself using first names more and more with *other* secretaries, often because he had never heard their last names. It continued to be strictly formal where he and Mrs. Shelby were concerned.

Born greeted Sayre warmly in the reception room, asked about Sayre's flight down and his evening at the hotel. Then Sayre followed Born downstairs to the conference room. Born saw Thompson at the end of the downstairs hall heading to the room, and he paused outside the conference room door to wait for Thompson, indicating to Sayre at the same time that this was the new member of the litigation team approaching.

"Bert, I'd like you to meet Dave Thompson. Dave, Bert Sayre," Born introduced them. Sayre and Thompson shook hands and exchanged pleasantries, as Born anxiously read their body language. He was not reassured by what he saw. Each man shook hands tentatively, definitely at arms-length, feet turned away from each other. "Come on in," Born invited.

Born thought it best to get right into the business at hand in the hope that Thompson and Sayre would thaw a bit. "Okay, we've got depositions starting tomorrow of

Sam Johnson, Bess Johnson and Doretta Anchrum. Oh, yeah, we'll also be taking the deposition of Sid Haley - he's the one who owned the van before Sam Johnson. I'll be taking the depositions of the Johnsons and Doretta Anchrum, and I thought Dave could take the Haley deposition, which is going to be down in Landon." Born and Thompson had already talked about dividing up the deposition responsibility between them, and Thompson understood the importance of the key witnesses and the fact that the client would naturally expect the senior lawyer to take those depositions. Thompson had taken a few depositions in his brief career, but not a lot, and he was looking forward to his first one in this case.

Sayre was coolly noncommittal, "Let's talk about the depos. Let's start with Sam Johnson. What are you going to try to get out of him?"

"Several main items, and anything else I can get," Born replied. "First, we know from Chaz Christopher's investigation that the van had 39,215 miles on it when Johnson bought the van at Citizens Tergano. We know the van had 98,554 miles when the accident occurred. So, one thing we need to know is: did Johnson put the tires on after he bought the van or were they already on it? This would help us pin down the mileage on those tires. Interestingly enough, he bought the van just four months after the tires were manufactured, in other words, nearly six years ago."

"But sometimes tires aren't bought by a consumer until maybe a year or two after production," noted Sayre.

"Still, this was a fairly popular size and popular trademark, the Surefoot, and there's a fair chance our tires were on the van most of the time Sam owned it."

"Another thing. We want to find out about Johnson's maintenance and care for the tire. We know he was no stickler about maintenance because the tires show it, but I'd like to tie it down with his own testimony. Next, I want to know all about how Bess came to be driving the van that day, and what Sam saw at the time he arrived on the scene. He'll surely be able to give us some perspective about the injuries, independently of the injured parties themselves. I also want to know his work history, who he knows and who's kin to him. The kinship will be very important later in helping us strike a reasonable jury. Certainly, I'll want to know about his relationship to the plaintiff lawyers and to other Phoenix County elected officials. I'll ask him about conversations he's had with other plaintiffs. You know the plaintiffs must have done a lot of talking among themselves about the case, and this would be very revealing - if he will just tell the truth."

"Bess, of course, is pretty obvious. Why did she go to Columbia that day? Why did she take the others with her? Where did they go in Columbia? Did she check the air pressure or add any air to the tires? Did she hit any road hazards she can remember? Exactly what happened when she lost control, and how badly injured was she? What is Katyna's condition? It might take me a while to finish her deposition, but the questions really jump out at you." Born ticked off the key questions.

Sayre nodded, and added, "You might want to ask her whether she'd ever driven a sports utility vehicle before. Also, you could touch on her driving record. You said Chaz didn't find any vehicle registrations in her name; you could ask her whether she regularly drives a car and, if not, how long has it been since she did."

"One more thing," Thompson suggested, "What were the children doing? Should we also ask about seatbelts?"

"I think we should ask about seatbelts, nail down who was and who wasn't wearing them. It might not be admissible in Court later, but discovery is broad enough we should be able to get answers about the seatbelts." Born offered.

"Okay, let's talk about Doretta Anchrum. We should ask her a lot of the same things we're asking Bess, of course. You understand I'll ask she not be present when we depose Sam and Bess, but I'm not sure I can keep her out because she's a party - not just a non-party witness - and parties have a right to be present at all proceedings. I'd sure like to see what she would say if she didn't get to hear Bess testify. Jimason's condition is going to be an important subject in her depo, maybe her own condition, but I don't think she was hurt much. I'll ask what she saw and heard. Bates tells me she doesn't drive. I'll ask a couple of questions about that. I want a long list of her relatives for jury selection purposes." Born sized up the Anchrum deposition. Then he turned to Thompson.

"Dave, you know what we need from Haley, the former car owner?" Born asked.

"Yeah. We basically need to know whether the Universal tires were already on the van when he traded it to Citizens, or did they get added later. How did the car drive and how'd it handle? That's about it." Thompson said.

Sayre added, "Well, there are a few other things. Maintenance on the van. Any major wrecks or repairs. And it's important we find out how well his first set of tires held up. See, the camber of the van and handling of the van could affect tire wear, and I'd like to know if he thought his first set of tires were wearing excessively or unevenly on that particular van." Thompson was not sure whether he detected a confidence deficiency in Sayre's tone of voice, but he said nothing.

"What do you think Tergano's lawyers might ask? We were first to send the depo notices and so we'll get to go first with the questions, thank goodness. We don't want to get crosswise with Tergano, but do you think they, in a subtle way, might try to make this a pure tire explosion case and get themselves out?" Born asked Sayre.

"Of course, I don't know. They might eventually try to focus on the blowout, but I think it's a little early for that in this case. Probably, they'll try to nail down the handling characteristics to show there was nothing wrong with the van or with its design. If it handled in the normal way, it should have been easily controllable on a straight road. What that means, is that Bess Johnson must have panicked and jerked the wheel, maybe slamming the brakes in the process." Sayre responded.

"That would be a tough sell to the jury. It's hard to blame an injured party who's suffered a lot. The jury probably is going to want to believe she was not at fault." Born counseled. "Anyway, we should know a lot more after we take the depositions tomorrow. We might even learn some helpful things this afternoon. Actually, we don't yet know the plaintiffs' theories about defects in the tire or in the van, so we - and Tergano - will have to try to cover all bases with these particular witnesses."

The group continued to bat ideas back and forth until Born again looked at his watch and saw that it was nearly noon. Born had arranged for the trio to see the remains of the van at Farley's garage that afternoon, after lunch. Born went to his office, followed by Sayre and Thompson, and introduced Sayre to Mrs. Shelby: "It's so good to know you, Mr. Sayre. You had a call a few minutes ago, and here is the call-back number. Is there anything else we can do for you, plane reservations or anything?"

"Not a thing," Sayre answered, favorably impressed by the hospitable warmth of her efficient messages, not just warmth, but genuineness. "Actually, I need a place to change into some jeans. I know I'm going to get dirty crawling under and inspecting the van."

Born offered, "How about my office across the hall? We'll all stand guard outside to make sure no one comes in on you. Wish I had thought to bring some myself. You can also return your call while you're in there." Sayre accepted the offer and retreated to make the change. "What do you think of Bert?" asked Born.

"He seems very nice," answered Mrs. Shelby.

"He's fine," said Thompson, smiling philosophically, "but I can see I'm going to have to prove myself. He's not too sure of me."

"Oh, Dave, he's only just met you. If it's any comfort, I'm having to prove myself too. He's not at all sure I can handle an exploding tire case. He'll be all right as soon as he sees more of us."

After grabbing sandwiches, the three men drove out to the garage. Marty Low, a paralegal/investigator for Bates & Ripps was waiting for them. He had arranged for the van to be set up on a hydraulic lift which could be raised or lowered for better viewing of the van. Born was careful to introduce Sayre only as the "client rep" without giving a name; he did not want to inspire the plaintiffs to take Sayre's deposition, which would not likely happen if Sayre remained anonymous.

Sayre was knowledgeable about vans as well as tires, and he went carefully through the ruins of the blue and white Logos, noting the odometer reading, car tag, vehicle identification number and similar data, as well as the absence of oil change stickers. Then he observed the deformed appearance of the driver's seat, bent backward severely at the top. The brake and brake light still appeared to be in working order; but the accelerator pedal was bent so that its left edge was slightly below the brake pedal. The single seat lock on the back seat had broken and the back seat had folded forward, almost certainly on impact. The shatterproof glass was shattered, but most glass clung to the clear sticky film sandwiched between the double panes of windshield glass. Sayre and Born together measured the dimensions of the V-shaped indention in the grille area.

They noticed that the front tires were angled to the right and that the left front tire was wedged immovably against the bent metal of the fender. "These front wheels were obviously in this right-turn condition at the time of impact and got frozen in that condition. I guess that still doesn't tell us much about the tire rupture," Sayre remarked.

"What do you make of it, Bert, overall, I mean?" asked Born.

"Not much," Sayre responded. "I'm still considering an accident reconstructionist. The only trouble is, I don't really see how he can help us. We know this much: Bess probably did not apply the brakes, otherwise the accelerator pedal would not be bent under the brake pedal. It seems to have been a steering problem mainly. She could have hit the accelerator, but if she floored it, I don't see how any of the passengers not wearing seatbelts could have survived the crash. We might be able to compute the speed of the van by calculating the force necessary to make the indentation in the grille and front bumper, but I'm not sure where that gets us."

"I don't, either," said Born. "If our tire was defective and blew out, the jury is not going to let us off the hook because Bess Johnson panicked and steered the van to the left, across the road and into the tree. And their decision probably isn't going to be affected much by Bess' speed. In the first place, the speed couldn't have been outrageously excessive because, as you say, there wouldn't be survivors; and even if it was, that only means Bess might have been contributorily negligent, but none of the passengers could be held accountable for her negligence. The worst injuries, and the death, involve people whose claims could not be affected by the driver's negligence, if any. I guess what that means is that we've got to prove the tire was a good one, because if it wasn't, we really don't have a defense."

"Yeah, the tire's the key," Thompson agreed.

The next day, lawyers for Universal and Tergano converged at the law offices of Bates & Ripps for Sam Johnson's deposition. He appeared in uniform, had a serious demeanor, was courteous but said little except when spoken to. He related a background of hard times, hard work and supportive parents. He had a part-time job delivering prescription drugs for the Phoenix Pharmacy and, since there were few drug stores in the county and a good many elderly and poor Medicare/Medicaid patients, Johnson got around to a lot of homes on his rounds. He would take a few minutes when he could to visit with them and, yes, he was proud that he knew almost every adult in Phoenix County. Those he had not met via private enterprise, he had met through his years of service in the Sheriff's Department, first as a deputy and now as Sheriff.

He first bought the Logos about five and a half years before the accident. The van had new tires on it when he bought it. For Johnson, the new tires had been one of the selling points for the van, one of the main reasons he bought it, and he had never bought any replacement tires. It was obvious then to Born and Thompson that the tires had at least 58,500 miles on it, subtracting the mileage on the van when Johnson purchased it, as shown by the title papers, from the mileage at the time of the accident.

Johnson said he never rotated the tires, never did any special servicing of them. He said he assumed the tires were properly balanced when he became owner and never balanced them or had the balance checked. Johnson denied he ever had a problem of low air pressure or leaks in any of the tires. He vehemently denied using tire sealant to retard leakage. In fact, Johnson denied ever having a flat or repairing a flat on any of the tires. He said he was not aware of the nail which was penetrating the tire as of the time of the accident, first he ever heard of it was at his deposition. Johnson claimed he usually changed his own oil and said he bought gasoline at two or three stations, but used them only for gasoline purchase, not for any service work. It was possible, but not easy, for an owner to change his own oil in the Logos, because of the way the oil pan fitted in, and the absence of oil change stickers lent some credibility to Johnson's testimony on that point.

Johnson related how he came to lend the Logos to his niece Bess, her telephone call that Saturday morning when he was shaving and trying to get off to work. He went on to tell about being one of the first at the scene after the van's accident. He professed to have had no discussions with Bess Johnson and Doretta Anchrum about the accident, on orders from his counsel. He knew little of the condition of the passengers in the car, except he knew of Sarena Miller's death. He told of getting Sarena's dress from the van, the only time he had seen the van since the accident.

One thing Sam Johnson was positive about was that the van had always driven well, no steering problems, no unusual vibrations, no shakes or shimmies or handling problems of any kind. He said his wife and others who borrowed the van from time to time all were complimentary of its smooth ride. Johnson denied using the van much for off-road driving, although he remembered using it off-road to pull a car out of a ditch some two weeks before the accident, the last time anyone had driven it before his niece Bess borrowed it that fatal day.

When Bess Johnson was called for her deposition, she acknowledged three speeding tickets within an eighteen-month period before she hit a cow and destroyed her last car. She told of her coping without a car for nearly two years now, getting rides to work and borrowing cars on weekends or hitching rides. No, she was not able to work after the accident, as she could no longer lift anything heavy.

She related the trip to Columbia that Saturday morning, how she stopped and got a fill-up of gas. No, she did not check the air pressure or anything else. She was in a hurry, and it was a self-service station.

The van drove well, no bumps or vibration, no

difficulty of handling. Then, on the return trip as the van was nearing the Driscoll property, she was driving at exactly 55 mph when she heard a loud popping sound and she tried her best to turn the steering wheel to the right. However, the van went out of control and continued pulling to the left despite all her efforts, until it hit the tree. No, the children did not distract her; they were very quiet, she thought sound asleep.

Every tooth in her head was knocked out in the accident; she had only had maybe one or two pulled in her life up to that time. She was badly hurt, in addition to the teeth: a broken wrist, a nasty gash in her hairline and an ugly scar on her knee. She did not quite understand what "consortium" meant, but she knew she was not as attractive to men, and her love life had suffered.

Katyna had a steel pin in her leg, might have to have it, or a re-sized replacement, the rest of her life, Bess Johnson said. Katyna hobbled around and could not participate in games with other children her age.

It took nearly all day to depose Sam Johnson and Bess Johnson, and Doretta Anchrum had heard all of it, as plaintiffs' counsel insisted (correctly, Born knew) that she had a right to be present. Furthermore, Bates and Ripps would have the evening to work with Anchrum further if they wished to prepare her for her deposition the next morning.

The next day after breakfast, Thompson drove off to Landon to take the deposition of Sid Haley, while Born and Sayre returned to the Bates & Ripps office to commence the Anchrum deposition. Born had hardly begun questioning Anchrum about the trip to Columbia when she volunteered, a little prematurely, that Bess Johnson had tried to turn right but the van went left. Yes, she also had heard the loud pop just before Bess Johnson lost control. Anchrum had never driven a car of any type and knew little about cars except you turned the key and they moved. However, she affirmed the van had at all times driven smoothly with no vibration, even right up to the instant when Bess lost control.

Born got mostly "I don't know," in response to many of his questions, until he began asking about Anchrum's health and Jimason's health. Anchrum still hurt a lot, she said, but had no broken bones. She verified she was the only person in the van wearing a seatbelt. Jimason was in bad shape. She had to bathe him, dress him, take him to the bathroom. He didn't make sense when he talked. The other children thought he was strange and didn't like to play with him. He was hard to control in terms of discipline. Also, he had bladder problems and had lots of medicine he was supposed to take.

Jimason's right arm and right leg did not behave properly, hung down limply and could be used only a little. A big surprise was Anchrum's assertion that Jimason seemed to be blind in his right eye. Yes, he was in school but some of his classes were special ed, and she wasn't sure how he was doing or how he managed to take care of himself while in school.

When the depositions were finished, Born and Sayre

accompanied Trip Gillespy back to his office, a few blocks away, to share thoughts. They left word with Fred Bates to send Thompson to Gillespy's office if he returned from the Haley deposition in Landon.

"They're conceding poor maintenance of the tire. Wonder why?" Sayre asked. Born responded, "My guess is, they are afraid to admit they've repaired or modified the tires in any way. You see, South Carolina has this Extended Manufacturer's Liability Doctrine which essentially says: if a product leaves the hands of a manufacturer and remains unmodified by the user and injuries occur attributable to the product, the plaintiff need only show a defect in the product, not necessarily negligence as has traditionally been required, in order to establish manufacturer liability. The plaintiffs probably see themselves in a dilemma. If they acknowledge repairs and maintenance, they might lose the benefit of the EMLD; if they do not, they could be guilty of product abuse. So, they don't know what to do, but apparently they opted for the 'no maintenance approach.' But, do you think it's possible Sam Johnson really did not maintain the tires?"

"I suspect there was very little maintenance, but one thing I believe they did do. I think Sam must have rotated the tires once. Otherwise, why would the two most worn tires be on the rear? Everybody knows front tires wear faster than rear tires, that's the very reason you're supposed to rotate them," Sayre opined.

"They've also got some sort of theory about my Tergano van," Trip Gillespy thought aloud. "She tried to steer it right and it went left. Looks like they're going to say something was wrong with the steering system. That's nuts, of course, but some of the jurors might believe it. I'll be interested to see what kind of expert opinion evidence they come up with to support that theory."

"We know it was probably human error, but can either of us - Universal or Tergano - try the case on that basis? Do we possibly dare to blame the accident on Bess Johnson's driving? That's not an appealing tack," Born observed.

"Apparently, the injuries are pretty bad, even accounting for some exaggeration by the ones we've heard in the last two days. We'll have to wait for the medical depositions to see just how bad, but they're bad. I'm just thankful Jimason is not a total vegetable. We certainly do have one death, in addition, and this case could set new records in damages, even by standards of the Phoenix County," Trip noted ruefully.

At that point, Dave Thompson joined them, having just returned from the deposition in Landon. "Well, the first owner of the van says it still had the original set of tires on it when he traded it in at Citizens Tergano at 39,215 miles, so Citizens would have had to have put the new tires on. We heard Sam Johnson say they were on the van when he bought it with a little over 40,000 miles on it. If we estimate the van had 39,500 miles on it when the new tires were installed, that would mean the new tires lasted -"

"Nearly 59,000 miles," Sayre interrupted, subtracting

39,500 miles from the terminal van mileage of 98,554.

"Yeah, pretty close to 60,000 miles, not a bad tire."

Born was thinking out loud also, "Nearly six years and 60,000 miles. Had to have been a great tire."

"Does that mean you win?" Gillespy wryly brought him down to earth.

"I'll let one of you answer that one," Born said, "We've got a blow-out, an out of control van that killed a beautiful little girl, brain-injured another child and caused other injuries. Our opposition is the Sheriff of Phoenix County and his friends and neighbors. The jury will be their other friends and neighbors. And juries in Phoenix County, even in less sympathetic cases, are giving huge multi-million-dollar verdicts. You tell me. Anybody think we can win this case because the tire was old and worn out?"

The room was hushed, and some looked down at their feet, others out the window, as if to crawl into their shoes or escape into another space.

CHAPTER TEN

PHOENIX COUNSEL

Rusty Loman was at his desk in his office on a side street on Courthouse Square in Groveton when the telephone rang. "Rusty Loman," he said into the phone.

"This is Ted Born in Greenville, Rusty. I wondered if you could help us on a case?"

"What kind of case?" Rusty asked.

"I represent Universal Tire and we're defendants with Tergano Motors in a lawsuit in Phoenix County. There was a death and some bad injuries."

"Is this the one involving the Sheriff and his relatives?" Rusty asked.

"Yes, it is," Born acknowledged.

"When is it set for trial?" Loman inquired.

"Not set yet," said Born.

"What would you want me to do?"

"Be a part of our trial team," Born replied.

Loman was relieved but still noncommittal. He was tired of out-of-county lawyers doing all the work on a Phoenix County case and billing the client for big fees, then calling him at the last minute to help just with jury selection. He had already vowed he would never be used in that manner again, that he would participate as a real lawyer or not at all.

Still, despite Born's assurance, he was ambivalent about this case. How wise would it be to get on the wrong side of the Sheriff?

"Can you give me a few days to think about it?" Loman asked.

"Sure," said Born. "We'd really like to work with you. To be quite frank, I would have called you earlier, but we'd worked with Jess Robinson in other cases and had talked with him about this one. But he's decided, I think, not to work on the defense side of these cases anymore."

"Okay, I'll give you a call as soon as I can see my way clear."

Ted Born had given up on Jess Robinson's committing to the case and had looked at alternatives. He made inquiries of lawyers who had practiced in Phoenix County, including Tergano's local counsel Trip Gillespy, and he studied the Martindale-Hubbell legal directory. Born ultimately rejected the idea of local counsel who did not in fact live in Phoenix County. "We don't really need trial expertise much from our local counsel. We need someone who really knows the county," he told himself. Born adhered to the traditional belief among lawyers that it is virtual malpractice to try a major case in a parochial county without good local counsel. From a technical standpoint, Born could try the lawsuit alone, but he needed local counsel to guide him through the local minefields. This called for a lawyer who did not merely live in an adjacent county - unless he could get a regional superhero like Jess Robinson - but someone who knew the people, knew the relatives, knew the local scuttlebutt, someone who had driven down Highway 53 many times, and all the backroads of Phoenix County as well.

There were essentially two lawyers who practiced law full time in Phoenix County, and the *other* lawyer had a conflict of interest. He had been local counsel for the Tokers firm in the first complaint filed in this case before Bates & Ripps took over. He had lost out when the lead attorneys changed, but having represented the plaintiffs even briefly, he would be disqualified from working with a defendant. That left Rusty Loman, a lawyer with eleven years of practice, but whom no one seemed to know well. Still, he was the only realistic alternative.

For Loman's part, getting started as a lawyer in Phoenix County had not been easy. Much of the local work was low paying, collect-your-fee-if-you-can work, and it had not always been easy to pay the rent and buy groceries. Even with more than ten years of practice, he was still regarded as the new kid on the block. But with the repeated big verdicts in Phoenix County, Loman realized that he had valuable local knowledge to sell, to plaintiffs and defendants.

Some plaintiffs' lawyers, like the Bates & Ripps firm, never hired local Phoenix County counsel because Bates felt he knew the county as well as anyone, and Ripps actually still lived in the County on its periphery not far from Columbia. The other main set of plaintiff lawyers plying their profession in the county seemed locked in with Loman's only local competitor. So, Loman had largely sat on the sidelines for much of the time while big verdicts in Phoenix County were making national headlines. He had once or twice helped with jury selection for corporate defendants in some big cases, but he had received minimal compensation for that, and he felt insulted they had not wanted him to function as a real lawyer, and he vowed never to let that happen again.

Rusty Loman was a true product of Phoenix County, not a transplant, had attended local Phoenix County schools, where he was one of the few white students. He had always wanted to be a lawyer and had always wanted to practice law on the beautiful little square in Groveton, where he could even walk to work, if he wished, or go home for lunch. There, in the pastoral countryside he could live and work and hunt and fish, where the sky was blue, and the air was pure. He could have his own vegetable garden behind a stately old house he was personally restoring in his spare time. It would take only a fraction as much money to live a far better life than anything a city could offer. Besides, it was home.

It had taken some persuasion to convince his wife to share the dream of a country lawyer, but now she too was a convert. It seemed so right, and so natural, to live in Groveton, in the heart of Phoenix County.

He talked over the call from Ted Born with his wife and with his parents. He thought of the frustration of trying to make a name for himself, frustration he had already experienced, watching the big cases go by without his involvement. "Maybe my problem is that I'm not black," Loman reflected. "The big city lawyers figure they only need a black lawyer in this county. Can't do anything about that. Well, Bates & Ripps haven't hired me, and they're not going to hire me. I'd rather be on the plaintiff side and hit the jackpot in one big case, but here is this Universal case. It *is* a big case and they want me, and no one else seems to be beating my doors down at the moment. Still better, they want me - they say - as a part of their team, not just for jury selection. Who knows? If Universal wins this one, which they probably won't, but *if* they were to win it, it would be a shot heard 'round the world. Everybody - plaintiffs and defendants - then would want me on their side. Why not? It'll be the best fee I'll get this year, probably."

So, after much thought, Loman signed on. "Ted, Rusty Loman," Loman called Born. "If you still want me, I'm ready to go. I decided the other side hadn't hired me, so why not? Sheriff Sam isn't going to like it, but he's so tied in with Bates & Ripps I don't know that it will ever matter. So here I am. What would you like me to do?"

"Delighted to have you aboard. Dave Thompson and I will want to meet with you soon. In the meantime, I'm going to send you a copy of our file on the case. Read it so you will be up to speed with us. I know of one project I'd like you to work on as soon as possible. I'd like you to make a survey of the big cases in Phoenix County over the last six years or so, you know, after the *Driscoll* case which I understand was the first big one. I'm not interested in the criminal cases or the divorce cases or the cases where a local resident sues another local over a cow or a property line or something like that. I'm interested just in cases brought by individual plaintiffs against good-sized corporations based on personal injury, wrongful death, products liability or fraud. In other words, cases where the jury had discretion to award big bucks for punitive damages or pain and suffering and such." Born wasted no time giving Loman the "GO" signal for the first assignment.

"Okay, I got you. I guess you want to know the type of case and the amount of damages?"

"Yes, and a few other things. What I want is information to help us find out what went wrong for the defendants in the other cases so we can maybe avoid the pitfalls. I want copies of the complaint, answer, pretrial order, verdict forms and post-trial motions, and any briefs. I want the names of the lawyers for all the parties, and if they are available, I want the names of all the jurors who served on the big verdict cases. One of the things we need to do is to begin building a data bank of potential jurors, with information about as many Phoenix County residents as possible."

Born definitely knew what he wanted, Loman thought. "That's a pretty ambitious program. I guess I'd better get started right away," Loman observed.

"Will you have any trouble, Rusty, getting access to all those files in the clerk's office? I understand it's a small room. I don't know how the clerk will react to your rummaging through all the files. I don't think any of us Greenville lawyers could get away with it. I know they're all public records and there're not supposed to be any secrets, but I suspect a hostile clerk could tell you she'll provide only specific files, one at a time, and not let you flip through them on a fishing expedition," Born probed.

"Shouldn't have any problem if I start right away. I'm on good terms with the present Clerk, but there's a good chance she will be voted out of office in the November elections and would then vacate office in January. Fred Bates has run the deputy clerk against her, and it's a black/white issue, and the present deputy who is black will probably win. I don't have any problem with the deputy, except she's beholden to Bates and might not want to help me - to put it mildly."

"Are Bates and Ripps into local politics in a big way?" Born asked.

"I'll say!" said Loman. "Fred Bates always represented the County Council and was in real good with the last head of the Council. That's how Bates got to know Sam Johnson: he represented Sam on a couple of police brutality charges, while Sam was just Deputy Sheriff, as a favor to the County Council executive. When he retired, Jack Ripps organized a big retirement party for him, acted as master of ceremonies in fact. Jack personally went to every business, every county official and lots of residents to get them to buy congratulatory ads in the program booklet handed out to everyone at the retirement party. With the money he raised, and with the extra money Ripps and Bates added, they bought a Lincoln Continental and presented it to him at the party."

"Bates and Ripps have also been heavy contributors to the County Council members" Loman continued. "Now the present Clerk, she's the widow of the man who used to serve as clerk and died in office, and she was ap-pointed to succeed her husband as Clerk. She's one of the last countywide white officials, and Bates has taken aim at her. He's backing her deputy, and she knows it. No love lost between Bates and the Clerk."

"I take it the Circuit Judge is immune to that kind of influence. At least I've heard nothing but good things about him," Born said, seeking assurance.

"Oh, yeah, Judge Andrews is outstanding. He's ap-pointed to a three-county circuit as Circuit Judge, and Phoenix is the smallest county in his circuit. Not much Bates can do to get rid of him, and Bates knows it."

"I'd guess Bates and Ripps obviously try to sidle up to him?" Born asked.

"I'm sure they do. They know he's going to be Judge regardless of what they do. But Bates can't influence Judge

Andrews, if that's what you're worried about. Last spring Jack Ripps sent out a letter to numerous Phoenix County residents asking them to support Judge Andrews for reappointment. Trouble was, Ripps never told Andrews in advance that he was going to do that. It made Judge Andrews hopping mad because he had no announced opposition and none was expected. The Judge saw through it, as an effort on Ripps' part to make people think Ripps had some special relationship with the Court. One thing you can count on is that Judge Andrews will be fair. Maybe more cautious than defense lawyers would like, but definitely fair."

When the two lawyers had hung up their telephones, Born felt good about the call, thought Loman just might do the job that was needed, and appreciated all those insights into local politics an outsider would otherwise never know. The whole idea of politics infecting the law was extremely distasteful to Born, but he was as realistic as he was idealistic, and he knew it was there, could not be ignored. It was good to be reassured that the Judge was fair; still, his fairness would not erase the fact of big verdicts, a few before Judge Andrews took the bench, but several on his watch as well. When all is accounted for, politics is everything in government, and law and justice are a part of government, ergo, no way to separate law from politics.

Born called in his paralegal, Nita Langley, asked her to take a seat and said, "We have this case in the Common Pleas division of Circuit Court down in Phoenix County. I want you to read the file and then we'll talk about it. The bottom line is, it's a serious case and we have lots of work to do. I'd like you to begin working with our local counsel in Phoenix County on a data base of potential jurors. I'd also like you to analyze the data on past comparable cases in Phoenix County. Be sure to bring to my attention any tidbits you think would be interesting, like irregularities in the trials of those cases. I'm really not entirely sure what I'm looking for, but we've had some extreme results in that county, and we need to try to identify what we're up against. Our local counsel is Rusty Loman, and he'll be feeding us information as he goes through the court records. Let me call Dave Thompson."

Dave appeared and sat in Born's office in a chair next to Nita Langley. "Dave, we're trying to get started on a data bank for potential jurors. Rusty Loman called a while ago and said he would work with us, and he'll be culling data from the court files on the bad cases, potential jurors and anything else we can think of, to send to us. But I thought maybe we could get started with the telephone book I picked up last time we were down there. Let's see. Here it is." Born began flipping through the book. "What is this! I can't believe it! A telephone book without addresses? I was going to have this telephone book optically scanned and then put into our computer so we could arrange Phoenix County residents by addresses, to see who lives near whom, who's a neighbor of whom. But there aren't any addresses!"

"That's not too unusual, Ted," said Thompson. "We

had the same situation at my home in North Carolina. Those little thin community telephone directories often don't have addresses. For one thing, most people just live on rural routes and don't really have street addresses."

"This is going to be tougher than I thought," Ted Born said aloud. "I guess we'll have to wait for Rusty Loman to send us something for our data bank."

"I'll call him and see what he might have, and I'll get started right away," Langley said.

"Okay, here's the file," Born handed it to her. She smiled and left the room.

"Have you ever worked with Nita?" Born asked Thompson.

"No."

"She's impressive. She'll figure out something. She's very mature, has children in college, and she's also efficient and imaginative. Looks like our team is pretty well put together now. Let's hope we're winners."

"Surely we can find twelve God-fearing people in that county who'll listen to us. I just believe that," said Thompson.

"I want to believe it too, Dave, but off-hand I haven't heard of any big case the defendant has won in Phoenix County in years. Not a single one. And the jury awards have been astronomical. The defendants in those cases weren't able to find those 'God-fearing people', but I sure hope you're right, that they're out there somewhere. What worries me is the thought that something may be going on that no one on the outside can see or prove, something skewing the results."

"Do you think it's a racial thing?" Thompson asked.

"Could be part of it," Born answered, "just a 'get even' feeling. But I think it's more than that. I just don't know what."

CHAPTER ELEVEN

MED-WISE

They knew the trial docket would move much faster in Phoenix County than in larger counties. It had now been nearly ten months since the accident occurred, and they were busy with discovery in the big case. The November elections had taken place, and there had been a lull in the discovery process during the Thanksgiving - to - New Year's period.

The Court generally scheduled two regular jury trial sessions each year in Phoenix County, one in February and the other in October, with occasional special settings at other times. The case would not be tried in February, as all parties had advised the Court the case was not yet ready for trial. But it might well be placed on the trial docket for the ensuing October, and that would arrive sooner than any defendant would want.

The lawyers for Universal and Tergano had been taking primarily medical depositions and at the same time had been responding to discovery initiatives of the plaintiffs' lawyers. Thompson and Gillespy had covered the depositions of paramedics and nurses. Not many surprises there. One of the main facts established was that no one who saw any of the van passengers shortly after the wreck detected any signs of life in Sarena Anchrum. The defendants had wondered whether plaintiffs would argue for damages attributable to pain and suffering, *in addition to wrongful death damages*, if it could be shown Sarena lived briefly after the accident and was in great pain. There did not appear to be any basis for such claim.

Jimason was the major focus of medical evidence in the case. A deposition of the neurosurgeon who performed the emergency surgery on Jimason in Columbia just after the accident elicited the observation that Jimason had sustained a "severe" brain injury. Born asked him, if the brain surgery involved Jimason's right frontal lobe, why was it that Jimason experienced no apparent problem with his left limbs but had considerable problems with his right arm and right leg. The surgeon explained that, while the right frontal portion of the brain generally controlled the left side of the body and the left frontal lobe controlled the right side, one had to assume the blow to Jimason's head severely injured both right and left frontal lobes - perhaps not obviously enough or visibly enough on the left to make surgery mandatory the day of the accident, but enough to cause the observed problems on the right side of Jimason's body.

Why was Jimason's left side apparently not adversely affected? Because, the surgeon explained, apparently there was not much damage to the part of the right frontal lobe controlling motor movement. In the surgeon's opinion, Jimason's brain injury would be related more to cognitive thinking than to motor movement.

Born showed the surgeon Jimason's report card for the first semester of the new school year and, for comparison, his report card for the preceding year. The surgeon shook his head, acknowledged that Jimason had performed better scholastically during the current semester than during the comparable period a year earlier. Born drew out of the witness that young patients with brain damage tended to compensate and bounce back resiliently, far better than adults. Born then asked whether it was possible Jimason might one day recover sufficiently so that no one would be able to tell he had sustained brain damage. "Yes, it's possible," the surgeon agreed. The witness had not seen Jimason since the day of the surgery and had no way to assess his recovery first-hand.

Ten or twelve days later, Universal hired a psychologist, Dr. Ralph Rumsford, to evaluate Jimason. Rumsford carefully studied Jimason's medical records and then tried to evaluate him. On the day of the examination, he telephoned Born. "What did you find?" Born asked.

"We weren't able to complete the examination," Rumsford reported.

"Why not?" Born inquired, puzzled.

"Let me start at the beginning. He came in this morning with his mother and with a paralegal from the Bates firm. He had had no breakfast and had not taken his medicine, I found out later. At first he did pretty well on the tests, but we would have to stop every ten to fifteen minutes for him to urinate. It wasn't fake either. He really produced. Then as the morning wore on, he exposed himself to my assistant and made some lewd comments to her. By eleven o'clock, he was saying he wanted to rest his head on the table. I encouraged him to keep trying, that we would be taking a break at noon. But before long, he simply could not go on. I had to stop the exam and let him leave."

"Did you question his mother about why he didn't take his medicine and had no breakfast?" Born asked.

"Yes, I did. I must say his mother is very limited. I'm not sure she's up to coping with Jimason and his situation. She said she forgot the medicine because they had to get up so early to get here, and she said they were running late and Jimason just wasn't hungry. I have to wonder whether the medicine was deliberately withheld so he would underperform on my tests."

"What kind of medicine is he supposed to be taking?" Born inquired.

"He's apparently taking several," Rumsford replied. "I don't know all of them, but his mother says one of them is a nasal spray. I suspect it's for the diabetes insipidus."

"Diabetes?" asked Born. "Is he a diabetic?"

"No, not the way you think. This is not the more common diabetes mellitus where you take insulin, which is what we usually mean when we say 'diabetes.' Jimason has diabetes insipidus. If you look closely at his medical records during his treatment in Louisville, you'll see it mentioned. It's what is causing the frequent and high-volume urination."

Born was still puzzled, "Did he have this diabetes insipidus before the accident?"

"Probably not," said Rumsford, "at least I don't have any indication of it in his records. It's a very logical consequence of the head injury, as I understand it. I'm a psychologist, not a neurosurgeon, but my understanding is that diabetes insipidus is often the result of pressure on the hypothalamus and/or the pituitary gland at the base of the brain. It could well have happened with the head injury, probably did."

"And you say this is treated with a nasal spray?"

"Yep. And if you spray once a day in each nostril, it will totally control the problem all day long."

"But this morning he didn't get any?"

"Right."

"How'd he do on the tests as far as you got with him?" Born asked.

"Consistent with the tests they administered in the hospital. Maybe a little better, but not much. He's got serious problems, Ted. He could answer certain rote memory questions, like he could recognize words and pictures and that kind of thing. But he would make statements which were contradictory, and he told me some things his mother and the paralegal said were wrong. For example, he said he had breakfast this morning, which his mother denies. He also said he watched a children's TV show this morning, but he would have been en route to my office when that program came on. He doesn't seem to have a sense of time and place and sequence of events. I've got to tell you I think his cognitive functions are impaired, maybe a lot. In other words, I think the test scores paint a more benign picture than the reality of it."

"I think I should have you see him again, and we will try to be sure he has taken his medicine next time. Don't write up a report until you see him again."

"One more thing, Ted. This might make you feel a little better. Remember, his medical records, especially his psychological exams they gave him in the hospital, suggest Jimason may be suffering from 'left neglect', an inability to see the left side of objects, like he had blinders on. If he ever had that, he's definitely improved. I asked him to follow with his eye as I moved my hand, covering each eye in turn, and he seemed to be following my hand movements perfectly. One hospital report I saw said he might have lost sight in one eye. You need to get an eye exam for him, but I suspect you'll find he is not blind in either eye."

Born hung up the phone but was still writing notes to himself on the conversation with Dr. Rumsford when Nita Langley appeared at his office door with his secretary Marta Shelby. "We've been going through the material

Rusty Loman sent up here and thought we'd better touch base with you," said Langley. "On the jury data base you wanted us to prepare, Rusty found a gold mine. I was afraid the jury lists from the past cases would have never found their way into the court files or would have long since been destroyed. Not so. They're all there, and the news gets even better. We not only have the names of the twelve members of each jury, but we also have the entire jury venire - jury pool - they were drawn from. And hold on, it gets better than that. The venire list shows which parties struck which jurors."

"Super!" exclaimed Born. "So, we will know the names of everyone who was on a jury that awarded fifteen million dollars, for example, and we'll know we don't want any of them on our jury. In addition, we will know that the plaintiffs struck so-and-so from the jury pool and must have believed therefore that so-and-so would be possibly favorable to the defendants, vice versa for those struck by the defendants."

"Exactly," said Marta Shelby. "I was going to set up several columns on the potential juror data base. First, in the far left-hand column would come the name of the potential juror. Next would come address, then age, then sex, then race and finally a box called comments. In that last box we'll make notations about who served on juries in what case and how much the jury awarded or, alternatively, whether they got struck and who struck them."

"Beautiful. Just the kind of thing I was looking for. Any other sources yet for potential juror data?" Born asked.

"Yes. Rusty sent us this program booklet on the retirement of the head of the County Council. It has all kinds of congratulatory ads from various groups, preachers, school boards, clinic workers and all sorts of others. Doesn't tell you a whole lot, but for example here's a note of congratulations from the Rainbow Senior Citizens' group, and it extols the honoree for serving on their board, and it lists the other members of the board. Would you be concerned if you had a juror who served on a board with the former Council head who was the mentor of the present Sheriff? I thought so, and I was going to make note of that fact." Langley answered. "Rusty's sent some other materials also, that I think we can get some names from."

"Any idea how many names you have so far?"

Shelby and Langley looked at each other, "I'd say maybe twelve hundred," said Langley, as Shelby nodded agreement.

"That's excellent. I'd guess there may be at most seven thousand adults in Phoenix County eligible for jury service, so you may have at least some information on about one-sixth of them. That's a great start. Anything else from Rusty?"

"Yes," answered Langley. "He's sent a master list of all civil actions filed during the last year and the disposition of each case. Of course, some of the more recent ones, like our case, have not been disposed of yet. Looks like an average of about a hundred ten civil actions get filed each year, but that's been increasing. No wonder, with the big verdicts, every plaintiff is trying to file here if possible. Then he sent us a copy of the entire court file on each case actually tried to a jury. That's about thirty-five to forty cases, the rest of them mostly being settled before trial. Of all the cases tried, I'd say fifteen or fewer involve wrongful death, personal injury, products liability or fraud. I have not read all the pleadings yet, but I've scanned the verdict forms, and I can tell you this: *no defendant* has won in that type case, and the *average* verdict is definitely in the millions of dollars."

"Let me have those fifteen files to look through, and maybe I will have a better idea how we ought to organize and use the data," Born suggested.

Just then Thompson knocked at the door and stepped inside. "Sorry to interrupt. But I thought you'd like to know what I just found out."

"Sure, Dave, have a seat and tell us all. You've just come back from deposing the dentist, haven't you?" Born remembered.

"Yes. And it turns out Bess was using her aunt's name for her dental work. Passed herself off as Cornelia Johnson. It took us the longest time to find her file, because it was filed under "Cornelia" instead of "Bess" Johnson. That's a fraud! And she just had twelve teeth left in her whole mouth, and she told us on her deposition she lost *all* her teeth in the wreck and had only had one or two pulled in her life before the accident. That woman is bad news. She's perjured herself, hasn't she?"

"Probably," Born answered calmly, not at all seeming upset. "We'll have to decide how to deal with that."

"Can't we ask for sanctions or at least use these facts to impeach her credibility at trial?" Thompson asked, obviously surprised at the equanimity displayed by Born.

"Let's think about it, Dave. First, she used her aunt's insurance. She shouldn't have done it, but a lot of jurors may excuse it because she works hard but still didn't have the money for dental work she apparently *needed*. They might give her a slap on the wrist, but that's about all."

"As for the teeth," Born continued, "she can probably say we didn't understand what she said in the deposition, that she meant she lost all the teeth she had in her mouth at the time of the accident, and I'm sure she'll find a way to explain her statement about having only one or two pulled before the accident. She can say she meant only one or two were pulled at the dentist's office on the Saturday of the accident, or something like that. Even if she can't explain it away, what's the average juror going to say? Won't the jury say, 'Well, she shouldn't have done it, but she's been hurt a lot and Sarena's been killed and Jimason's been brain-injured, and Bess' little white lies don't amount to a hill of beans compared with the enormity of the injury and death'? Instead of helping us, anything we could do might actually hurt us. It might be interpreted as two large companies persecuting a poor, hard-working single woman."

"Then, are you saying she can just get away with *anything*? If she bribed the jury, couldn't you say the same thing?" Thompson pressed his point.

"Dave, I'm not saying we won't do anything about

it. I'm just not sure what. We need to think about it. Maybe I'm insensitive because unfortunately I rarely take a deposition where I feel the witness was a hundred percent truthful. Maybe it's a matter of degree. It's good work, Dave, and I'm glad we know for sure Bess Johnson can't be trusted, because we can factor that into our planning. But I am not sure about the right way to use this information."

As the meeting broke up and Dave Thompson returned to his office, he thought, "Can this be right? Can a witness lie with impunity? Was it possible there was a trace of racism in Ted Born's reaction? Was Born really thinking, `I'm not surprised because Bess Johnson is black and black people are supposed to lie and cheat, and other blacks will ignore it when they lie and cheat'? `You just can't trust those blacks'? Would Born have been so casual about it if Bess had been white and the jury all white? Maybe, charitably, Born was justified in his attitude in one sense, the sense that all-black juries had seemed to be out of control in past cases." Still, Thompson didn't like it. In North Carolina where he came from, he had grown up very religious, and that included being truthful. It was all very troubling.

CHAPTER TWELVE

LITIGATION LEGACY

Ted Born was reading the pleadings of the fifteen
Phoenix County cases Nita Langley had left with
him. "Unbelievable!" he was telling himself as he jotted
down notes. "This stuff is so bizarre, why hasn't it been
on the pages of the *New York Times*, or at least a national gossip rag? Talk about news! The public has no idea
what's going on in the courthouses. No *idea*!"

Most of what Born was finding out came from post-trial motions and briefs filed by losing defendants who had
tried vainly to persuade the Court to overturn the jury
verdict and award them a new trial. There were affidavits and counter-affidavits and excerpts from transcripts
supporting and opposing the post-trial motions and elab-
orating on the facts. "Better call Dave," Born mumbled to

himself. Just as he was reaching for the telephone, Dave Thompson appeared at the door. "Hi, Dave, I was just about to call you. Come on in. What's on your mind?"

"I've been wrestling with our responses to the plaintiffs' interrogatories and request for production, and I've got problems. For one thing, they want to tour our tire plant and I know Universal wants to avoid that at all costs. They want our adjustment data, too, and they apparently want our green tire specifications. The client's gonna' fire us if we turn over all that confidential trade secret stuff to them, but you know how broad discovery is. I don't know if we can stop them, gonna' be hard," Dave reported.

"I know, I've been wrestling with the same problem. Seems to me we ought to draw the line at preventing a plant tour. Universal doesn't even let its own lawyers inside the plants. There's a decision from a California court—I forget the name of the case—where the court refused to permit a plant tour. The facts in that case were a little different from ours, but at least it might help some. Anyway, let's fight that one."

"What about the green tire specifications? Actually, they asked for the specifications of Goodyear, obviously the lawyers just copied the wording from some other file and forgot to change the name to 'Universal'. But that's technical," Dave said.

"Maybe it's technical, but it could help us with the Judge because he'll know their discovery request is canned garbage and wasn't carefully tailored to the needs of this particular case. My main problem with the request, though, is that Alton Fox has never provided us with his theory of what was the alleged defect in our tire. They should have to articulate some reasonable theory of a defect; otherwise how can we determine the relevance of their discovery request? As it stands now, nobody can say whether the green tire specs are relevant or might lead to relevant evidence, because they haven't favored us with their liability theory, beyond saying vaguely that the tire somehow was defective. We need to force their hand and withhold the specs until they commit themselves."

"Okay," nodded Dave. "As for the adjustment data... ."

"Yeah," said Born, interrupting, "the adjustment data on this tire are excellent, few customer complaints and very few adjustments or credits due to customer dissatisfaction, but Universal still doesn't want to produce this information because Universal's afraid it might set a precedent in other cases where the data aren't so good. Universal feels when customers come in and want a new tire or some kind of adjustment, this doesn't mean the tire is defective, because most adjustments are made simply to preserve customer goodwill, usually because the customer has a change of mind and wants a different brand or type of tire. But still, some jurors could think bigger adjustment figures must mean the tires weren't well made."

"So, what do we do?" asked Dave.

"Go ahead and resist it and, if we lose, it's not the end of the world. On the other hand, if we have to allow a plant tour, that pretty much is the end of the world as far as Universal's concerned. And Universal might go out and find itself some new lawyers!"

"All right, I've got the plan. Thanks," said Dave, starting to rise from the chair.

"No, wait if you have the time. I was about to call you anyway to share with you a few tales of Phoenix County justice." Dave was definitely interested. "I've made notes here on this pad. Let's go back to the first BIG ONE, the *Driscoll* case. You remember reading that opinion in the Supreme Court reports when we first got into this case, don't you? It's the one where Mrs. Driscoll bought the used car and then claimed they sold her more credit life insurance than she needed."

"Yeah, I remember it very well, and I know about Mrs. Driscoll's house on the hill," Dave nodded.

Born continued, "In connection with the motion for a new trial filed by the defendants, affidavits were submitted which were sworn to by eight of the twelve jurors. In each affidavit, the juror identified anywhere from one to five material witnesses known by them, but whose friendship or acquaintanceship they had not disclosed when asked during the jury selection process. In other words, when the jury was being chosen, the defense lawyers had asked the entire jury pool, 'Do any of you know any of the following material witnesses?' and none of the eight jurors raised their hands at the time."

"So, what you're telling me is that the jurors were chosen without the lawyers having the full and truthful information they needed to select impartial jurors," Dave summarized.

"That's right. In that instance the lawyers just did not get the information they needed to strike a fair jury. Voir dire examination of prospective jurors is critical, and it's supercritical when you are trying your case in a small county with numerous cross-ties among the residents."

"What did the Court say about that?" Thompson asked.

"The Court said this was not an adequate showing prejudicial to defendant's rights because defendant had failed to strike one or two jurors who *had* raised their hands; therefore, the Court could not assume the defendant would have struck any of the eight. Of course, given the fact you are not likely to be able to get perfect jurors, you might well waive a potential juror's acquaintance in one instance but not in another, weighing a multitude of factors, but I should think you need accurate information in order to do the weighing."

"Then there was the case where a fast food chain franchised a store to a black man in a neighboring county. It did all right for several years, then the franchisee began neglecting the business and it failed, got hooked on gambling trips, apparently. He sued the franchisor - the chain - for fraud, claiming the franchisor didn't disclose to him that a larger percentage of African-American franchises failed than white franchises. This one, mind you, was a Fred Bates case like *Driscoll*. They brought the suit in Phoenix County, even though none of the parties lived in Phoenix County and the store was not located in Phoenix County. In fact, there was no connection whatever with Phoenix County except that Bates thought he could get a big verdict there, and unfortunately state law permits suit in any county where a corporation `does business'. The only `business' the fast food chain did in Phoenix was that it had billboards in that county and sometimes bought local produce there for some nearby stores."

"That's crazy," Thompson remarked.

"Oh, of course that kind of thing ought not to be allowed, but it's really beside the point," Born continued. "More important is what came later. Bates made a big black/white issue out of the case and it got a lot of notoriety. Bates even hired a well-known civil rights leader to come to the trial, ostensibly as an expert witness on the chain's affirmative action record. The Court ruled his testimony would not be admissible and ordered Bates and Ripps to keep him away from the jury. But it turned out he was highly visible anyway. They got the message he was on the side of the plaintiff."

"Pretty bad," Thompson said.

"I'm just getting started, you haven't heard the half of it," Born said in a lay-it-on-you kind of voice. "Then Jack Ripps procures Mrs. Driscoll to come down to the Courthouse. Now, Mrs. Driscoll had no connection whatever to the dealership case, but she'd become quite famous in Phoenix County, and everybody knew about all the money she won in her lawsuit with Bates & Ripps representing her. So, she came into the courtroom dressed in finery and she proceeded to give Fred Bates a big hug, which Bates enthusiastically returned, right there in the courtroom in front of the jury. Then she sat in the spectators' part of the courtroom right behind counsel's table where Fred Bates and Jack Ripps were sitting, obviously reinforcing her support for plaintiff who - remember? - was not even a Phoenix County resident and she probably never saw him before in her life. Hold on now, Dave, because it gets even better. At the lunch break, Mrs. Driscoll took two of the jurors to lunch with her."

"You mean the Judge let her do that?" asked Dave Thompson incredulously.

"No. Of course, the Judge didn't know anything about it until the Court session reconvened after the lunch break. When he found out, he dismissed the two jurors who went to lunch with her, but the problem is that these incidents which are seen and reported are probably just the tip of the iceberg. Jess Robinson was local counsel for the manufacturer in that case, and he got numerous anonymous telephone calls saying that the jury was being bribed. Of course, if it had been a white lawyer rather than a popular black lawyer like Jess Robinson, it is questionable whether there would have been any calls reporting the bribery. Robinson reported to the Judge, but the Judge said he couldn't act on anonymous tips. There had to be proof. Proof is hard to get when you're in the middle of a trial, and when honest lawyers are trying to observe the Court's instructions to stay away from the jury except when addressing them in Court."

"So you think there's jury tampering?" Thompson asked.

"I don't have any doubt about it," said Born. "There's

too much smoke, too much evidence of improper conduct, and the verdicts are too big and disproportionate to the offense and out of kilter with verdicts in other counties in South Carolina."

"For example - and I'm not going to relate every one of these incidents to you, you can read them yourself - but at the last term of Court, a good many members of the jury did not show up for jury service and the Judge ordered them rounded up and brought into the courtroom. Several of them told the Judge they had not come because they felt uncomfortable. Seems they had been personally contacted by the recently retired head of the County Council. Remember him? He's the one Bates & Ripps sponsored the retirement party for and gave him the Lincoln Continental. The former Council head, now in retirement, was employed by Fred Bates to provide him with `jury information'. Remember here, too, that Bates claims he already knows everybody in Phoenix County, so why does he need jury information? Anyway, this `jury consultant' had a very direct approach to getting the information: he personally called the homes of the jurors to ask them or family members a series of questions. Aside from the fact he probably already knew all the prospective jurors and did not need to call them for information, the obvious message conveyed by his telephone calls - directly or indirectly - was that he personally was interested in the plaintiff's side of the case. Here is probably the most popular person in Phoenix County, a virtual icon in that county, essentially calling the jurors on plaintiff's behalf

in advance of trial. Of course, the Judge, who truly is
fair and conscientious, sent home the whole jury pool and
specially set the cases for trial later. The Council head -
former head - just said he didn't realize this was wrong,
entirely innocent, you understand. You can bet that, one
way or another, our trial will not be played out on a level
playing field."

"Is it legitimate to try to get jury information? Don't
we try to get it, too?" Thompson asked.

"Absolutely. But you don't call jurors or their families personally for the information after they've been
summoned for jury duty and are waiting to serve. That's
a very sensitive period of time when they should not be
approached for fear of improper influence," said Born.

"I hear you saying, bottom line, that we as defendants
can't expect to get accurate and truthful information in
answer to questions you might ask the jury pool at court.
That's problem number one. And I think I also hear you
saying that, even if you did get good info, the plaintiffs
would find some way to poison the jury with improper
contacts or outright bribes," Thompson said.

"That's why we have to file a motion to transfer the
case to another county, probably to Richland County,"
Born announced.

"You know I looked into the possibility of transfer
awhile back, before we ever found out any of these things,
and the law is just dead against us. Here the plaintiffs
are all residents of Phoenix County and the accident took
place in Phoenix County. The precedents all say plaintiffs

have a right to a trial in the county of their choosing and especially if that county is where they live and where the accident took place. The law is real strong against us," Thompson stated.

"Even if we can't get a fair trial?" Born asked rhetorically.

"The law presumes you can get a fair trial. The Court has the power, at least theoretically, to give protection against anything that would prevent a fair trial."

"It didn't work in the past. We've got a series of victims of Phoenix County's `fair trials.' "

"You know the plaintiffs are going to make a racial issue of it, don't you? I mean, I know it's not racial, but they'll say we're contending we can't get a fair trial in Phoenix County because it is predominantly black," Thompson warned.

"Yeah. I know you're right. But I can't let that stop me. Fact is, we can't get a fair trial, no one else has, and I'm not going to be led meekly to the slaughter," Born said firmly.

"But I don't see what good this motion does you. No way in the world the Judge is going to grant it. Not only is the law against us, but he'd be admitting we can't get justice in *his* Court. He'd be slapping himself in the face. What good's it going to do?" Dave Thompson reasoned and pleaded.

"In the first place, I think we're right. I'm not sure there's ever been as strong a showing in any other case as I'm prepared to make. If there's bad law out there, maybe we can change it, probably not, but maybe. Besides, knowing what I know about Phoenix County justice, I'd probably be guilty of malpractice if I didn't try. Most important are two reasons which apply *even if we lose on the motion.* First, it will make an impression on the Judge that we don't think we can get justice in his Court. If we are polite enough and don't make him too angry with us, we might at least convince him to bear with us and give us some extraordinary protection later to help promote a fairer, or less unfair, trial. Second, I want the plaintiffs to know we'll be watching them. So the making of the motion could be helpful even if, as is most likely, the Judge denies it."

"I hope you won't be offended at me, but I'd rather not sign the motion," Thompson said politely. "I mean, regardless of what we do and regardless of our true motives, this motion is going to be played up as a racial thing, an effort to get out of Phoenix County because it's mostly black. I might even want to get in politics someday and run for something, and someone would drag up this motion with my name on it and accuse me of being against black people, African Americans, even though I am one."

"I can understand that, Dave, and I totally respect your feelings. I think, for a similar reason, I will not ask Rusty Loman to sign it. He has to live down there and practice law there, and I don't want to put him in a position where he's saying litigants can't get a fair trial in Phoenix County. Anyway, when I draft up the motion, I'll send you a copy. I'd appreciate your comments anyway."

"Sure, I'll be glad to help behind the scenes if I can. Well, better go back to my office and work on this discovery."

Dave Thompson left the office wondering whether he had done the right thing, wondering again whether Born - and maybe most of the other white lawyers in the firm - were latent racists. It just didn't have the same opportunity to surface with other people unless race turned out to be an unavoidable issue in a particular legal problem. Then he wondered if he was being fair to Born. Maybe Born was not racist, just a realist, as he seemed to be claiming. Time will tell, he thought.

Born at the same time was reflecting on Thompson's resistance to filing the motion, and his absolute refusal to sign it. Would there be more problems down the road? Would Thompson be a team player? Was it an immature kneejerk reaction? Was Dave's position well founded? Would it be a mistake to file such a motion? He would draft the motion, he thought to himself. Then he could see it on paper, read it the way it would be read by others, then decide what to do.

CHAPTER THIRTEEN

TIRES AND WIRES

D ave Thompson had gotten a response of calculated vagueness when he pressed Alton Fox for the theory he would offer at trial concerning any tire defect. It was a written response which read: "belt separation caused by contamination probably occurring in the manufacturing process." At least it was *something*.

Neither Thompson nor Born felt comfortable dealing with tire technology, for Bert Sayre had not yet conducted the promised private seminar, because, he said, he didn't know where to start until he found out what Fox claimed was wrong. The response from Fox was meaningless, but Born did not expect a better one any time soon. Meantime, he needed to get on with his tire schooling and hoped the response would at least be a catalyst for Sayre to provide some lessons on tires.

Born telephoned Sayre and got a receptionist on the line who said Sayre was out of town. She would tell him Born called. Later the same day Sayre called back from California. "Hi, Bert. We finally got something from the plaintiffs on their liability theory. You won't like it. Obviously not adequate, but it's all we have now. They claim contamination in the factory that caused belt separation."

"That's bull," said Sayre. "There isn't any *belt* separation. A small amount of belt *edge* separation, maybe, but nothing out of the ordinary."

"Here's our problem, Bert. We need a crash course in tires. First, we've got to go before the Judge in Phoenix County and argue about the scope of discovery, those issues about the green tire specs and the tire molds and the plant tour and all that. I don't know enough about tires yet to plead our case with confidence. I'm a pretty quick study, I think, but I need some help on that," Born urged.

"My second problem is that I need to be getting ready to take their experts' depositions pretty soon, and I need to get my Ph.D. in tires for that reason – the main reason, actually. I ought to know more about tires than their expert, if possible, to do my best job in the deposition, and time's running out. I need to get started," Born continued.

"Tell you what," offered Sayre. "Let me schedule a date to come to Greenville with our tire expert and we'll give you the works. I can't patch him in from this phone. Can you get him on the line?"

With Bob Tegrit connected, they agreed on a visit the next Wednesday. That would be two days before the specially set court hearing on discovery disputes in Phoenix County.

Born arranged to borrow the tire once again from Alton Fox who had custody of it. Any contact with the plaintiffs' lawyers always seemed accompanied by acrimony, but this time the arrangements were smoother than usual. Once before, Fox had left a hotly worded message on Dave Thompson's voice mail. It had shaken Thompson, and also bothered Born because he was afraid there was a racial component in the outburst, or at least that Thompson would think there was. Born, too, had had problems with Fox who seemed to get very upset over Tegrit's removal of the tire from the rim during his examination, an obviously necessary action, Born thought, which did no harm.

This time the tire arrangements had gone smoothly, and as Sayre and Tegrit convened with Born and Thompson the next Wednesday in a conference room at the law firm, the ruptured tire was there, lying on the table.

Tegrit had brought with him drawings and charts illustrating the radial tire building process. He explained that a steel belted radial tire was mainly a handmade product, built up from various individual pieces and then vulcanized.

"First, you start with the innerliner," Tegrit began. "That's the piece on the very inside of the finished tire that serves the same purpose as the old-fashioned innertube. Then you put in the polyester tire cords or body plies, as they are sometimes called, which go around the tire from bead to bead, 90° or perpendicular to the length of the innerliner. You know what the beads are don't you? They're the steel cables encased in rubber that form the circular edges, one on each side of the tire, that seal against the rim when the tire is mounted, in other words, the circular edges which make the inside circle of the tire donut."

"Next, you have the belting, and this is very important, so listen carefully," Tegrit advised professorially. "There are two belts. They are essentially brass-coated steel wire embedded in tacky, sticky rubber and cut at an angle so that the wires run at about a 15° angle relative to the belt edge. You lay the two belts on top of each other so that the wires would seem to intersect, or run criss-cross rather than run parallel, if you could see the wires through the sticky rubber in which they are embedded. In other words, you take two strips of belting and lay one down, then you turn the second belt around, so the angle of the wire is opposite from first belt, then lay the second one on top of the first."

"This might sound stupid," Born said, "but I've never really understood the advantage of the steel in the belts, except in a vague way I know that steel is strong. Can you help me out on that?"

"Sure. The steel reinforces as it improves the cornering capabilities of the tire," Tegrit explained. "It took a lot of experimentation, though, to get the angle of the steel wire just right. That's because you give up something with steel belted radials; the ride is not as soft and comfortable. But an angle of about 15° from left to right on one belt, and the same angle from right to left on the second belt, gives good cornering and a reasonably soft ride."

"Why do you brass coat the steel of the wire?" Thompson asked.

"An excellent question," Sayre answered. "Go ahead and tell him, Bob."

"Yes, it is a good question," Bob concurred. "Steel won't adhere to rubber, but it will adhere to copper. So you coat the steel with brass, which is an alloy of copper and zinc, and it will vulcanize and fuse together with a nice, strong bond. There's only one problem. When you cut the belts to the correct width for a particular type tire, the cut ends will expose raw steel. There's no feasible way to put copper or brass on those ends, so there's inevitably going to be imperfect bonding along the edge of the belts where those cut ends of steel wire are exposed to rubber. This means there is absolutely inevitably going to be some separation of the rubber from the belting along the edges where the cuts have taken place - belt edge separation - in *every* steel belted radial tire, but the separation generally does not advance enough to be a significant problem in a well-made tire."

"But there can be problems?" asked Born.

"Yes. In some cases, the rubber/wire bond begins to weaken along the edges and works its way to the center of the tire where the entire belt loosens from the surrounding components of the tire. Then you've got real problems. I'm talking blowouts."

"Is that what we had in this tire?" Born asked.

"No. There is some belt *edge* separation, all right. It might be a little worse than you usually expect, but, then, you don't see that many six-year-old tires with sixty thousand miles. I say for an old, worn out and abused tire, the belt edge separation has been held within very reasonable bounds. In fact, I'd say it is excellent. Of course, you do see some belt separation right along the line of the rupture, but that was caused by the blowout, not by advancing belt edge separation. If the whole belt really separates, it will usually peel off in a strip when there's a blowout. That didn't happen in our case," Tegrit noted.

"Then you put on the sidewall rubber and the tread rubber. Along the way you have taken these components and stretched them into something roughly resembling a tire, which we call a `green tire' before it is vulcanized to `ripen' it. Then you heat or vulcanize these components just right, molding the tread pattern into the tread rubber and pressing an inflated bladder from the inside. You also put all the lettering and serial numbers and that kind of thing on the tire while you are vulcanizing it."

Sayre offered an addendum, "There are many different types of rubber in a tire, because they all serve a different purpose. The sidewall rubber, for example, is made by an entirely different formula from the tread rubber, it has to be pliable and flex easily. So, when you get through and it's vulcanized, it all looks like a single piece of rubber, but it's really many different types of rubber fused together. Our rubber formulas are some of our best guarded secrets."

"Let's talk about tire problems," Born proposed. "We got a six-year-old tire. Are tires supposed to last that long and still be good?"

"Theoretically, yes," said Tegrit. "But obviously, the older a tire is, the more possibility there is for abuse, wear and impact damage. The tire could have been run underinflated for extended periods - terrible for a tire. The tread could be real thin, the carcass could have been punctured a half dozen times without proper repairs. It could have stood outside in the weather, with the severe heat of summer and the cold of winter. It could have hit curbs and potholes and objects in the road. These things could weaken or destroy a six-year old tire, which has had that long for bad things to happen to it. Because of these factors, most tire manufacturers - including Universal, I think - limit their tire warranty to a period of years. What's yours, Bert?"

"Four years," Sayre answered.

"How about the mileage?" asked Thompson. "Aren't tires warranted for only a certain mileage, like 40,000 miles?"

"We used to do that," Sayre interjected. "But then we realized that the abrasiveness of roads, which is a big factor in tread wear, differs a lot from place to place in different areas of the country, and so we went to a system of giving pro-rata credit for the remaining usable tread in case a defect developed. That means down to two thirty-seconds of an inch. The last two thirty-seconds is not considered usable. The tire's worn out and has served its useful life at that point."

"Does thin tread make the tire less safe?" Born wanted to know.

"Definitely. The most obvious problem is that the traction is not as good, so you have bad problems in wet weather, trying to drive with slick tires. Of course, it wasn't raining the day of the accident in this case, was it? No? But it's still not as safe, even on a dry road, because it is very much more susceptible to impact damage, being thin and lacking the cushioning protection of the tread. Plus, it's probably had plenty of other opportunities for damage and abuse by the time the tread gets worn down."

"How thick is the tread on this tire?" Born asked, rotating the tire on the table.

"It ranges from slightly below two thirty-seconds to slightly above. Problem is, there are basically three main tread grooves running around the tire in the crown area. The tread near the edges and the two outer grooves is worn pretty bad, due to chronic underinflation. But the tread in the center, and surrounding the center groove, is not as badly worn. That's the normal pattern in underinflation, the two opposing edges of the tire wear the worst," Tegrit explained.

Looking at the nail and plugged hole, Born asked: "I've never understood about puncture repairs, the right way and the wrong way. Can you tell me something about that?"

"Sure. The right way to do it is to take the tire and rim off the vehicle, then take the tire off the rim, plug the hole and put a patch on the innerliner. That way, the inflation pressure of around thirty-five pounds per square inch is confined inside the tire and the tire performs perfectly. But this takes time, is labor intensive and costs more money, and a lot of motorists don't want to take the time or spend the money to do it this way."

"So they plug it," Sayre volunteered. "And service stations like it better too, because it's easy to do, doesn't tie up their limited service bays, and they can quickly send customers on their way for, maybe, a third of the price of doing it right."

"Yeah. What they do when they plug it is, a service station guy will find the nail or screw or whatever and pull it out. Then he takes something like a screwdriver, and he reams out a hole about the size of a pencil where the puncture hole is. He then takes a plug which is like an oil impregnated fibrous cord and pokes it in the hole and twists it into a knot, then pulls out the insertion tool, snips the plug flush with the tread and checks to see if air is leaking out."

"So why is this bad?" Born asked intently.

"The problem is that the seal may be good enough in the beginning to show no apparent leak, but there probably is at least a small one which may grow worse. Remember, the reaming has produced a larger hole, usually, than the nail, going all the way through the tread, the belting and the innerliner. The inflation pressure within the tire is pretty strong and air inside will try to force its way out through the tiny irregular spaces between the hole and the plug. If that was all that happened, it would just mean deflation, a new repair job. But it's worse. Once the integrity of the innerliner has been destroyed and not patched back from the inside, air can work its way under the innerliner and between other layers of rubber. Air can then migrate around the tire in between the various layers of rubber where the bonding has been disturbed by the puncture and the reaming. This can cause belts or tread to separate and come off the tire. Then you get a blowout."

"But that didn't happen here?" Thompson and Born asked almost in unison.

"Certainly, the belts and tread did not separate, but you can see excessive wear in the areas of the plug and the unrepaired nail, and the process could have been occurring without yet being in an advanced stage. I don't think it caused this particular accident. It's more of an indication of tire abuse in this instance."

"As for the tensile fractures, Bob, do you feel entirely confident about that, or might it help to hire a metallurgist?" Sayre asked Tegrit.

"I've testified about it lots of times and I'm quite comfortable with it," Tegrit responded. "But it never hurts to have a fully qualified metallurgist, especially if you can get a good one who's local and who can provide a little local flavor that I can't give."

Born knew some metallurgists through patent work he had done, but he picked up the telephone and made a few calls to get some other opinions. Weighing his own judgment and the advice he had gotten from others, he told the group he tended to think one Bill Edmonds might do a good job.

"While we're all here, why don't we call him and see if we can meet with him and then we can evaluate him?" Dave Thompson excused himself to handle an afternoon motion docket. The remaining trio drove to Edmonds' office.

The metallurgist's office was in a grimy industrial area of small machine shops, garages and vacant run-down buildings. "Not sure I'd want to come to this place at night," Sayre observed, surveying the neighborhood. Edmonds himself had apparently been sufficiently concerned that he had posted no signage of any kind suggesting the presence of a business within his building. The visitors could identify the location only by the numerals on the door representing the address.

The front door was bolted and there were burglar bars at the windows. Born rang the doorbell. A gray-haired, fatherly-looking man came to the door. It was Edmonds. He was slight, about five/seven or eight in height and wore rim glasses. There was no receptionist, but Born saw a secretary or clerical employee in a room to the left and a good-sized office to the right. "I'm Bill Edmonds," he smiled, extending his hand. With introductions made, Edmonds ushered the group into his office.

Born and Sayre explained they were considering employing an expert witness, and confirmed that Edmonds had no conflict, that is to say, had not already been hired by Bates & Ripps. They approached the subject gingerly, not at all sure they wanted to employ Edmonds. Certainly, his premises had not necessarily been reassuring as to his qualifications. In fact, the tire had remained in the trunk of the car on account of doubts engendered by Edmonds' office location.

But the visitors quickly warmed up to Edmonds who was careful and deliberate in his speech but hospitable, with a twinkle in his eye. When Born noted the twinkle, almost an involuntary wink in his grey-blue eyes behind his wire-rimmed glasses, he thought to himself that he had never before known what writers meant when they referred to a "twinkle" in someone's eye. Here's a real twinkle, for sure, he thought.

Edmonds held undergraduate and master's degrees in metallurgy from fine universities and had had years of work experience in metallurgy before becoming a consultant. He acknowledged he had never worked with tires before. Tegrit and Sayre explained that groups of three filaments were intertwined to form what at first glance appeared to be individual wires embedded in rubber in the tires. "Then it's like a wire rope," said Edmonds. "I've done an awful lot of work with wire rope."

"Have you studied tensile fractures and shear fractures and fatigue fractures in wires?" Sayre asked.

"Oh, yes. I've done extensive studies with cable and

larger diameter wires woven to form wire ropes. I'll confess I've never done much with really fine wire, I mean, not in connection with types of fractures. But I can't conceive there would be any difference in what a tensile fracture looks like in a fine wire or a cable."

At that point Born offered to bring in the tire for Edmonds to see. When Edmonds first saw it, he reached for what appeared to be an ordinary desk magnifying glass and looked at some of the wire ends. "Yes. I can see what looks like tensile fractures, maybe some shears. I could probably see it better under my stereo-microscope."

Edmonds led them from his office back out into the entry hall, then toward the back of the hall to a door which he opened. Beyond the door, the visitors' jaws dropped when they saw the impressive-looking equipment, with several men in white lab coats apparently very busy. Although it had not been apparent when they first entered Edmonds' office, the office actually occupied two adjacent relatively narrow storefront buildings with depth of perhaps 150 feet, really a good-sized metallurgical laboratory. Born's confidence immediately got a boost, and he could see the same written on the faces of Sayre and Tegrit.

Edmonds steadied the tire as best he could to view the exposed wires in the rupture area under the stereo-microscope. "This will go up to 50 power," Edmonds explained. "I've got it on about 35 power now, and I can see this particular wire very clearly. Problem is, this process is a little slow. You can only look at one wire at a time, and then you have to get the focus right for the distance. This tire is a little awkward to deal with. I don't suppose we could cut any wires, could we?"

"Oh, no! Fox would have an absolute fit - he's the tire lawyer working on the other side of this case, and Judge Andrews might put me *under* the jail." Born responded quickly and firmly. "We've agreed not to do any destructive testing."

After looking for about fifteen minutes, Edmonds announced he had readily seen tensile and shear fractures, but thus far no fatigues. "Bill, do you understand why you get both shear and tensile fractures when a wire under tension is subjected to a blow? I've never understood the mechanism," Tegrit admitted.

"Yes, I think I can help you. It's all a part of wire rope theory. You won't get shearing unless wire ropes are present. What you've got in this tire is a bunch of tiny three-filament wire ropes. When a wire rope suffers a sudden impact, the impact causes the wires to cut into each other, causing shear fractures."

"I'll be damned!" said Tegrit. "I never understood that before, but now it makes perfect sense. Never could figure out why or explain it. I just knew you got both tensiles and shears."

They left the tire with Edmonds for further studying and photographing under the stereomicroscope. It was five o'clock in the afternoon when they left Edmonds' office. "I think we've got us a metallurgist," said Born.

"Yeah, I think we have!" agreed Tegrit.

CHAPTER FOURTEEN

THE HEARING

Ted Born and Dave Thompson were driving to Groveton for a hearing on a discovery dispute two days after the visit by Bert Sayre and Bob Tegrit. They were talking about sports and how the Atlantic Coast Conference was strong in basketball and how football was king in the Southeastern Conference. Born and Thompson both had ACC connections, Born having been graduated from the University of Virginia and Thompson from the University of North Carolina, more than twenty years separating them.

Born talked of Thomas Wolfe and *Look Homeward, Angel,* and chided Thompson for never having read it. "The greatest American writer, a Carolina graduate too, and you, a Tar Heel, have never read it!"

"No, but how do you feel about Virginia – or do I even need to ask ?" Thompson countered.

"Well, I lived one year on West Range and the next year on West Lawn, in the shadow of Mr. Jefferson's Rotunda. I loved Virginia, got into my blood, great friends there, some of the nicest people in the world, and a great professional experience in law school. " Born smiled.

"I notice you always talk about Virginia, and I can see you love it, but didn't you go to an Ivy League college? I don't hear you mention it much," Thompson said.

"Well, there are not as many graduates of my college around here. It's natural since I'm a lawyer and we have other Virginia law graduates in the firm - and UVA law-yers practicing in Greenville - so I guess Virginia comes up a lot more often in conversation. You're right. I love Virginia. I've never been happier in my life than during those three years I spent in Charlottesville. I went there not having the foggiest idea what the law was all about, and I developed this love affair with the law. Virginia was something special," Born reminisced.

"And college?" Thompson asked.

"College has a special niche in my psyche, but a different one from Virginia. I don't have quite the same warmth, no, when I return on a visit to college, it's like going to a shrine, where I feel this reverence and respect. That's where the biggest changes occurred in my life." Born stopped for a moment, swallowed and blinked his eyes to clear them. "I was a small-town boy - parochial, dogmatic, benignly narrow, very fragile in other ways.

Then I took the Greyhound bus with one large suitcase in hand and went to the northeast. There I met Plato and Aristotle, Aquinas and Hegel, Royce and Tagore, and the other great thinkers. I never knew people really had thoughts like that, I mean, with so much depth. I even dared to imagine that I also could think creative and different and constructive thoughts with a new perspective on great issues. I've been an amateur philosopher ever since. I studied the great books, too, from Homer to Dostoevsky, took art humanities and music humanities. I tell you, it changed my life." Born almost got carried away.

"But you studied engineering. How? Why? And then law school!" Thompson virtually protested.

"I had always been a pre-law student, but I was looking for wisdom and truth. So I majored in philosophy, minored in engineering. Simple as that," Born teased.

"Okay, what's the catch?" Thompson asked.

"No catch. I really was just that idealistic. I thought if there was any such thing as truth, it would have to be in science, or at least science would bring me closer to truth than could anything else. So, I was being a philosopher while trying to learn about the magnetic moment of electrons spinning around the nucleus of an atom."

"Did you learn wisdom and truth?" Thompson grinned.

"Can't say that I did. I'm a little wiser and more critical, and I'm still hungry for the right questions and the right answers. No, wisdom and truth are still elusive, but the search goes on. Every now and then I see a glimmer of new light in the darkness and I keep hoping that one day

I'll walk in full sunshine."

"How about Carolina?" Born asked Thompson.

"I never changed universities between college and law school and don't have anything to contrast. But Chapel Hill is probably a lot like Charlottesville, small college town in the South with a fine university. I studied statistics, and I've got to say I was more interested in making a living and less in philosophy than you seemed to have been, but I picked up an awful lot of philosophy and good literature anyway, even as a statistics major. I love Carolina too, and owe everything to that school. But I'm sorry to say I never read *Look Homeward, Angel.* I ought to do that," Thompson remarked.

They turned south on Highway 53 and grew silent as they began to approach the scene of the accident. Born slowed as they passed the spot, shook his head, but said nothing. Thompson looked at the scene as they passed by, then looked at Born, also said nothing. Five minutes later, they were walking up the spiral steps to the upstairs courtroom.

From Universal Tire's point of view, the hearing at the Courthouse on the discovery went about as well as could be expected. The Judge ordered Universal to turn over the tire mold designs and a substantially narrowed set of green tire specifications, but no rubber formulas had to be revealed. Nor did the Judge order Universal to allow a plant tour.

Judge Andrews at the conclusion of his discovery rulings asked the parties whether the case could be ready for trial in October. All the lawyers said "no", the case would not be ready for trial by that time. However, Fred Bates urged the Court to go ahead and set the case for trial the following February, about ten months hence. Born requested the Judge to hold off on the setting or, if set, to make the date tentative. He pleaded that plaintiffs had not yet identified or designated who their expert witnesses would be, that the defendants would need to see a summary of the experts' proposed testimony, prepare for their depositions, take the depositions, and then get defense experts to rebut the plaintiffs' experts. This would take time. Moreover, the factual discovery was still incomplete.

Bates promised that the plaintiffs' side would designate its expert witnesses shortly. The Judge did not clearly indicate exactly what he would do about setting the case for trial.

After the hearing, Born suggested a meeting at Rusty Loman's office with Tergano's lawyer Trip Gillespy who had also attended the hearing. The relationship between the Universal/Tergano lawyers had been cordial and fairly co-operative, but one could not say they were completely open with each other. The Universal side feared that, despite the don't-point-the-finger-at-each-other pact, Tergano would be tempted to say or imply the accident never would have happened without the blowout of the Universal tire. Tergano similarly feared Universal might stress the principle that vehicles should be controllable with minimal effort when a blowout occurs on a straight road, thus suggesting some possible validity to the plaintiffs' defective steerage argument.

Gillespy mentioned he had already commissioned a professional surveyor to survey the elevations and other key features in the vicinity of the accident. Born wanted to know if Universal could obtain a copy of the survey if it paid its share of the survey's cost. It would help, Born argued, if both defendants had consistent surveys. Gillespy was noncommittal. Such sharing might cause the jury to think Universal and Tergano were somehow in cahoots, and he silently reminded himself Tergano wanted to distance itself from Universal. Tergano hoped that, even without pointing a finger at Universal, the jury would get the idea this was basically a tire case. After all, the tire definitely blew out but there was no obvious failure in any other aspect of the van. He would think about sharing the survey, talk with Tergano's lead counsel in Atlanta and get back to Born with an answer.

"Rusty and Trip," Born said, changing the subject, "Do you think this case will be tried in February?"

"I think there's a good chance," Loman replied.

"I agree there's some danger of that," Gillespy added. "But I think there's still a tremendous amount of work to do. Once we see what their expert says about our van, we'll then have to hire the right kind of expert to rebut plaintiffs' theories. We really can't intelligently get the right expert with the right expertise 'til we know what the hell they're going to say. Then we'll probably need to do some field tests on steerage with exemplar vans to simulate the conditions. That's all going to take some time. Bates says he's going to get us the information soon, but he won't do it. He'll try to get us in a bind, wait to the last minute to give us any information, and then press the Court to honor the February date. You wait and see if I'm not right."

"Unfortunately, this is not the only case I'm working on, although judges seem to think lawyers handle just one case at a time - the case that's in that particular Judge's Court," Born said with an air of frustration. "I have a major, major antitrust case set for trial the first of December, and it will take a good two months to try. I'll be spending loads of time in the fall getting ready for that trial. I'm already over my head in depositions in that case. I'll also have some smaller trials along the way, some patent applications to draft, some licensing agreements, and I'll be trying to keep dozens of other clients happy. It seems like a lot of time, between now and next February, but I'm so stressed out as it is, I've about lost my sanity."

"I've got cases coming out my ears too," agreed Gillespy. "I can predict what will happen. Bates will take his wife to Europe this summer, and Ripps and Fox will get busy on other cases, and along in October they'll give us the names of their experts. Then we'll be expected to compress all our work into the period just before Christmas, because we aren't allowed to do any discovery in January, the month before trial in February. You'll be tied up in November-December, and so will I, but the Judge will think we have plenty of time."

"I'm going to have problems, too, not as serious as yours and Ted's, but serious for me," Thompson volunteered.

"I'll tell you what I'm planning, Trip. You'll say I'm nuts, but I'm gon' tell you anyway," Born said. "I'm going to file a motion to transfer. All right, go ahead and smile, like I'm nuts or naïve. Dave and Rusty think it's ridiculous, but we've researched what's been going on in Phoenix County. I know it's your county, Rusty, but you're the one who got me the information I'm using as the basis for the motion. Incredible things have been happening in Phoenix. And if we don't get a transfer and if we later get hit with a big verdict in Phoenix, I'm going to say to the Court, 'Okay, I told you we couldn't get a fair trial, and we didn't, so now we want you to set that verdict aside.' I have to file it. I just have to, but I'm not asking Dave and Rusty to sign it. I've got some ideas and I just ask you to bear with me 'til you see what I work up."

"Ted," said Trip, "You haven't got a ghost of a chance. We're all going to get hit with a verdict which will break all records and immortalize us as the chumps of Phoenix County, probably the chumps of the whole state. All we can do is hope the case is postponed and then postponed again, and maybe we'll be saved by the intervention of the Second Coming before we take the bath. Face it. This is reality. This is life. This is Phoenix County. There's no way out."

CHAPTER FIFTEEN

THE MOTION

Ted Born was talking with Marta Shelby and Nita Langley about his project, to put together the backup for a motion to transfer. "Nita, I'd like you to review these boxes of pleadings from Phoenix County. Rusty's copied them from the original Court records. I want you to compare them against the originals and verify that we haven't missed any relevant cases in the Court file. I know you already picked the comparable type cases from these boxes, but I need you to sign an affidavit, and you have to go to the original records to do that. Rusty could do it, but he has to practice down there and can't afford to make anybody angry at him. So, you should go with Rusty to the Courthouse in Groveton, and let him walk you through the files so you can make the affidavit based on your personal knowledge."

"Mrs. Shelby, I'd like you to help Nita get it all put together," Born continued. "See, the affidavit will read something like this: 'I examined the files of all civil cases filed in Phoenix County in a six-year period and have listed the number of cases by years. I have excluded domestic relation cases, and other cases involving purely local Phoenix County residents. I have further eliminated cases that do not involve wrongful death, personal injury, products liability or fraud. Exhibit A is a listing of all such cases showing their disposition. X number of cases are still pending and have not yet been disposed of. Y number have been settled, and Z number (I think maybe one or two) were cases which have been dismissed or summary judgment granted. The remainder are 'comparable cases' for which there were jury verdicts, and here are the results.'"

"Yes, I understand. And we already know the results," Nita responded matter-of-factly. "It's just a matter of verifying our data against the original Court files. Result number one: No defense verdicts. Result number two: The *average* jury verdict in favor of the plaintiff was about $6.15 million. Now you know, of course, that some of those verdicts were reduced somewhat by the trial Court or on appeal, and in one case a new trial was granted. Are we correct in not taking those modifications into account?"

"Well, we do take them into account in that we note in the affidavit any reductions or modifications, so that this information will be fully disclosed in your document. But keep in mind that the question we are initially addressing is whether we can get a fair trial by a Phoenix County jury. This is a separate and distinct question from what a Court might do to the verdict later. We will, of course, deal also with the issue of Court intervention to modify the jury award, but our initial focus is on whether a jury in Phoenix County is likely to render a fair verdict."

"I think we know what you need," said Marta Shelby. "Nita, just call me when I can do something to help. I take it you'll be meeting with Rusty in Groveton to do the check against original records."

"Right," confirmed Nita Langley. "Guess I'll go call Rusty and get the arrangements all set up."

Mrs. Shelby continued to sit in her attorney's office as he thought out loud about what else he would need. He wondered if the Phoenix County Judge could take judicial notice of the contents of its own Court files, in terms of some specific material Born intended to use. Or should he be safe and support the material with affidavits? Nita could probably provide such an affidavit if one was needed, perhaps make it a part of her first survey-type affidavit they had just been discussing.

Born indicated to Mrs. Shelby that she need not stay any longer. He had just had an idea he wanted to check out, which would call for contacting a distinguished South Carolina lawyer. It would need to be someone with unquestionable credentials as a trial lawyer, a dean of the state bar, but not someone identified strongly with either the defense bar or the plaintiff bar. Born thought he knew the perfect lawyer for the purpose he had in mind. "Tillman Bailey," he said to himself. "If only he will do it!" He picked up the telephone and called.

"Tillman," Born addressed the older lawyer, visualizing his steely green eyes, white mane, his often-ruddy complexion. "I have a case in Phoenix County... . Oh, you know about Phoenix County cases, huh? Well, this one is worse than most, and I need to try to get out of that county if I can... . Yes, I know I haven't got a snowball's chance, but if I let that stop me, I might as well just ask them how much they'd like us to write a check for. Anyway, we've analyzed the results of jury trials in comparable cases in Phoenix, and they're pretty extraordinary. I was wondering if you could do this: Could you review the files of about a dozen cases I'll send over to you? You can assume these are the comparable cases that have resulted in jury verdicts. We'll have backup affidavits verifying the accuracy of what you'll be working with. I'd like you to look at the records of those cases and express an opinion, based on your many years of experience, whether the verdicts are excessive in relation to jury verdicts you have seen in similar cases with similar degrees of injuries and other damages. And further, I'd like your opinion as to whether the verdicts are so far out of line as to indicate prejudice, bias, passion and so forth?"

"Well, send them over and let me look at them, Ted. I'll let you know what I think," Bailey said. "I'll try to be open minded, and God knows I've had my share of plaintiff cases, but I also have an obligation to the bar as a whole, and to the law. I do worry that the whole justice system is in danger. I'm not sure I can help, but send them over and I'll see."

"They'll be right over," promised Born, delighted that Bailey had at least been willing to look at the material. "And I'll send a chart to help you walk through the cases."

He called Mrs. Shelby in, told her of his conversation with Bailey, and asked her to put together a duplicate set of the case files for Bailey.

Born had one further idea. He was intrigued about a possible statistical approach. What if, he thought, the jury pool is considered to be a randomly selected cross-section of the County which statistically should be reasonably representative of the County as a whole? If eight of the twelve eventually selected for jury duty have not been candid in their disclosures during voir dire examination - as had occurred in Phoenix County in the past - could the selected jury then be used as a statistically meaningful sample to project back to the whole county the likelihood that any other randomly selected jury might also fail to make candid disclosures? If so, then Born would have statistical proof, or something close to it, that he could not expect to get a fair trial. He could argue that he would not be able to get full and accurate information needed to select a fair jury, ergo, no possibility of a fair trial.

Born made telephone calls, got recommendations for several statisticians and finally settled on a professor of statistics who after a period of study made some probability calculations. He found the probability of

Universal's getting a jury of *twelve* candid and upfront jurors was vanishingly small, and the chance remained slim that even *half* of the selected jurors would make fully truthful disclosures in answer to voir dire questioning. He furnished Born an affidavit detailing his analysis and computations.

In due course, Born contacted Bailey again, and found that Bailey had in fact worked up some enthusiasm for the project. Bailey prepared an affidavit that he had reviewed the Court files on the set of twelve comparable cases and found them grossly excessive based on his experience and judgment. He concluded the pattern of consistent excessiveness could be explained only on the basis of prejudice, bias or passion. He volunteered that in this opinion, Universal could not receive a fair trial in Phoenix County.

Bailey refused to take an expert witness fee. "This one is a part of my dues to the bar. You will not be getting a bill."

Born put together Nita Langley's affidavit, with the excerpts of specific as well as survey evidence of Phoenix County verdicts. He put the statistician's affidavit and Tillman Bailey's affidavit with the proposed submission, wrote a brief tying it all together, and then he sent the whole packet to Dave Thompson for his comments.

Thompson kept it overnight and came back to see Born the next morning. "This is powerful," Thompson said. "It really isn't a racial thing at all."

"There are some white lawyers we know," Born

predicted, "who will say it's racist, with great indignation."

"I agree they'll say that," Thompson acknowledged. "My feeling that it will be perceived as racist still has not changed."

"We're not talking about perceptions, though, are we?" Born asked rhetorically. "Bates won't really perceive it as racist. It just makes good press for him. He comes off as the defender of the downtrodden, champion of the black community against this white lawyer from Greenville who's insulted the good people of Phoenix County. If there's a newspaper reporter there - and Bates will probably see to it one is there - it will make for a sensational article. Of course, I'll come across as the villain."

"Is it worth doing?" Thompson asked.

"Yes, Dave. It's worth doing. It's worth doing because I'm a lawyer, and it is my obligation to do the right thing for my client, and to absorb the punches if they're unfairly directed at me. It's worth doing because fear and intimidation are the worst enemies of justice. I have a passion for justice, and I won't be intimidated - regardless." Born answered with thoughtful determination.

"Are you sure you're right, Ted?" Thompson probed. "Like I said, it's powerful stuff, a lot more powerful than I ever thought you could put together. But that doesn't mean I don't have questions. For example, does it really ring true to you that it's statistically impossible to get truthful answers from a Phoenix County jury pool? I have a hard time with that one."

"You should have a hard time with that, Dave. But,

statistically, it's true unless... Tell me what you think could skew the statistical results," Born invited.

Thompson frowned, looked puzzled, and then his expression changed as he looked intently and seriously at Ted Born, "You mean, maybe the jury pool was tampered with before it was convened!"

Born nodded. "I want the Judge to understand that jury tampering is an alternative explanation for what appears to be a ridiculous conclusion compelled by statistical analysis."

"What a game this practice of law is. Here we are being sued by a popular Sheriff and some of his relatives in a county, where practically all the residents, from whom the jury will come, consider themselves his good friends, where the death and injuries are terrible, where the track record on fair trials is awful, where our opposition is sure to play the race card, and where the Judge feels compelled to defend the integrity of the justice system by keeping us in his Court. No rational system would allow us to be tried in Phoenix, but we all have to walk around on tiptoes and whisper platitudes about how great our system is and all the wonderful safeguards, pretending it's fair when every actor on this stage knows it's rotten." Thompson visibly showed his frustration.

"Watch it, Dave," Born said. "You're beginning to sound like me. Someone will be calling you a racist, if you don't watch out."

"Ted, you don't know how this gets to me. I mean, I know there's discrimination out there. I know there's racial injustice out there. I've sworn to do something about it. Then I come face to face with this, and it makes me ill. I mean it's embarrassing and disgusting, and I grit my teeth about it in my sleep. We'll lose everything - African Americans will lose everything - if they stand by and let Phoenix County type situations to continue and fester.

"Ted, you know what makes me furious," Thompson continued. "It's two things. The first thing," said Thompson, "is that I understand it, and I don't want to understand it. I want to believe I'm wrong."

"What do you mean?" Born asked.

"Ted, you probably can never know what race means to me, a black man, yeah, a black man, let's dispense for the moment with this African-American bit. I live with my race twenty-four hours a day, seven days a week, fifty-two weeks a year, every year of my life. I wake up black and I go to bed black, and I look in the mirror and what I see looks fine to me, but then I go to school or to work or anywhere and I see people who aren't black. I wonder, should I offer my hand in a handshake? Will someone be offended, coldly polite but offended, if I sit next to them? Will they be thinking, this is someone I should politely tolerate, or can I possibly have a real friendship? Will they be thinking, is he going to rape my daughter? I try to be easy-going; I try to prove myself and not let these things infect me and destroy me. You see, I've been lucky, and I can afford to be progressive and liberal. But what about the poor, unemployed, fatherless teenager in Phoenix County whose highest possible hope is to push some drugs and escape that way, or to take the drugs and escape *that* way? So, I'm afraid I can understand the seething anger and the crime and the frustration. I can understand why classic liberalism, born of the Age of the 'Enlightenment', is laughably irrelevant in Phoenix County and why the niceties of fair trials don't inspire them. The second thing I understand is, they are fodder for money-grubbing white lawyers, joining in this unholy alliance with people like Bates and Ripps. I understand it, see, and I don't like what I understand. It's not what I'm living for and standing for. I understand it, and I don't like it."

Ted Born was silent. He looked Dave Thompson in the eyes. He started to reach his hand out to Thompson, to offer the gift of touch, the gift of love and acceptance and kinship. He did not extend his hand. Dave might think he was being patronizing, Born thought, as if trying to prove that Born didn't mind shaking hands with him. Born merely sat there, looking at Thompson with warm, watery eyes.

"Sorry about that," Thompson said. "I forgot myself for a minute. Do you remember a while back when we were talking about Virginia and Carolina?"

"Yes, of course I do," Born answered.

"You kidded me about not having read Thomas Wolfe, remember? The reason I didn't read Thomas Wolfe is that I was busy reading Richard Wright and James Baldwin and Dr. King and Malcolm X and Angela Davis, and of course the standards also. I was looking for information about who I was, about what it means to be an African

American, and I didn't think I'd find out about myself in a white man's book like *Look Homeward, Angel.* Then something happened to me, and I went back to the faith. I guess you know my religion means a lot to me. Oh, I still read a lot of black authors, and I read accounts of people who said Abraham and Moses and even Jesus were black. But I decided I was asking myself the wrong questions. It was relevant to me that I was black, but it became a whole lot more relevant to me that I was a person, a human person with a mind and a spirit and a soul. I decided there were some things, like religion and all that religion represents, which meant more to me than my color or anybody else's color. The race monster is still after me, I see it creeping up behind me, and that's true of the rest of the world, too - every person of every color is stalked by the monster - but I'm trying not to let it catch and consume me. I can't live that way. *We* can't live that way. There are things more important, and that's why I'm an African American defending a big corporation against African-American plaintiffs, because I believe - I mean *I really* believe - that justice is the most important thing here on earth." Then Thompson grinned and said, "I'm still not going to sign that motion to transfer, though."

"Thanks, Dave, for sharing that," Born spoke softly and low. "I'm sure you are right. It would be arrogant of me to say I understand. I know the gulf is wide. We just still have to try to swim or float or jump across it. The race monster is after me too – you're right. It is after all of us, and it seems that no matter what we do, no matter how much 'progress' we make, it is still haunting us all. It ought to be simple. We all came out of Africa, so we are all blood kin. I'll tell you a true story. I know a man who was Egyptian, with somewhat olive complexion, and he applied to attend a graduate school in the U.S. When he filled out his application papers, he had to check a box designating his race, you know, the usual categories. He did not quite feel he could say he was 'Caucasian,' and when he looked at other options, he decided the one that said 'African' was the best fit, so he checked it. When he got to the States and was processed into the University, he was questioned about his choice, and he said, 'Well, I am from Egypt, so I checked African.' The clerk scolded him and said, 'You are messing up the whole diversity system. Egypt is in Europe!' My friend was amazed at such ignorance of geography, but just shook his head. The school still honored his admission. Race and culture – we make them complicated, even when they ought not to be. We need to find a way to make this cancer disappear, although that is elusive and sometimes seems futile. Speaking of futile, and to get back to what is immediate-ly staring me in the face, I'm going to file this motion, come what may."

The motion was indeed filed the next day. It created a stir among the plaintiffs' lawyers, and word of it began to get out to defense lawyers who had cases in Phoenix County, and they asked for copies.

Fred Bates convened a meeting with Jack Ripps and Alton Fox to discuss their response. Ripps wanted to feed the motion to the press. "Look, how can we lose? You know the Judge isn't going to transfer this case. There'd be all kinds of hell to pay politically, no he's not gonna' do that. So, it's not a question of deciding how to win this motion. The main question is: Can we get something else out of it besides a win? Seems to me we paint Born and Universal as racists, stir up the citizens of Phoenix, make this a '*we'll* show *them*' kind of case, and that should insure a big verdict."

Bates was more circumspect. "Not quite so fast, Jack. Remember, this motion is a helluva document with some sensational stuff in there about some of our past cases. I for one don't want any reporters nosing around about any of those cases. I hope they're behind us for good. Besides, my experience is that you can never tell what reporters will write. We can hope they'll paint it as a groundless racial thing, but then again, they may not. After all, Universal has this affidavit by a Ph.D. in statistics and another affidavit by one of the most respected members of the bar. I agree Judge Andrews ain't about to grant the motion. I'm not worried about that. But it's pretty risky to get the press involved. Seems to me our best bet is just to argue to Judge Andrews that this is a racist motion and try to poison him against Universal and Tergano."

Fox sided with Bates. "Don't mess with the press on this thing. It might help, but I'm not sure we need that help. I'm more concerned it could hurt, and I'd rather not take the chance. Once the press gets involved, we lose control."

Ripps acceded to the judgment of Bates and Fox, and the decision was made not to try to weaponize the press, with possible dubious consequences.

The motion was set for hearing the first Wednesday in September. Born, Thompson and Loman had had conferences about how to handle the oral argument. It was decided that a critical point was Sam Johnson's status as Sheriff of Phoenix County while being a plaintiff. While the history of big verdicts and at least arguable past jury tampering would be strong points, all the defense counsel agreed that nothing else was quite as strong as Sam Johnson's status of Sheriff, the chief law enforcement officer whose identification as a plaintiff would have a chilling effect on jurors' ability to decide the litigation on the merits.

At the argument, Born began by emphasizing Sam Johnson the Sheriff, and even told the Court Johnson's status as a powerful county official was the single most important of the factors favoring a transfer. At this point at the beginning of Born's argument, Jack Ripps interrupted and told the Court, "He's resigned from that position. It's a thing of the past."

CHAPTER SIXTEEN

EXPERTS FOR THE PLAINTIFFS

Born tried to conceal how stunned he was by Ripps' statement that Sam Johnson had resigned. It seemed unbelievable that Johnson would have resigned a position of good pay, retirement benefits, power and prestige after spending so many years working toward that goal, but he had no time to reflect on such matters. He looked at his local counsel Rusty Loman who raised his eyebrows and also looked surprised. Born continued with his argument, shifting gears quickly to point out the "other" strong reasons for transfer. The Judge looked impassively at Born as he went through his argument.

When Born had finished, the Judge looked over his reading glasses at Bates, and Bates rose to say he would not respond to each of Born's points but would only make the observation that this motion was a blatantly racist assault on the good people of Phoenix County, that Bates especially resented the insinuations or outright accusations that the all-black juries in previous cases were corrupted or somehow incapable of being fair, arguing there was no race-neutral reason for a transfer.

Born on rebuttal pointed to the statistical evidence which had never been disputed by any counter-affidavits, so it was an uncontested fact that fair juries could not be selected, and the history of huge jury verdicts confirmed it. Judge Andrews wanted to know if Born really meant all, or almost all, Phoenix County residents lie, and Born responded, "Alternatively, the results could have been skewed by improper intervention with the jury."

"Judge, can I hit him?" Bates said with righteous indignation, perhaps prematurely asserted. "If you're accusing me of bribery, Mr. Born, I want you just to say so."

Born answered calmly, "I say only that one of two things must be true: either the statistics are true, or something intervened to skew the results."

The Judge asked Bates to calm down. He then announced his ruling that he was denying the motion.

Born huddled quickly with Thompson and Loman in a corner of the courtroom, as Judge Andrews took up the next case on his motion docket. "What's this about Sam Johnson resigning?" Born asked Loman.

"It's news to me," Loman said. "I saw Sam in his Sheriff's car just a couple of days ago. Let's go downstairs over in the Annex and ask in the Sheriff's office."

The trio of Universal lawyers, plus Trip Gillespy for Tergano, went to the Sheriff's Department and asked about Sam Johnson and whether he had resigned. No, he had not resigned. He had switched to the night shift because of expanded daytime responsibilities in his drug delivery sideline. "I can't believe it!" Thompson said. "Ripps got up and said Johnson had resigned, right to the Judge's face. Why would he do that? He must have known we'd find out the truth."

"I'm pretty cynical, Dave," Born said, "but I suspect it's because they wanted to take the wind out of our sails, get the Judge to rule for them, and they knew that - once the Judge ruled and was committed - he probably wouldn't change his mind, even if the truth was revealed. Well, I'll tell you. We're going to find out."

The entourage of defense lawyers went back to the courtroom where the Judge was still hearing arguments in other cases. Bates was nowhere to be seen, having apparently already left the courtroom. However, Ripps was still there, waiting his turn to argue a motion in another pending case he was handling. Born waited impatiently but politely until the motion then being argued had been disposed of, then he asked the Court for leave to say a word.

The Court recognized Born, and Born then reminded the Judge of Ripps' statement about Sam Johnson's resignation and how the Sheriff's Department had just confirmed Johnson in fact had not resigned. Judge Andrews looked at Ripps, his dark eyes peering sharply over his glasses.

Ripps shrugged and said, "It was my understanding he resigned. I know he expanded his private job. We'll all find out."

"I cannot understand how a lawyer would make an unqualified representation of that kind, interrupting my argument to do it, without being sure his information was correct." Born stated firmly. "Universal asks the Court to reconsider its ruling and to transfer this case to Richland County."

The Judge thought for a moment, looking at his bench notes where he had already written in the denial of the motion to transfer. "Well, I don't think I will disturb my ruling. There were other considerations supporting it."

The defense lawyers left the courtroom shaking their heads in disbelief at the Judge's tolerance level for such conduct on the part of lawyers in his Court. "Rusty," Born asked, "what's that jail cell for in the back-left corner of the courtroom?"

Loman said, "That's an old holding cell where they used to keep prisoners who were waiting for their turn to come up to the bench for a hearing or sentencing in criminal cases. When they restored the Courthouse, they decided to keep the cell in the courtroom as a historical oddity. Of course, they don't use it anymore."

"I disagree with you, Rusty," Born said. "I felt like someone grabbed me and put me in that cell today. I feel hemmed in, helpless, with justice in sight, but totally out of reach."

CHAPTER SIXTEEN

The defense lawyers paused outside the Courthouse to assess the situation. "Do you still feel you did the right thing filing the motion?" Gillespy asked. Tergano had joined in the motion but Gillespy had said little at the hearing, keeping a low profile.

"Yes, I still think so, although my confidence is a little shaken," Born answered thoughtfully. "Judge Andrews didn't say much, but I believe we've gotten his attention. Of course, I didn't expect him to grant the motion, would have been astonished if he had. For the first time, some-one has made a broad-based assault on the state of justice in Phoenix County. I think he'll remember this a long time, and maybe he'll try to prove to us we *can too* get a fair trial in Phoenix. If it helped soften him up so he will give us some relief we need in order to get a maybe halfway fair jury, it'll be worth it."

"I'm amazed," Thompson said, "that Judge Andrews let Ripps get away with something like that. Did it surprise you?"

"I don't really know what to make of it," Born confessed. "I'm sure it offended Judge Andrews. I even thought for a moment, as he paused and gave Jack that searching look of his, that he might actually reconsider the motion. My guess is, he decided it wasn't quite clear-cut enough to make a disciplinary issue out of, but at least he'll be watching Ripps. Jack will have a credibility problem with Judge Andrews for a long time to come."

"Ripp's lie paid today, though," Thompson observed deliberately, "but I hear what you're saying. It might hurt him with Judge Andrews in the long run. I guess he just sees one day at the time, he sees what happened today, and he's the big winner. He's probably convinced himself that this is the way to be a winner all the time."

Taking advantage of this occasion to get together, the defense lawyers discussed among themselves the dreaded prospect of a possible February trial but they shared a common hope it would not be set at that time, feeling they should not be put to trial when the plaintiffs had failed to identify their experts. Gillespy reminded Born and Thompson of his prediction it would be October before the expert information would be forthcoming, that it was now September, and the prediction was about to be borne out, could even prove a bit optimistic. Gillespy emphasized he was not complaining, even hoped the plaintiffs would delay a lot longer, since he felt Judge Andrews would not set the case for February trial if plaintiffs were delinquent in identifying the experts.

Born was surprised the trial setting had not come up at the hearing on the motion to transfer, thinking the Judge might clarify the uncertain status of the trial setting left murky at the prior hearing some months earlier. Gillespy, who was more familiar with Phoenix County practice, advised that the trial setting probably would be discussed at the October motion docket, the first week in October. It was customary to set cases for the next term four months in advance, which translated into an October firming up of next February's trial docket. Gillespy said he was sure Fred Bates and Jack Ripps would be very familiar with this pattern and would probably scurry around at the last minute to try to get the case set for a February trial.

Born observed that he still was set for a December/ January trial in his big antitrust case but added he had filed a motion for summary judgment and had a glimmer of hope he might get out of that case without having to undergo trial. There were several other defendants, and they were planning to file for summary judgment also. At this point, it was all up in the air, but for planning purposes he had to assume he would be in trial for a good solid two-month period beginning in early December, with mountains of preparation in November.

Although the defense lawyers could not have known it, Fred Bates at that very moment was on his way to meet with Alton Fox about the status of the expert witness on the tire part of the case. He felt reasonably good about the hearing on the motion to transfer. He had won, and it's hard to do better than that.

"Maybe Jack went a little too far on that stuff about Sam Johnson's resignation, but we won," he told himself as he drove back to the office for his meeting with Fox. "Anyway, I think I scored some points with the Judge on the race issue. Every Judge in this part of the state has got to be 'right' on the race issue, and Judge Andrews has to handle this case from here on out so as to prove he's not favoring those racist defense lawyers."

"Of course, I have to deal with the fact they've got this nice young black fellow Dave Thompson, but I think I can predict what's going to happen," Bates mused to himself. "Ted Born will parade Thompson before the jury like some kind of trophy, but they won't let him do a damn thing. The jury will see right through that. Yeah, a token black, that'll just confirm in their minds that the defense lawyers are a bunch of racists. That's a theme we have to make the most of."

When Bates arrived at his office, he found Fox in a small conference room with the tire and rim and some papers organized in several stacks. "Okay, Fred, how'd the hearing go?" Fox asked.

"Victory was ours," Bates beamed. "Didn't expect anything else, but it's good to know for sure. Now we can get ready for trial. Alton, I'll tell you like it is, if I hit it big on this one, I'm gone. I'm going to leave it with you, and you might never see me again. I'm going fishing, and my wife can probably persuade me to take us on a cruise around the world. The way I see it, I need one more big one, and I'm counting on you to come through on the tire part of the case. So, tell me, where do we stand?"

"All right, here's the situation, Fred," Fox explained. "I've had two potential experts look at this tire. The first one I sent the tire to was a guy in Michigan. I've used him before, and he's effective with a jury, relates to them pretty well. Problem is, he's kind of wishy-washy about this tire. He points out it was old, fairly well worn, and apparently failed from impact. Of course, he's willing to say there's evidence of belt edge separation which could have progressed inwardly from the edges across the crown to make a weakened area near the blowout. You can't really see

214

it today because of the disturbance caused by the blowout. It's probably enough to get the case to the jury, but it really isn't all that inspiring."

"What about the other expert?" Bates asked.

"He's an Aussie, Fred. Now don't lose your drawers, he's been doing some testifying here in the U. S. and had some luck in a big case in San Francisco and Chicago and a big one against Universal in Houston." Fox had expected Bates would be leery of an Australian expert, and he soon found he was not mistaken.

"I don't care, Alton, if he's the world's greatest, Groveton ain't San Francisco nor Chicago, and it's not even Memphis. You get somebody who comes in and talks funny, and it just might bomb with our favorite kind of jury," Bates warned.

"Fred, hear me out," Fox argued. "He's good, and I think he'd go over just fine in Phoenix County. You know the old saying about how an expert is someone who comes from a place at least a couple of hundred miles away. His accent would certify him as an expert in the minds of those jurors. Plus, you've got to remember, jurors today spend a lot of time watching television, especially in Phoenix County where lots of them are unemployed and there's not much else to do. I doubt they'll think Australia is as strange as you suppose."

"Well, we're gon' have to think about this one. I know you're the tire lawyer and know what you're doing, but I've tried more cases in Phoenix County than anybody alive, maybe more than anybody who ever lived, and I'm not real thrilled with an Aussie. Next thing I know, you'll be suggesting some Limey." But Bates was willing to listen. "Go ahead. Tell me who he is and why he's so great."

"His name is Wrack Kelly. He's got good credentials. Worked for tire companies in quality control for many years, first in England and then in Australia. Really, he's an Irishman who first went to work in the tire industry in England and eventually ended up in Australia. He got terminated from his last job - admittedly a bit of a problem - but he's got that part covered pretty well. He passes it off by saying they fired him because he wouldn't compromise his high standards and principles on quality control. He's been a consultant for the last ten years or so, mainly testifying for plaintiffs in tire cases, as you might expect. He's been hired to speak to consumer groups about tire safety and has done a good bit of writing about tires. That sometimes worries me, because I don't like for my expert witnesses to have committed themselves too much in writing, because they can get tripped up with their own words. In this case, it doesn't worry me much, because he's been writing purely from a consumer's and plaintiff's standpoint, and I don't think he's ever said anything that would help a defense lawyer cross-examine him. And, as I said, he's been having a run of success in this Country after making a name for himself in Australia and Europe."

"What does he have to say about the tire?" Bates wanted to know.

"A beautiful approach. He acknowledges the

well-worn condition of the tire and the failure from road hazard impact. But he's got this `sweat theory' that explains everything," Fox began.

"He's got this *what?*" Bates frowned.

"That's right. He's got this sweat theory. Here's how it goes. During the manufacturing process some worker touched one of the rubber components, most likely the belting, with sweaty hands, and when that sweat got on the rubber it sort of acted like a contaminant which prevented the touched rubber component from bonding properly to the adjacent rubber component. This would produce a spot weakness in the area where the blowout occurred." Fox smiled as he explained it, knowing that Bates was not understanding much of what he was saying.

"Sounds pretty weird to me," Bates pronounced. "How can you prove it?"

"You can't 'prove it'," Fox grinned. "The blowout would destroy all signs of any contamination. The beautiful thing is that no one, no defendant tire maker, can disprove it, either. That means the case will go to the jury every time."

"All right, Alton, I'm no tire lawyer," Bates acknowledged. "But seems to me there are lots of holes in this sweat theory, could even say it smells. Ha! First, I assume tires get touched all the time in the manufacturing process, and if Kelly's theory is right, why don't we have blowouts of every tire?"

"Well, tire components get touched more frequently in some tire plants than in others, and we have reason to think there's a lot of touching in Universal's plant, more so than in most. Also, the Universal plant is over in Georgia where it gets really hot in the summer like our South Carolina summers, and the plant is not air conditioned."

"Didn't you tell me these tires were manufactured in April of some year?" Bates asked.

"True, but even April in Georgia can sometimes get very hot, especially toward the end of the month, and this tire, all four tires, were made the third week of April. I haven't yet checked the climatological data for the plant site during the week of manufacture, but if the *outside* temperature reached 85°-90° F during even one hour of one day during that week - and it probably did - the jury will believe the temperature got above 100° F *in* the plant. They'll imagine the workers inside that plant were sweating like pigs."

"Why weren't there blowouts in the other three tires on the van, made the same week at the same factory?" Bates probed, still far from convinced.

"Easy. Those tires didn't necessarily get touched by the same worker or by hands that were quite as sweaty. Furthermore, if they'd had another week or another month of use, maybe they would have blown out. *Some* tire had to be the first to blow. It just happened to be this one." Fox had a smug look on his face.

"Why wouldn't the sweat problem have shown up earlier? I mean, these tires had a helluva lot of miles. Wouldn't there have been vibration or something? Remember, everybody and his brother who's given a deposition in the case says there was no vibration. It drove great." Bates showed he was adept at cross-examination.

"Admittedly, this is one of the toughest problems. But remember this contamination starts out as a *local* problem. The tire was probably well vulcanized, as far as we can tell, and it held together everywhere except in the area of the blowout, where the sweat contamination occurred. When you have a really localized contamination and the vulcanization has fused the different rubber components well except in the local area, it can hold together pretty well for a long time until there ends up being an unusual amount of local wear which gradually enlarges and gets worse. There probably was some vibration near the end, but on that rattly van, it could easily be missed, especially by Bess Johnson who wasn't familiar with how it was supposed to ride."

"I'm full of questions," said Bates, "but this is sounding pretty good, I have to admit. How does he deal with the fact the tire was felled by a road hazard?"

"Ah, that's one of the things Kelly does best," Fox explained, savoring this trump card. "Kelly says the tire was already `dead' from the contamination before it hit the road hazard. As Kelly tells it, the road hazard was something trivial, like a reflector in the road, a small stone, something which a normal well-made tire can handle safely, with no difficulty. However, a tire like this one, with the sweat contamination, was an accident waiting to happen, and it was set off by something trivial. In other words, there was a road hazard that it hit, but that's not the real cause. The real cause was the weakness which came from the contamination. He uses this analogy: He says everyone eventually dies because the heart stops beating, but this doesn't mean they all really had heart problems. The real cause of death might have been the underlying pneumonia or cancer or something else. The stopped heart just finished off the underlying disease, just as the trivial road hazard finished off the tire which really was already dead from the effects of the local contamination. Well, what do you think?"

"Let's go back to first principles. One way or another, the jury's going to be with us - I think. I mean, we've got the Sheriff as a plaintiff and we've got a death and brain injury and all that. It's a thousand times more sympathetic a case than any I've had in a lifetime of practice. This is such a dream case, the jury probably won't need any prodding," Bates replied.

Bates paused, lit a cigarette, and then continued. "Anyway, assuming the jury's gonna' be with us, the main questions are, first, how do we make sure we survive summary judgment or a directed verdict, so the jury can do its thing? Second, how do we make sure the verdict's appeal-proof once it's rendered? That leads us back to your Australian. If he doesn't turn the jury off, and if he can get enough 'evidence' in the record to get us to the jury and protect us on appeal, then it's okay with me. Have you ever met him?" Bates asked.

"No," Fox replied, "Australia is a long way from South Carolina, but I have talked with him by phone. Had to call him at midnight to reach him, with the time zones and all that. Seems like a nice chap. A little expensive, but with what's at stake... ."

"You know it doesn't take much to get the kind of record we need to protect us. A guy gets on the witness stand and says he's an expert, and that makes him one. He can say damn well anything, and it's evidence. You might do just as well with someone a little more domesticated, but what the hell! You're in this case because you're a tire man, and we ought to take your advice, I guess. Only thing is, I've never used an expert I hadn't met. What if this Kelly turns out to have a red bulbous nose and bloodshot eyes and hair in pigtails and rings through his lower lip? Check him out, if you can, at least get a good recent picture. Now let me tell you about my van expert."

"Yeah, I'd like to hear about it," Fox said.

"I found him down in Atlanta. He's an engineer, so that makes him an expert, right off the bat. He can speak the language; well, I should say he can do about as good a job with the language of Phoenix County as anyone who's not literally from there. He's never had any direct experience with design of vans or automobiles, which is something of a problem. But he once was employed by someone who had a NASA contract to design a better moon rover. Frankly, he wasn't on that project too long, but long enough to make him an expert in vehicular design, I guess. He's a consultant, and I got his name from an ad in a trial lawyers periodical."

"What's his theory - or has he gotten that far

yet?" Fox asked.

"Yeah. He's got a theory. He says the center of gravity of the van in an unloaded condition is at its geometric center - in other words at the intersection of diagonal lines running from the left rear tire to the right front and from the right rear to the left front. When the van is loaded, as in this case with more than twenty sacks of groceries and other things, the center of gravity shifts to the rear. That's true even when account is taken of two adult passengers in the front seat and three children in the rear."

"So?" Fox was waiting for the tie-in with the accident.

"So, if the weight of the van is concentrated rearward from the geometric center and you have a blowout of the left rear tire, what's going to happen to the front wheels?" Bates asked rhetorically.

"I guess the left rear obviously is lowered by the blow-out and the right front would be raised a little, maybe raised off the ground?" Fox reasoned.

"You've got it!" Bates said with the smile of a teacher delighting in a student's learning breakthrough. "Now remember that this van was being driven in two-wheel mode at the time of the accident, and the front wheels controlled the steerage of the van."

"Okay, I'm with you. Go on," said Fox. "Well, if the front right wheel is lifted off the road by this fulcrum or see-saw effect, that leaves only the left front controlling the steerage. Now the left rear is totally flat and acts as a drag. When power is applied to make the van accelerate, or even if it is already being driven at a fairly high speed - I think fifty-five mph is fast enough - the van has to go somewhere, so it goes to the left."

"Okay. I'm trying to follow this." Fox said, thinking aloud. "Is it something like this? If you take a string and put your finger on one end, let's say that is like the drag caused by the deflation of the left rear tire, and then you have motion at the other end, it can't go forward, it has to go either left or right by centrifugal force. You've just got one wheel on the ground up front. But what makes it go left instead of right?" Fox was struggling. "Wait! I think I see. The left rear is deflated and creates the drag, and the right rear is pushing forward, creating a torque which forces the left front to go left! Eureka! It finally got through to me."

"Hey, you did pick up on that. You know what the clincher is: Practically all vans manufactured in the last two or three years, including the newer Tergano brand vans, now have the center of gravity considerably forward of the geometric center, which to me is an admission that the earlier design was bad. See, if the center of gravity is toward the front, both of the front wheels critical for steerage remain firmly on the ground no matter which of the four tires blows out, and you don't lose steering control," Bates smiled.

Then Bates continued, "For a while I thought our best case was against the tire maker because the blowout was indisputable, but then I realized it's a little worrisome that the tire was old and pretty worn. I was bothered by the fact that, usually, vehicles ought to be controllable when a blowout occurs on a straight road. But Peter - Peter Justin is the name of our van expert - pointed out that most of those control tests were made using cars, not trucks, and cars almost always have their center of gravity forward of center, so naturally there was no loss of control. It was the advent of the van which caused this potential steerage problem. Now that I see how logical it all is, I'm beginning to think we could possibly have a better case against the van maker than the tire maker. Hopefully, it won't matter. Hopefully the jury will give us big verdicts against both of them. We'll be rich, and we can claim we did some good for the public in making sure the tire designs and van designs of the future are better."

There was a knock on the door. It was Jack Ripps. "Come in, Jack," Bates invited.

"I just got my ass royally chewed out," said Ripps. "Born and his group found out Sam Johnson hadn't resigned, came back and told the Judge. They asked Andrews to change his ruling. Of course, he didn't. In fact, he didn't say much at the time, but at the end of the docket, the good Judge said he wanted to see me privately. Everyone had left, and there I was in the courtroom with Judge Andrews. He told me in the toughest words I've ever heard him say, that he was going to be watching us, and specially watching me, and we'd better not step over that line, or even give him reason to think so. He was looking at that animal cage back in the rear of the courtroom. I told him I was sorry, that it was a mistake, that I'd be more careful in the future, and I was sure there wouldn't be any more problems."

"I hate that happened," said Bates. "It means we *will* have to be more careful. It's too late in my career to go to jail. You know, you too could retire on this case, Jack, if it just comes out right. So no more screwups. This kind of thing can affect our program for the case, if nothing else. In just a few weeks, we'll be trying to get Andrews to confirm a February trial date. I don't want him to punish us by continuing the case. You know damn well the defendants are goin' to be kickin' and a screamin' for a continuance. I'm gonna be fighting like hell against one, not only for my retirement, but because I don't think I can stand anymore of those phone calls from Bess or from the Millers."

"Ain't that the truth!" Ripps agreed. "I almost wish I hadn't told that Bess woman to stay home from work. Got nothin' on her mind but this lawsuit. Doretta's not too bad. She don't seem to know what's going on or care. But Bess, I tell you what, I've quit returning her calls, and the Millers, they ain't much better. My father would have had some choice words about this situation, where I am and what I'm doing, if he was still here, but I'd just have to say, 'Daddy, it's a living. You did what you had to do. *This* is what I have to do. No big difference, really. Just a living.'"

Bates laughed. "It's all about doing the best you can with what you've got, right? Coping, just coping, is the living end. What the hell! What's it matter? You do what you have to just to get along, but you guys can keep wrestling with Phoenix County as long as you want to. I'm gonna' make my getaway soon as I win this case. I gotta gorgeous lot down on the bay, with gentle breezes and lots of palmettoes to help me forget this place."

CHAPTER SEVENTEEN

TRIAL SET

It was the last week in September when the mail brought to defense counsel a notice designating Wrack Kelly as plaintiffs' tire expert witness, specifying that he would testify the Universal Tire was rendered defective by contamination during the manufacturing process.

Just as Born had been warned, the plaintiffs were supplying expert information, such as it was, at the very last moment. "They want to be able to say they've already given us this information when we go over for the conference with Judge Andrews to argue about whether to have a February trial. I'm sure they are going to do their best to get us in a bind, to squeeze us time-wise so we won't be able to do a good job," Born thought.

He decided to call Bert Sayre about this development.

"Bert, we received this notice designating a fellow named Wrack Kelly as plaintiffs' expert witness on tires. He's apparently from Australia. Ever heard of him?"

"Sure have," Sayre answered immediately. "He was a witness against us out in Utah, where we got a summary judgment, and then again in Houston, where Universal got hit for forty-four million dollars. The Utah case was mine, the Houston case was somebody else's, thank God, but, yeah, we've heard of him. In Houston, he came up with this crazy sweat theory."

"Sweat theory?" Born asked, incredulously.

"Yeah. The plaintiffs in Houston had this video tape which came from our own records, we produced it to them - unfortunately - in discovery. No one really remembers how the tape came to be or why it was made, but apparently it was supposed to show the various steps involved in making a tire. It was never intended as a model illustration of good tire making procedures in terms of sanitation and cleanliness, and there was an awful lot of human touching of the green tires in process of being made, mainly because hands and fingers were being used to point to, touch and identify parts of the tire for instructional purposes, most of which would not really happen in an actual plant setting. Anyway, the camera lights shined down on one worker who seem to be gleaming with sweat on the forehead, and he even wiped his brow and slapped his hand against his work apron."

"Okay, I'm following you about the video and the man with the sweaty forehead. How did Kelly use it?"

Born inquired.

"Kelly said that workers just like the man in the video tape would get sweat on their hands and then touch the rubber components. He said the tape proved workers sweated, that they got the sweat on their hands, and with all the hand contact on tire components, there would inevitably be sweat deposited on the rubber components." Sayre explained, then continued, "Kelly claims sweat can be a contaminant which prevents good adhesion between rubber tire components, causing the tires to fail."

"Can it be?" Born asked.

"Not usually. We've never seen any problem with that. Of course, if you get enough moisture of any kind on a tire component, it can be a contaminant, whether human sweat or plain tap water or anything else. But if you got that much moisture trapped between, say, two layers of belting, the heat of the vulcanization process would turn the moisture into steam which would tremendously expand in volume, producing a bulge or distortion which would certainly be detected at one of the inspection stations." Sayre answered.

"You say the Houston jury bought this theory?" Born asked.

"Hook, line and sinker," Sayre answered. "We've got to try to keep out that video tape in this trial."

"You must have some of his old depositions and trial transcripts then. What can you get me on Kelly?" Born wanted to know.

"As you say, we have some depos and one trial

transcript. He once wrote a little tire handbook, and I can send you a copy of that. Also, he's written quite a few articles on tires. Most experts don't write much, because of course they don't like to commit themselves and thus give future defense lawyers, like yourself, some ammunition to impeach them later. Apparently, he felt like, operating out of Australia, he had to write a lot to make a name for himself so he could break into the lush testifying pastures of this Country. I'll get you up a big bundle of this stuff and send it to you."

Born mulled over his conversation with Sayre, thinking about Kelly's sweat theory. It seemed like a nutty, cockeyed theory. But, of course, a jury bent on awarding big bucks to plaintiffs might seize on anything to justify their verdict. If Kelly tried to use this theory in our case, Born thought, he would have to earn his expert witness fee. "First, we'll try to keep the tape out of evidence. Second, we've already won a battle on a plant tour, there won't be one, the Judge has ruled. There would then be only one way for plaintiffs to introduce any evidence of sweat - through a Universal employee. This could be a problem," he thought. "Any employee in the plant is going to have to admit tire components *did* get touched by human hands at times." If all else failed and evidence of touching, with the possibility of sweat contamination, actually ended up being admitted in evidence, then Born would argue that no detectable contamination was found post-accident, that tell-tale signs of contamination would have shown up earlier if they were there, that the whole sweat theory was, well, just plain crazy.

It then occurred to Born that he had not seen any comparable proposed expert testimony as to the van design, the Tergano part of the case. Did they forget to send him, the tire maker's lawyer, a notice about the van expert? Or had the plaintiffs not yet designated a van expert? He confirmed that Gillespy also had not received any information as to proposed testimony from plaintiffs' van expert.

"I'm not going to push them," Gillespy said. "If we go to the docket call in October and they still haven't designated a van expert, we've got a real good chance Judge Andrews won't set this case in February."

"By the way," Gillespy continued, "I think it would be a good idea for you to meet our Atlanta counsel. They've let me carry the ball pretty much up to this point, but they'll be taking the lead, I assume, as we move closer to trial. I think it would be good for you to get to know them."

"Sounds fine, Trip," Born agreed. "I hope we continue the good working relationship you and I have had. Will they be coming in for the big October docket call?"

"Yes," Gillespy said, "That's really what I was coming to. Could you come by my office on the way to Groveton and let's talk for thirty minutes or so?"

"We'll be there," Born responded. Born wanted to turn his attention to the reply brief on his summary judgment motion which was due to be filed by the end of the day. First, though, he looked briefly at the long list of messages and telephone numbers of clients demanding a piece of his time. He picked out a couple of messages he had to handle immediately, told himself the others would have to wait until he put the reply brief to bed. Then he commandeered a vacant conference room and left instructions that he not be disturbed.

When Born arrived home that night at eleven forty-five, his wife Lydia was propped up in bed, reading as was her custom, before turning out the lights and going to sleep.

"You look tired, honey," she said. "It hurts me that you have to work so hard. You haven't been home a night this week before eleven. I worry about you."

"I don't like it, either," Born said, as he emptied his coat pockets and put the contents in a compartmentalized caddy on his bureau. "I can spend so little time with you. I feel like a captive. I'm locked into my law practice, and it's exhilarating and rewarding in many ways, but I also feel like I'm not really living, or alive. I never seem to have even a minute for myself. But don't worry. I'm psychologically connected, just tired."

"It's been a tough year, hasn't it?" Lydia asked sympathetically.

"One of the toughest," Born said. "I keep thinking, as I get older, that things will get easier and better, that I can just delegate the stressful, hours-gobbling work to younger lawyers. I'd like, in my dreaming, to be an office lawyer, a telephone jockey, where trusting clients call me for advice and cling to my every word, as I pontificate about the law." Born smiled weakly and shook his head.

"It's not to be. At least, I'm afraid, not for me. I guess I'll turn out to be like one of those batteries that, instead of gradually attenuating their output as they get older, just put out the same level of current until finally one day they go `Poof!' and it's all over. I guess it'll be like that for me. I want to escape, but I can't escape. I'm locked in and can't help it."

"How about early retirement? Would that work for you? You've always wanted to be a writer and never had the time. We could go up to Maine, and you could sit on the deck of the house and look out at a glacial lake, through the birch trees along the shore. And you could write." Lydia said, at least halfway seriously.

Ted Born at this moment yearned to be in Maine. The fall foliage was not yet quite at its height, but would be by mid-October, give or take a week. "Maybe," Born answered, "Maybe. You just hit me in my Achilles' heel. You know I'm vulnerable." He slipped into bed and cut out the lights.

In due course, the first Wednesday in October arrived. Born and Thompson were driving to Columbia, and they were talking about Wrack Kelly and his sweat theory. "That theory has got to be the craziest thing I ever heard of," Born said. "What do you think?" he asked the younger lawyer.

"It sounds crazy to me, too. You know, I imagine a lot of those Phoenix County jurors do a lot of hard work with their hands. They probably don't think of sweat as being any big deal. That's if their minds are open,"

Thompson answered.

"Tell me something, Ted," Thompson said, looking over at Born who had his eyes fixed to the highway in front of him. "I notice you never cuss. I mean, maybe I shouldn't even say anything, since you're a lot older than I am. I think most people would have had some choice words about that sweat theory, and I can think of some myself. But I've never heard you let go like that."

Born laughed. "You really want to know?"

Thompson smiled.

"Well, when I was a child I had some good Baptist friends who lived down the block from me. My family was Lutheran. But I used to spend lots of time at the Baptists' house. They had a boy one year younger than I was, and they had a couple of boys a little older, and that's where I learned to play baseball. The two older boys would get on first and second bases, and I and my younger friend would try to steal base while they threw the ball back and forth and closed in on us to tag us out. But, anyway, they told me in no uncertain terms that, if I said any bad words, I wouldn't go to heaven. The same thing about lying, only they didn't call it 'lying'; they called it 'telling stories.' So, I grew up sometimes hearing colorful language like all kids do, but in the back of my mind I had this subconscious taboo about cursing. My theology in the meantime has advanced a little beyond that, but still... ."

Dave Thompson grinned. "I'm a Baptist. I don't cuss, either. Do you ever feel like you ought to cuss, just to be part of the group, if you're standing around with other men and stuff?"

"Really, no. To tell the truth, it does make me a little uncomfortable, when other people let out with a stream of obscenities, like Fox did with you. But it's just not part of my vocabulary. I learned I had to face problems and things I didn't like, and it didn't do a bit of good to cuss about it. Maybe let off a little steam, but I always figured the best way to let off the steam was to solve the problem or win in competitions," Born answered.

They pulled into the parking lot of Trip Gillespy's law office and went inside where they were ushered to a conference room. "Hi, Ted and Dave," Gillespy said warmly, "I'd like you to meet Butch Cassidy and The Sundance Kid. No, seriously, Brad Mansfield and Chet Bernhardt."

"Yeah, Chet's my sidekick and we're both gunslingers," laughed Mansfield.

"Come to think of it," Thompson offered, "That's how Fred Bates described you when Trip mentioned to the Judge you would be in this case. I guess he actually called you a 'hired gun.'"

"Close enough," Bernhardt smiled.

Mansfield was the senior lawyer, probably mid-fifties, Born guessed. He had mostly gray hair which seemed to be combed in parallel strokes from front to back. He had a serious business-like bearing, small black eyes, a Cyrano nose, ruddy complexion and a thin wiry body that suggested he ran marathons on weekends. Chet was in his late thirties or early forties, pleasant, blue eyes, sandy blond hair, a trim build, however lacking the wiry emaciation of a habitual runner.

"Still no word about a van expert?" Born asked.

"Not a word," Mansfield answered, eyebrows raised to show he did not understand why.

"I need a continuance badly," Born said. "this is such an important case, and we've just gotten our expert designation and you still don't have yours. There's no way I can do an adequate job with what's on my plate. If I'm lucky and get a summary judgment in my antitrust case, it would help tremendously, but I'd still be covered up. Judge Andrews will never be able to appreciate how bad my situation is, but unfortunately I'm not sure he would even care."

"Remember, Ted," Trip Gillespy pointed out, "It's not a sure thing we're even set for February. Bates pushed him for that setting, but Judge Andrews never said he was doing it. Maybe we'll be in luck."

They left in separate cars to drive on to Groveton for the docket call. When they arrived, Rusty Loman met them and handed them a copy of the docket, hot off the press. A sigh of relief floated among them as they noticed their case was in a sort of no-man's land, not yet on the February trial docket, but with its status yet to be determined.

Ripps approached the defense lawyers huddled in a corner of the courtroom, looking at the docket sheet. "Did we send you a copy of our designation of the van expert?" he asked.

He knows damn well they didn't, Gillespy thought to

himself. "No, Jack, you didn't."

"Well, I'm sorry about that. Some sort of mix-up in the office. It was supposed to have gone in the mail." Ripps pleaded.

Some forty minutes later, Judge Andrews called the *Johnson* case, and the lawyers on both sides came up to the bench. "Did we agree that this case would be taken up at the trial docket next August?" the Judge asked.

Bates quickly jumped in, "No, Your Honor. We specifically asked and we understood you agreed to set it in February. These plaintiffs are hurt, and we need to get this case to trial."

"Judge, we didn't understand it that way," Gillespy responded. "Mr. Bates did ask for a February setting, but we objected, and I don't believe any decision was made one way or the other. If there's any doubt about it, Your Honor should understand that the plaintiffs promised us a prompt designation of expert witnesses, and we came here today still not knowing who their expert would be, or what their theory of liability is. Jack - Mr. Ripps - just handed us his designation a few minutes ago after we arrived in this courtroom today. There's no way we can get ready for a deposition, take the deposition and understand their theory of liability, get our own expert, give him time for preparation and for his own deposition."

"That was a foul-up in our office, Judge," Bates responded. They should have gotten the designation earlier. We did send Universal the designation of our tire expert-"

"Not much earlier, Your Honor. We got no notice

until last week," Born interjected, "and I have a terrible litigation schedule between now and February. I'll probably be in trial all of December and January in Federal Court. Not much hope for a Merry Christmas."

"That's not a proper reason for a continuance, Your Honor. The cases should not be set for the convenience of the *lawyers*. That was the old way. But now the courts are supposed to set cases for the needs and convenience of the *parties*. They keep saying that over and over in bar/bench conferences," Bates argued.

"But, Mr. Bates, aren't you the one who didn't follow through with your designations? My concern is how fair it is to the parties to have to go to trial when it is your fault they don't have time," Judge Andrews observed.

"Judge, the defendants have plenty of time. It's four months between now and February. This is one of the oldest cases on Your Honor's docket. It needs to be tried in February, for the sake of these injured and bereaved plaintiffs," Bates insisted.

"I don't know," the Judge thought aloud. "I'm not sure the case is going to be ready for trial in February, and I'm not sure whose fault that is."

Bates frowned and looked at the Judge imploringly. Then he sensed that the case was about to be set on the August docket. Now's the time to play his trump card, he thought to himself. But he'd better clear it with Ripps and Fox. "Your Honor, may I have a moment - just one moment - to confer?" Leave was granted, and plaintiffs conferred in whispers for perhaps a couple of minutes. Fox seemed unhappy, even agitated. Then the huddle ended and Bates reapproached the bench. "Your Honor, in an effort to serve the interests of the parties and the Court, and to show our good faith, plaintiffs are willing to waive the taking of defendants' expert witnesses. All we expect is a reasonably thorough Rule 26 summary of their testimony. This should clear the way for trial in February."

"Are you saying you will promptly produce your experts for depositions and will waive the deposing of the defendants' experts?" Judge Andrews asked, peering between his dark bushy eyebrows and the top of his reading glasses.

"Yes, sir," Bates confirmed.

"Seems to me that ought to do it. With prompt depositions of their experts and not having to prepare your own, you ought to be able to get ready in four months," the Judge addressed the defendants. "The case will be set for February. If the plaintiffs don't follow through with prompt proffers of their experts, come back to see me and we'll revisit it, but for now the case will be on the February docket."

CHAPTER EIGHTEEN

A DAY IN AUTUMN

"Thank goodness it's comin'," Bess declared to Louis Goodlett and Doretta Anchrum. "I'm 'bout to go crazy, not doin' nothin' but sittin' 'round here. It's gon' be February. They say we're gon' hit it big. They talk 'bout millions of dollars. Lord, I don't even know what a million dollars is, but I'm ready to find out. How 'bout you, Doretta?" They were sitting on the front porch of Bess' small house, a porch in need of paint and new flooring.

Doretta Anchrum also was ready. Goodlett smiled faintly and thought about all that money. It wouldn't be his exactly. Bess might be too good for him, if she woke up a millionaire. Talk about the competition. There'd be suitors who'd put up with an awful lot to be Bess' consort.

Goodlett never wanted to be the marrying type. What good is it but ties a man down. Plenty of women out there. Yet the money - the money made him think.

Doretta Anchrum never said much. She just rocked and talked about how she could use some help with Jimason.

Bess Johnson chuckled. "It's nice to be so pop'lar. I reckon ev'rybody comes up to me, no matter where I am, and they say they're with me, that I do deserve it, how proud they are. All that."

"Yeah, same here," Anchrum agreed.

"Attorneys say talk it up. They say let ev'rybody we know, find out our case is goin' to trial in February. Well, I done the best I can, but see, I ain't got no car or nothin', and I hate to just call up people on the phone. I do some of that. I set down yesterday and just thought of people I ain't seen in a while, and I called up a couple. They seemed glad to know. Really, though, I'm lookin' to Sam to make sure people know. He sees - Lord, he must see - he's gotta see a hundred people a day, in and out o' that Courthouse and on his rounds and delivering for that drugstore too. I cain't hold a candle to Sam. He's the one what's got to do it."

"I ain't called many, neither," said Anchrum. "I 'spect the word'll get around, though. My preacher - he's gon' remember me and Jimason in his prayers ev'ry week in January and February. You know, the `out loud' prayers at the service. That'll help lots. If you ain't done that, Bess, be sure to tell your preacher. Preachers can influence lots of people."

"Amen," said Goodlett. "You cain't do no better'n that. These preachers, they control lots o' votes, at the polls and in the jury room. Gotta get them preachers on your side. Anywhere you've got a contact with a preacher, that's who you need to be calling, and Sam, and Ben Miller too, they need to help with the preachers."

It was a gorgeous October day in Groveton, the temperature moderate and the usual sticky humidity in remission. A brilliant yellow hickory tree stood out across the road. Doretta Anchrum asked what time it was. It was two o'clock in the afternoon, Goodlett advised. "Guess I gotta go home," Anchrum announced reluctantly. "I got things to do."

Bess Johnson and Louis Goodlett found themselves alone. Her children would also be coming home, but with the bus, they probably would not arrive before four o'clock. Goodlett moved his chair so it nearly touched the woman's. He reached over and put his hand on her hand. They smiled. "It's a beautiful day. Don't your mattress need airing out? We could just pull it outside, into the back yard? Wouldn't it be nice to sit there on the edge of that mattress and see them leaves fallin'?" Goodlett suggested.

"Maybe that mattress could use a little airing, a little sunshine," Johnson responded with interest in her eye. "Think you could help me move it?"

"I 'spect so. Let me see if I can." Goodlett rose and pulled Johnson up, and into an embrace. He released her and playfully pushed her into the house, meeting little resistance.

The backyard had a wooden fence on one side, a wire strand fence on the other two sides. A square area with better fencing enclosed a small chicken yard, where a rooster and two hens were kept. Johnson's mongrel dog Jake lay sunning in the back. Occasionally an acorn or a sweet gum ball would hit the tin roof of the house and roll off, adding a percussive contribution to the outdoor sounds, which seemed especially intense. There were no other houses within sight.

Bess and Louis sat on the edge of the mattress they had dragged outside, and Louis began to urge her to recline and look up, up at the blue. Bess tugged back, gently resisting, looking into Louis' eyes. They said nothing to each other, they said everything to each other. "Louis, what do you feel? I mean what do you feel when ...?" she asked.

"I guess I feel like a king, you know. There I am, with you, and lookin' you in the eyes and readin' your eyes with ev'ry movement, and feelin' alive - more alive than I've ever felt - and knowin' that you feel, too, I mean, really feel, you know. I'm a man and you're a woman, and we know each other. Lord, we know each other! And ev'ry nerve I got is on edge and I can see ev'rything and know ev'rything. And then the drums roll - and then there's that high note, that long high trumpet note that answers back and keeps goin' on an' on. Then there's peace and there's warmth, and I keep holding you, touching you, and I want to hold you to me as I slide off into peace, sweet peace." Louis' muscles tightened and his eyes watered.

"That makes it all fine, Bess. Ain't nothing here in this world that's fair, except for you, Bess. You even it all out, make it right for me, when ev'rything else seems wrong."

Bess reclined in his arms and looked up at a cloudless sky. They would not have to hurry. The children were not due for a while.

CHAPTER NINETEEN

THE SWEAT THEORY

Ted Born was sitting at his desk as the telephone rang. It was the law clerk to the federal judge handling the antitrust case. "Judge Benson asked me to call all the parties and tell them to stop work on the December trial. He has decided to grant summary judgment. An opinion and order will issue in probably a couple of weeks."

Born tried to control his emotions as he thanked the messenger. Simultaneously, he felt joy, release, pride. He felt like celebrating. There was ample cause for celebration, for the opposition had spent over a million dollars in *out-of-pocket* expenses pursuing this litigation, and thousands of hours of lawyer time. Two hundred and twenty depositions had been taken. Ted Born had won, he and the young associate, Chip Sturdivant, who worked with him on the case. To be sure, there were other defendants and other defense counsel, but Born knew this was his and Chip's personal victory, and every other lawyer in the case knew it likewise. It was they who mobilized and led the defense. It was Born who filed the initial motion for summary judgment and the first brief, and it was he who had mainly argued the motion on behalf of the defendants.

Yet there would be no celebration. Well, perhaps a small dinner with the other defense counsel, months later, when time permitted. At the present, time did not permit. The impossible situation which had confronted him a few minutes earlier had now become merely difficult. No longer would he spend all of November feverishly working to get ready for a December antitrust trial, nor would he spend December and January in trial. Instead, he would spend most of his time in those months getting ready to try a case in February that was unwinnable.

The contrast between the two cases struck Born. This victory he had just learned about would be one of the high points of his career, but few would know about it. Certainly, there would be a half dozen or so who would see him in the hallways and congratulate him on getting summary judgment in some case they had only vaguely heard of and which they would not even remember a week later. But he would probably lose an unwinnable case in Phoenix County in February, no matter how well he tried it, millions in damages awarded, and *everybody* would know about *that* one. Everyone would remember it forever. "They won't have much room on my tombstone,"

Born thought, "just a few lines to sum up my life's work, and it will probably read: 'He lost a one-hundred twenty-million-dollar verdict in Phoenix County.'"

Even as he basked in the warm glow of winning the big antitrust case, he knew that it would not be a defining moment for him. Like it or not, his defining moment would be the Phoenix County case.

"I don't want my life's work to be assessed by the yardstick of the Phoenix County case. It isn't fair! Why can't my professional life be defined by this antitrust case, or by the multi-million-dollar verdict I got as a plaintiff in that unfair competition case that was appealed three times to the Fourth Circuit? Or the zoning case where the decision revolutionized the law? Or the criminal defense of the appliance manufacturer where I won, and where the Government lost for the first time in that type of case? I'd rather be remembered because I wrote the legislation on mandatory education for retarded children," Born protested. "I'd rather be remembered for a thousand things I've done, good things, constructive things, hard things - things I've done well, and where I won. Why can't I choose what will define me as a lawyer, as a person? Why must it be this guillotine, poised for my naked neck, in Phoenix County?"

He knew the answer, he knew that human beings are mostly products of their circumstances, that they are required to cope and - at least here on this earth - some one or two incidents in that process will be deeply etched in memories to define an entire lifetime. It need not be the most important thing, or even typical. "Circumstances just come together in a way that obliterates everything we've ever done, except that one thing, and we become defined to the rest of the world, defined as champs or chumps. Here on earth, it matters little how you play the game at that crucial moment. It only matters that you win, that you lose," Born thought pensively to himself.

Will people understand if I lose? Not a chance! Oh, they'll discount it slightly for the difficulty, but mainly they'll say, patronizingly, "He wasn't up to it, couldn't deal with it, couldn't cope." The patronizing would hurt worse than the criticism. Worst of all would be the silence, those who would not say much, where Born would be left to wonder what they were thinking. "I have a responsibility to Dave," he thought. "A terrible responsibility, because I'm in charge and he has to work with me. Sure, I'll get most of the blame, but Dave will get some too. That's something else that's not fair either."

Dave Thompson had not yet heard of Born's big win in the antitrust case, but he had parallel thoughts. He wondered why he had not politely opted out of this case in the beginning, after he saw the picture of Sarena. It was not too bad as long as trial seemed distant, when there was hope something, anything, might come *deus ex machina* fashion to make it disappear. Now he knew it would not go away. There would come a day in February when a trial would take place, when a jury verdict would be handed down. He had made some emphatic statements about finding twelve God-fearing people who would render a fair verdict. As trial approached, those statements seemed hollow, canned sociology, little relevant to the reality of Phoenix County.

Thompson had always respected Born as a lawyer, but he knew Born was a *white* lawyer and wondered if he could ever relate to a mostly African-American jury. It had taken some time before Thompson felt comfortable with Born, and that process still had a ways to go. Born seemed tolerant, he seemed to have a capacity to understand, to be trusted. Thompson marveled at the similarities between the two of them, like hard financial times in boyhood and youth, the influence of fundamental religion. "If his skin was different, could pass as one of the brothers," Thompson thought, then honed his observation. "No, he still wouldn't really be quite a brother, but I guess he doesn't have to be."

Thompson's opinion of Tergano's counsel was guarded. Trip Gillespy was likeable, no doubt about it, a good lawyer too, but could he relate to *this* jury? Thompson was sure Chet Bernhardt could not relate, was doubtful about Brad Mansfield. What did he mean, "to relate"?, Thompson asked himself. "It's got to mean somebody you'd like at a subconscious level to be intimate with, not in a Freudian sense, but more like soul-mates."

Thompson was good-looking, and he knew it. He also had a smiling, no-chip-on-the-shoulder disposition that reinforced acceptance. Thompson could relate, he knew, but he wondered if it would be enough in Phoenix County, with this death and these injuries and being a lawyer for a big corporation. The closer the trial date came, the more he doubted it.

Ted Born appeared at Thompson's office door. "Congratulate me, Dave! We won the antitrust case. Now maybe I won't be guilty of malpractice getting ready for this one."

"Hey, congratulations!" grinned Thompson as the two shook hands. "Are you and Chip going to celebrate?"

Born noticed that Thompson still turned his body slightly to one side as they shook hands. "He's straightening toward me, but we're not quite there," Born said to himself, but he answered: "Afraid not, not right now, anyway. I took time to call Chip, and then I called Lydia, and then I came to see you. The next thing I'm going to do is set the date for the deposition of the tire expert, Wrack Kelly. Alton Fox gave me some dates when Kelly could fly over from Australia, but my schedule's been so horrendous, I haven't firmed up a date. Now I can do it. Maybe I'll even be able to read some of the materials Bert Sayre has been sending me on this fellow!"

The date for the Kelly deposition was set for a Thursday in November, to provide a two-day Thursday/ Friday window for completing the deposition, which Born thought would probably be adequate.

Kelly was a tall, thin man, slightly humped back, snow white bushy hair, with wire-rimmed bi-focals. He was in his late fifties, his speech a blended medley of Irish, English and Australian accents.

Born took the deposition, which turned out to require

only one day after all, and Sayre was present. Kelly conceded the tire failed from impact with a road hazard, though he said he thought the hazard was "trivial." When pressed, Kelly could not point to any evidence that the road hazard was "trivial" and conceded the hit object could have been several inches high, as far as the evidence showed. He acknowledged the tire was "well worn" and said he would not have put it on his own car, because "it hasn't got much further to go." It was worn, but not quite "worn out," he said.

Kelly had taken tire x-rays, which he called "radiographs", of approximately thirty degrees on each side of the rupture. He pointed out some belt edge separation, but acknowledged such separation was inherent in all steel belted radial tires. He had other criticisms of the tire construction but conceded none of those supposed shortcomings could have caused the blowout.

The culprit, he said, was contamination. He did not find any hard evidence of contamination, but, then, one never does: All evidence is destroyed with the blowout. Why did he suspect contamination? Because the tire failure occurred in a highly localized area, no sign of bad vulcanization. He was sure there had been a bulge or protrusion in that localized area before the blowout occurred, and the bulge should have caused vibration. He had no explanation for why no driver or passenger in the van ever felt any vibration, except they perhaps did not recognize vibration in the tire for what it was.

He was not absolutely certain what the contaminant

was, but he strongly suspected it was sweat from workers' hands. It would not take much sweat, according to Kelly, to contaminate the tire. No, an employee need not be dripping with sweat. "There is always sweat on your and my hands and fingertips," said Kelly. "We are not conscious of it, but it is there. I'm talking about minute, infinitesimal amounts of sweat. There's something about the content of human sweat, I've never determined what it is, which prevents rubber from adhering to rubber. If someone touches the rubber, it will not bond securely to the adjacent rubber at that spot."

Kelly said other contaminants could theoretically be responsible, but he thought it unlikely in "an operation such as Universal's." That left sweat as the most probable contaminant. He mentioned he had seen a Universal video about tire making where he observed excessive touching of tire components with the human hand. He knew nothing about who made the video, the purpose of the video, the date it was made or the identity of the plant shown in the video.

Kelly acknowledged he had conducted studies of controllability of vehicles after blowouts and had reached two major conclusions: first, when the blowout occurs on the inside of a curve during a turn, "cornering" as Kelly put it, the vehicle was almost impossible to control at highway speeds of forty-five to sixty miles per hour. Second, on a straight road, the vehicle was controllable by the driver one hundred per cent of the time, regardless of which tire blew out and regardless of the speed. He had no explanation why Bess Johnson had lost control on a straight road.

The witness denied seeing any signs of underinflation, but he agreed that underinflation is the single worst abuse a tire can sustain, resulting in excessive wear and excessive buildup of heat - another enemy of tires.

One of the things Born had been most concerned about was a "failure to warn" theory. He feared the plaintiffs would not only say the tire was defective, but that Universal should have given consumers some kind of warning about the tire which it did not give. The Complaint had only hinted at such a theory, and possibly Fox had not yet focused on it, but Born knew a failure-to-warn theory could emerge. These were the toughest kinds of charges to defend against, because it always seemed there was an infinite number of potential warnings a fertile plaintiffs' lawyer could think up in hindsight.

Born quietly, very low-key, asked Kelly if he could think of any warnings a tire maker could give which might have averted the accident, then held his breath as he awaited Kelly's answer. "Only that vibration of any kind must be taken seriously. A motorist should proceed slowly and cautiously to the nearest garage for inspection and service if there is any significant vibration."

Born asked if there were any other warnings he would recommend. Kelly answered, "No, just that vibrations should be taken very seriously." Born allowed himself to settle back slightly, knowing Kelly's answer should go a long way toward eliminating the failure-to-warn issues as to Universal.

Kelly had not been inside a North American tire plant ever, and since losing his job he had seen the inside of only two or three tire plants, mostly in the Pacific rim or in third world countries. Mainly, he spent his time testifying on behalf of plaintiffs in lawsuits. Almost casually, in connection with some background questions about his citizenship and multi-national work, Kelly stated he paid no income tax to the United States on income earned by testifying in American litigation.

"Bert," Born said, "that deposition went well enough, I think we ought to get summary judgment across the board, probably won't, but ought to. I think we'd be justified in filing a motion for summary judgment as soon as we get this transcript back from the court reporter, at least on the charge that Universal somehow could have and should have provided some warning which would have prevented the accident. Kelly seems to have given us what we need to get rid of that theory of liability for sure, if there's any justice in Phoenix County."

Sayre agreed, "I'm not a lawyer, but I'm supposed to be managing this case as the Universal rep. I know we need to get out of this case, hopefully, *entirely* out of this case. If you think we've got a decent chance, let's go for it."

"I like summary judgments, obviously," Born commented. "When you can get them, it's a great way to win. Of course, they're not quite as appeal-proof as a jury verdict, but anytime I can get out on summary judgment, that's what I try to do. When you win, you don't get the credit for it that you do with a jury verdict, but it's really a higher form of lawyering than winning with a jury. In other words, if I got you out of this case on summary judgment, I'd be saving you the cost of trial and the risk that the jury might go haywire with damages. That would be a better deal for you - by far - than a crap shoot with an unpredictable jury."

"No question," said Sayre. "Are you going to win it for us?"

"Please, Bert, don't push me back into reality," Born said. "I was enjoying fantasyland. No, I doubt it. I can't see this Judge giving us a summary judgment regardless what we do. You know what? The sad thing is, he's as good and honest and conscientious as any judge I know. It's just that he's scared of reversal, so I feel sure he'll let the case go to the jury. Still, we can't leave any stone unturned."

"Obviously, we can't count on summary judgment, Bert, at least not a total summary judgment, just possibly a partial one. We'll give it everything we've got, but it's a very long shot," Born continued. "We've got to go ahead, getting ready for this trial just like it's definitely going to happen. That has to be our assumption. I'm going to suggest a couple of things I believe will be helpful. First, I want your authorization to employ a communications expert, some people call them jury consultants. I know someone I've worked with on possibly ten or twelve earlier cases, some of which went to trial and some of which settled, but she made a tremendous difference in all of them. I've never had anything but good results in every case where I've used her. Her name is Dr. Phyllis Maxwell. She has a Ph.D. in Communications, and she's been doing this jury work for about twelve years. She's good. I'm a believer."

"What's the second thing?" Sayre inquired.

"I'd like to do a mock trial, a mock *jury* trial. I think we will learn an awful lot about what works and what doesn't work with a demographically similar jury. With so much at stake in this trial, I think you should do it. It's expensive, but well worth it."

"I'm inclined to say 'let's do it,' but get me some cost estimates and I'll take it up with my bosses," Sayre answered.

"I don't have any problem getting you the information and I'll get some estimates immediately, but remember it takes some time to set up the mock jury trial, so let me know as soon as possible. Thanksgiving and Christmas are coming up, and it'll be hard to get anything set up before January. This would leave us a narrow window, as we'd have to be finished by mid-January in order to have time to get ready for the real trial and digest what we learn at the mock trial. I won't waste any time getting you the cost information," Born responded.

There was a knock on the door. It was Dave Thompson, returning from some deposition cleanup work in Columbia, Mrs. Driscoll's son and the wrecker operator. "The depos went fine," Thompson reported. "Nothing much there. Driscoll didn't actually see the accident, just heard the crash. How'd Kelly's deposition go?"

"Fine, we think," Born replied. "We're going to file for summary judgment and believe we can make a pretty respectable showing, though realistically we're not optimistic. I've been talking with Bert also about getting ready for trial if we don't get a summary judgment, which is a long shot at best. Among other things, we've been talking about a communications expert and a mock trial."

"Oh, yeah," said Thompson, remembering he and Born had briefly discussed it. Thompson had been especially doubtful that a white woman could help them much with communicating with a black jury, but he had not voiced any opposition.

"Well, as I said," Thompson continued, "not much happened in my depositions, but I did get served with a request for production, to produce that video tape. Guess we knew it was coming. Ripps delivered it to me at the depositions. And they also served me with a notice to take the deposition of a Universal company representative."

"I knew it was coming!" Born said. "This will be a real battle. They want the video tape in order to show a lot of hands touching tires during manufacture, to bolster Kelly's sweat theory, and they want to reinforce the touching with testimony from a company representative."

"Can we do anything to head this off at the pass?" Sayre asked.

"Probably not a lot," Born confessed. "We'll object to the video tape, but discovery is so liberal, we probably won't succeed. As to the company rep, the way they worded this deposition notice, we're obligated to make available the person most knowledgeable about tire making procedures at the plant at the time this tire was made. No question they'd be entitled to take such a deposition. We'll just have to do our best to protect against trick questions and so forth. Got anybody in mind, Bert, who would fill the bill? Someone who knows the manufacturing process and would make a good witness?"

"As a matter of fact, there is somebody," Sayre answered. "His name is Al Gifford. He's retired now, but he was head of quality assurance the year this tire was made. We're on good terms with him. He testified in that Houston case, where we lost big, but we really can't blame the loss on him. Want to talk to him? I could stay over, since I set aside two days for the Kelly deposition and it took only one day."

"Okay, and I'd like you to meet him too, Dave. Can we give him a call, see if he's available?" Born asked.

"Sure," Sayre responded, opening his laptop computer to retrieve his telephone number. "He lives in Georgia, worked there and retired there, even though he hails from Ohio originally. Here's the number. Can you dial it?"

Gifford would have to reschedule a golf game set for the next day, but he agreed to come to Greenville instead.

When Gifford arrived late the following morning, after a three-hour drive from his home in northwest Atlanta, Born and Thompson joined Sayre and Gifford in a conference room. Al Gifford was sixty-seven years old, lean and healthy looking, salt-and-pepper hair, with a small mustache, and he was sporting an outrageous,

flowery sport shirt, Hawaiian-style. Gifford was matter-
of-fact and strictly honest. There was a certain amount
of hand contact with tire components, and if asked on a
deposition, he would have to admit it. "Doesn't have a
damn thing to do with quality or safety, but Kelly can
make it seem so, to someone on the jury who doesn't
know what the hell is involved in tire making. That's what
Kelly did in Houston. I was just sitting there, nothing I
could do, but he made this so-called sweat contamination
seem plausible."

"Can they use the transcript of the Houston case in
our trial?" Thompson asked.

Born started to answer, but Sayre broke in, "All the
Houston testimony is under seal and is confidential by
order of the Federal Court in Houston, while the case
is on appeal. Kelly shouldn't have a copy of it. I'm not
saying he doesn't have one, but he's not supposed to have
it and would be subject to severe sanctions if he admitted
having it. By the same token, Alton Fox is not supposed to
have a copy either, and if he does, he can't use it. It would
be like the water torture to have what you regard as a
valuable piece of evidence which you can't use. So he'll
try to develop the same thing independently."

Gifford walked them through the procedures
Universal had in place to guarantee quality. Born and
Thompson were impressed. "The only thing is, Universal
does have some touching, not a lot, but some. For example, the worker at the belt station lays the belts on top of
each other just right, using his hands."

"Why couldn't he wear gloves?" Thompson asked.

"Two reasons," Gifford answered. "First, gloves are awkward, and it would be hard to line up the belts precisely enough wearing gloves. The second reason is, if you're worried about contamination, gloves would give you a tremendous problem. Gloves would pick up and shed lint and dust and particles of all types, and it's complicated to wash them frequently. They just plain don't work."

"What do other plants do?" Born wanted to know.

"Some are like ours; some are more automated and have less hand touching," Sayre answered, "but, Ted, let me assure you it's just a matter of normal evolution of a plant. When we get around to automating the process more, it won't be because we're trying to solve a contamination problem. In fact, there might even be more contamination with advanced automation, because contaminants could creep in unseen, whereas today the workers look at every green tire component and make pretty doggone sure there are no contaminants. No, the only reason for automating out the hand-touching is to get more perfect machine alignments of components, has nothing to do with minimizing contaminants."

"You've convinced me," Born said. "The question is, can we convince the jury?"

CHAPTER TWENTY

JURY SCIENCE

In Atlanta, Brad Mansfield and Chet Bernhardt were assessing the deposition they had just completed of the van expert, Peter Justin. "This guy's out of sight," Bernhardt said with disgust, "but we've got our work cut out to prove it."

"Some van expert!" agreed Mansfield. "He's never driven a sports utility vehicle in his life, except his own, and it's a Logos like the one in this case! His theory has some superficial plausibility, but - "

"But his model is static, and the real situation was dynamic," Bernhardt interjected. "He ignores the role of the suspension system in the van which counters the seesaw effect he talks about. He makes a bunch of assumptions about the weight of the groceries, and he doesn't recognize the need for a centered weight mass for better, evenly distributed traction for off-road use - which is what these vans were primarily designed for."

"Yeah, when this van was designed, the manufacturers thought it was *really* going to be used for off-road travel," Mansfield mused. "Then a few years later, they find out they're rarely used for that purpose. They're either bought for driving around in snow and ice - not a big problem in Phoenix County - or they are bought for their rugged macho image. You know, the urban cowboy type, pretending to be an east coast Marlboro Man or something. So now they've shifted the center of gravity forward, and Justin's going to say this shift recognizes the error of our past design."

"Did you follow what he said about the lack of a stabilizer bar?" Bernhardt asked.

"Not really. I don't think he has a theory yet. He just observed there wasn't a stabilizer and said he'd have to think about whether one could have prevented the loss of control. If he tries to testify about that, I'll raise holy hell. He was supposed to have his theories fully developed before we took his deposition. Bates effectively represented to the Court that his experts were ready to go and there was no reason to delay the trial beyond February. If he keeps thinking of new theories and revising his old ones, we'll at least be entitled to a delay of the trial. It's clearly prejudicial to us." Mansfield felt strongly about the possibility of any "new and improved" theories from Justin developed just in time for trial, too late for discovery.

"I'm bothered about one of his theories that does seem to be well developed, the seat latch problem," Bernhardt posited. "How do we handle that?"

"I think he's saying we had only one latch retaining the back fold-down seats in an upright position for seated passengers," Mansfield said. "He's claiming we should have had two latches, one on each side of the seat, that it would have retained the seat in position and prevented it from folding forward on impact. If I'm understanding him right, he's saying the latch failed on impact, folded forward and propelled the children to death and injury."

"Hard to argue there shouldn't have been a second latch. How much would it have cost the van maker, four bucks maybe?" Bernhardt asked rhetorically. "But hon-estly, those kids weren't propelled forward by the back of the seat. It was inertia that sent them flying forward a split second before that latch broke."

"Right. No proximate cause. The latch system might or might not have been good enough. Even a double latch might have failed, I dunno. But, with no seat belts on, those children were going to fly forward anyway. The latch would not have prevented that, even if it had held. So, there was no causal connection between the failed latch and the death and injuries."

"What if they had been wearing seatbelts?" Bernhardt asked.

"That's troublesome," Mansfield frowned. "It's argu-able that the failed latch might have caused the kids to have broken backs if they had been strapped in as the latch failed and the seat folded down, doubling them up, with tremendous force. There's still another practical problem about seat belts."

"What's that?" asked Bernhardt.

"There were *only two seat belts* in the back seat. Even if they had tried to buckle everyone up, one child would have been unprotected. If we could legally raise the seatbelt issue - which we can't - they might eat us alive. They could say, `Does Tergano want you to believe these mothers should have had to choose which one of the children ought to die? Tergano should have installed at least three seatbelts in the back seat.' The back seat, of course, is a bench type seat where three persons, even three adults, could comfortably ride. Of course, the front has two bucket seats, and two seatbelts. I suspect we'd better leave the seatbelt issue alone, even if we could raise it."

"Well, we're not supposed to raise it as a defense. The plaintiff bar saw to that. I understand from Trip," Bernhardt explained, "that the plaintiff bar for years opposed mandatory seatbelt legislation, because they were afraid failure to wear seatbelts would then be prima facie evidence of contributory negligence of injured drivers and passengers. Finally, under intense pressure from public opinion, they compromised and let the mandatory seatbelt legislation get adopted, but *only* if failure to wear a seat belt could not be considered contributory negligence at trial, and they wrote that into the law."

"What do you think Born's view is?" asked Mansfield. "We don't want him going off on his own tack and screwing us to the wall in the process."

"We haven't really talked about it in any detail, but from things Ted has said, according to Trip who's been with him a lot on this case, I think he may be planning to get in some evidence about the seatbelts, ostensibly not as evidence of contributory negligence but just as a part of the general description of the condition of the van and passengers as they were discovered after the accident."

"We need to head that off," said Mansfield. "I don't know if Bates and his plaintiffs are aware of our problems with seatbelts, but let's don't take a chance. Meanwhile, I see Universal has filed for summary judgment. I think Ted is being a little optimistic, or maybe overreaching, in asking for total summary judgment. But they're right that something along those lines needs to be done. If we don't get greedy and ask for too much, we just might get some relief. My thought is we ought to file for *partial* summary judgment just on the latch issue. If we won on that point, it would remove one of the most troublesome issues, our obvious problem in not installing an inexpensive second lock for greater security. At the same time, we would also go a long way toward solving our two-seatbelt-three-passenger problem, since it's most likely to come up in the context of the seat and latch. We'll hit hard on the lack of any proximate causation. One good thing is that Bates has told me he won't really oppose a summary judgment motion as to Citizens Tergano, the dealership, so we can hopefully get it out of the case. It's all such crap. Bates never would have named Citizens as a defendant in the first place except to defeat diversity grounds of federal jurisdiction and keep us in state court. Now that Citizens has served its purpose, and we're stuck in state court, they'll let Citizens out. Nice of them!"

At the moment, Ted Born was not thinking about seatbelts. He was engaged in the difficult job of convincing Dave Thompson of the value of a communications expert.

"I don't have any problem with her helping us with jury selection or helping some of the witnesses do a better job, but I'm going to have a big problem if she tries to tell me how to talk to the jury," Thompson was saying. He was trying hard not to say a white woman, whom he had never met, could not possibly help an African-American lawyer talk to African-American jurors. Yet that was what he really meant, and Born knew it.

"Dave, all I'm asking is that you and I meet with her and listen to what she has to say. If you don't think it helps, that's fine. But I've been working with Dr. Phyllis Maxwell for years, and I'm telling you, she's been very helpful. You may be thinking she could not possibly understand African Americans, and I don't doubt that in certain respects you're right. But I think there are some universal principles which cut across racial and cultural lines, some of them logical and psychological, others not so logical, that she has studied and put into practice. She's done lots of jury research, some of it on predominantly African-American juries, and she might have some points you would find useful."

"Sure. I'll listen to her and what she has to say, but I

come from a tradition of extemporaneous speaking. Take, for instance, preaching. I know one preacher here in Greenville who's always well organized and has his notes and gives a good sermon - if you were reading it. I know another preacher who hardly ever uses a note and doesn't do much planning or organizing. Well, the first one is a fine man, but he puts people to sleep, and the second one has everybody standing in the aisles, shoutin' and saying 'Amen' and really getting with it. Dr. King, you know, knew how to speak to people, and he moved the whole country with his 'I have a dream' speech. I don't think this Dr. Maxwell could've helped him." Thompson was very firm and obviously convinced of his position.

"Dave, I'm sure Dr. King thought long and hard about his 'I have a dream' speech. I doubt it just happened extemporaneously. But, be that as it may, I just ask that you listen to her. Incorporate what you think is good and forget the rest. That's what I'm going to do. I'm going to pick what I think I can use from the menu of ideas she offers. Even if I use just a fraction of her ideas, as I usually do, they'll be valuable. One thing she brings to this entire process is objectivity. No one is totally objec-tive about himself or herself. All of us have tunnel vision and lack perspective, in one degree or another. Give it a chance," Born urged.

"Oh, I'll give it a chance. Let's see now, the plan is to meet with Dr. Maxwell tomorrow and then we meet with the mock trial people the next day - Jury Science, is that their name? Will Dr. Maxwell be in that meeting too?" Thompson asked.

"Yes," Born responded. "Tomorrow is a preliminary meeting, and then the full group meets the next day. I've gotten Carl Heimat to agree to take the role of the plaintiffs' lawyers at the mock trial, and Tim Archer will be the lawyer for Tergano on the van issues."

"I guess it wouldn't be a good idea to do this mock trial jointly with Tergano's lawyers, would it?" Thompson asked.

"I've thought about that but decided against it. The reasons for getting them involved would be to split costs with them and maybe get a more accurate read from the mock jury, since the mock jury would have seen the real lawyers for both Universal and Tergano. The negative is that we lose control of the process—I want to be in total control, we need to learn something about the way our two defenses mesh or clash with each other, and how the mock jury assesses our relative strengths and weaknesses. I'm not sure I necessarily want to share that information with Tergano. For example, if we learn from the mock trial that certain issues help Tergano but help them only at Universal's expense, it might be something we'd just as soon keep to ourselves." Born had thought it through and added that he had discussed this with Sayre who agreed to keep it purely a Universal show, with a simulation to the mock jury of both the plaintiffs' and Tergano's roles.

The meeting with Dr. Maxwell was low key. Born had warned her of Dave Thompson's feelings, and she was aware that she needed to tread lightly with him.

Actually, Born need not have warned her, for Thompson's cool distance-keeping manner told her she needed all her psy-chological skills to thaw the doubt and skepticism. They discussed the case as a whole, its facts, Wrack Kelly's sweat theory, the Tergano factor, the type of probable jurors, Universal's "message," and how best to get across the overall message. Dr. Maxwell wanted some time to think about the case. If there was any narrowing of the icy divide between Thompson and Maxwell, it was not perceptible. Still, it seemed useful to be talking to-gether about the case as a whole because of their shared goal of winning.

The next day, the firm's largest conference room was filled with participants in the contemplated mock trial. Rusty Loman had come over from Groveton to join Ted Born and Dave Thompson. Bert Sayre was down from Universal. Nita Langley and Marta Shelby had come in order to be sure they understood what was to be done. Carl Heimat and Tim Archer attended as the surrogates for plaintiffs' and Tergano's counsel. Phyllis Maxwell was there. Jury Science was represented by Dick Santos and two staff members.

After Ted Born made introductions and outlined the basic facts and mission, he turned to Dick Santos and asked him to explain the mock trial services of his compa-ny, Jury Science. First, a locale demographically similar to Phoenix County would be selected, Santos explained. He assumed Phoenix itself would not do, because of the twin threats of information leaks to the plaintiffs and also the possibility of indirectly influencing potential jurors. Born agreed a Phoenix County situs would not be feasible.

Once a statistically comparable county is found within one day's driving distance, a facility for the mock trial would be rented, either a motel, schoolhouse or other building. A scientifically selected group of mock jurors would be hired to come on the appointed day, to be paid generously to participate in a "judicial research project." They would not be told anything about the case in advance, or even that the judicial research was a mock trial.

The mock jurors would all assemble in a central meeting room or auditorium set up as the mock trial room. There would be no judge, but Santos would act as a kind of moderator, giving instructions, answering questions and keeping it all going. The mock jurors would fill out information sheets on themselves, so their demographics and personal data could be correlated with their conclusions.

The session would begin with "opening statements" by lawyers for the parties, plaintiffs' surrogate lawyer Carl Heimat going first, followed by a lawyer for Universal and Tergano's surrogate lawyer. After each of these opening statements, there would be a pause while the mock jurors filled out questionnaires, showing how they were leaning at that point, what facts seemed most important to them, and how they rated the lawyer's presentation.

Then someone would outline basic background facts which might not have been brought out in the opening statements. After lunch, there would be the closing arguments, with questionnaires again filled out after each lawyer's presentation.

At that point, the group of mock jurors would be subdivided into smaller groups of six to eight persons who would retire to separate rooms to deliberate their respective verdicts or, in the event of a plaintiffs' verdict, the jury would be asked to assess damages.

Each mock jury room would be wired with microphones and unobtrusive video cameras which could be monitored from adjacent rooms. Also, since it would be impossible for all lawyers to monitor all mock jury rooms simultaneously, the mock jury deliberations would be videotaped so the deliberations in each room could be viewed in their entirety later, at the lawyers' leisure. "What leisure?" Born thought to himself wryly, but said nothing.

At the end of deliberations, the mock jurors would receive their pay for participating and would go home. Santos, for Jury Science, would give some on-the-spot general conclusions he had picked up in the course of the day, then a week or so later, would give a slide presentation with commentary and more detailed conclusions. He would also, at that time, distribute a notebook of conclusions, with pie charts and statistics. For example, his presentation would compare the relative plaintiff/ defense leanings of jurors with demographics of age, sex, race, marital status, home ownership, employment status, automotive experience and the like, also showing how opinion shifted throughout the day between pro-plaintiff and pro-defense positions as each lawyer in turn made a presentation.

Thompson wondered aloud whether the real names of parties, witnesses and locales should be used in the mock trial, versus fictitious names. Santos explained it depended a lot on confidentiality considerations. If real names and real locations were used, was it possible some of the mock jurors might try to telephone some of the parties and tell then all about the mock trial? They would have to think about how to handle that aspect.

Tim Archer asked whether it would be helpful to have "actors" read key portions of depositions in lien of a summary of evidence, as Santos had suggested. Santos answered there would likely not be enough time to read from depositions, without making a two-day event of the mock trial, with logistical problems connected with keeping the jury intact, minimizing intra-juror communication prior to deliberations and conflicts with work or church or other activities. Besides, Santos explained, mock jurors tend psychologically to confuse the actor with the real person, even when they intellectually know otherwise, and the mock trial is then saddled with that baggage: if the jurors like the actor, they might react one way; if they do not like the actor, they react another way. Better simply to have a neutral summary of the uncontested facts, with the mock advocates stating their contentions on the contested facts, Santos advised.

Born inquired about the size of each mock jury panel after the big group is subdivided into smaller parts. Would the dynamics within the jury room be different with only six to eight mock jurors, compared with twelve in the actual jury? Not significantly, Santos assured him, the group had to be large enough to get some pro-and-con discussion, with the possibility of leadership developing within the jury group, but once it reached a certain size - say, six to eight - the quality of the deliberations and the information to be gleaned did not improve. Anyway, most participants in a jury room tend to be followers who line up behind one or more leaders in the room and do not really enter into the deliberations in an active way.

The group continued to work on the mechanics of the mock trial and settled on a target date of Friday or Saturday in the second week of January, depending upon location and availability of facilities.

As the group eventually broke up at the end of a long planning session, Dick Santos walked over to Born and Thompson, shook hands, and said: "I look forward to working with you on this project. You get a lot of useful information out of a mock trial. I just want to be sure, though, you don't have any unrealistic expectations. There are some things with the mock trial that will be very different from what will happen in Phoenix County. For one thing, the jurors in Phoenix will know Sam Johnson and probably some of the other plaintiffs - personally - and they'll know Highway 53 and they might even know that mock orange tree. Plus, they'll be influenced by all the other big verdicts in the past in that county."

"Hm," mused Born, "a staged mock trial, versus a real mock orange. Yeah, I know, I know. But thanks for the reminder."

CHAPTER TWENTY-ONE

MERRY CHRISTMAS!

Thanksgiving had come and gone. Ted Born had been thankful for one day with his family and was especially glad to see his daughter Rebecca who was a junior in college, home for her Thanksgiving break. He worried that he did not give enough time to his family, that it would be all his fault, if some catastrophe occurred in his family life.

On the other hand, it seemed arrogant to suppose his greater involvement with them could really affect the course of their lives. He remembered his own hard-working father, whom he as a child had seen generally for only a few minutes a day as their paths would cross. His father hadn't been around a lot physically, really could not be, as he worked one job in the daytime and another on night shift. From such a father, Born had learned of a husband's and parent's love and sense of responsibility, which did not necessarily depend on close handedness.

Even on a real family occasion around the Thanksgiving table, Born had been unable totally to close out the hovering, brooding specter of the upcoming trial. To the blessing which he pronounced at that Thanksgiving meal, he added his plea for strength and wisdom for the trial, an addition to the blessing that was unusual, reflecting his own tension about the case. His wife Lydia tried to be supportive. She alone knew Ted well enough to appreciate the Catherine's-wheel stress gripping him as he looked into the eye of the hurricane from which he was unlikely to emerge unscathed in psy-che and professional reputation.

It was affecting Born in every way. No longer was he the light-hearted romantic, the eternal optimist she had always known. He seemed to make room for an almost mock romance, like his mock trial, as and when his schedule would permit, another item on a busy agenda. He loved her. She loved him. It was something beyond romance, more a committed personal partnership and friendship. The bond was strong, they renewed it each time they kissed goodbye in the morning and looked into each other's eyes. They knew, though, that life was not intended to be lived this way, that an unseen powerful undercurrent had taken from them a large part of the life they had known and now missed.

Dave Thompson could relate to some of those feelings,

although he and Born rarely discussed their private lives and families. Thompson's young eighteen-month-old daughter Cherie had shocked him by refusing to let him pick her up and hug her. "She's forgotten who I am!" Thompson said. Thompson's wife Candry was sympathetic, but occasionally she reminded him he was still a young man - was he going to burn himself out? "There's light at the end of the tunnel," he would say. "When this case is over, there'll never be another one like it. I'm just getting baptized with fire now. After this, I can take anything." She warned him not to get scorched. It was hard work and long hours, he knew, but the greater problem was the stress, the tension, more even than the sheer volume of the work. To have so many millions of dollars of your client's money riding on your performance, and your professional reputation too! It helped somewhat with Thompson's stress, but not much, that Ted Born was in charge of the case. Thompson felt a high sense of responsibility far beyond the staffing hierarchy for the case.

At the December motion docket, Judge Andrews had overruled Universal's objection to production of the video tape showing the sweaty workers. Born took some consolation from the Judge's remark that this ruling was merely a discovery matter and that he doubted the tape would be admissible at trial. Yet Born had practiced law long enough to know that Judges always reserve the right to change their mind as to such initial reactions, that indeed they frequently did so. "If the plaintiffs can tie that tape in and show it's representative of the production situation at the plant where this ruptured tire was made, you can bet he'll admit the tape," Born told Thompson and Bert Sayre. "We've lost the first battle on production of the tape, and I think we're gravely at risk to lose the battle of admissibility. One day at a time, I guess."

The week before Christmas, plaintiffs took the deposition of Al Gifford, Universal's corporate representative designated to be deposed under Rule 30(b)(6), as plaintiffs had requested. Born prepared Gifford as best he could. "The bottom line is," Born told him, "if they ask you the right questions - and they probably will - you obviously have to tell the truth, you'll have to admit that, yes, there's a good bit of human touching. But don't make it easy and don't volunteer anything. Make them work for that answer and try to parry and fend them off as long as you can. A deposition is a battle of minds and wills. Do your best."

When Born and Gifford arrived at the Bates & Ripps office, they learned that Alton Fox was not yet ready for them, even though the scheduled starting time for the deposition had been some minutes earlier. They waited thirty minutes, and the receptionist told them "something had come up" which delayed them. Finally, Fred Bates emerged and told Born he and Fox would be ready shortly. When the deposition finally commenced, some forty minutes late, Fox seemed agitated and kept looking at his watch as he asked about the steps in tire production and Universal's various quality safeguards. Born kept waiting for the key questions about human touching of the tire components. Finally, Fox asked: "How are hands used in the manufacturing process?"

Gifford answered, "Hands are used to the extent necessary to build a tire." What a beautiful parry, Born thought. That statement doesn't necessarily mean the tires are ever touched, *could* be interpreted to mean only that workers punch buttons and do other things not involving any physical contact with the tire.

"Well, let's look at the video tape," Fox suggested to Gifford as the deposition continued. Born's heart sank. This is it, Born told himself, he's going to go through that tape with Gifford and make him admit the ruptured tire was made under similar operating conditions, including the touching - which was largely true. Fox began fumbling with the video player and monitor, obviously having trouble getting them to work. He summoned a female employee into the conference room, who also failed to get them operational.

Frustrated, Fox looked with embarrassment at Bates. "Whew!" Born said to himself. "Close call. I'm beginning to believe there really is a *deus ex machina*. At least, the god is not in this machine!"

Fox continued, "You've seen the tape, haven't you, Mr. Gifford?"

"What tape?" Gifford answered innocently.

"The tape about tire making which your counsel produced to us. Here it is," said Fox, pressing the "eject" button on the video player, removing the tape and handing it to Gifford.

"This just says 'Tire Making' on this gummed label," answered Gifford, "I've seen lots of tapes on tire making."

"Have you ever reviewed a tape with Universal's counsel which they told you was produced to us in this litigation?" Fox pressed.

"No," Gifford answered truthfully. Born and Gifford had certainly discussed the tape produced, but Gifford had not reviewed it with Born. It wasn't necessary. Gifford had wrestled with that tape in the Houston litigation and had no need to review it again with Born.

Still frustrated, Fox looked again at his watch, changed the subject and asked Gifford ten minutes' worth of further questions. Then he announced he was finished. Born said a quick silent prayer and left the room with Gifford as fast as he could gracefully get out of there, lest Fox call them back for more questions.

When they got well away from the Bates & Ripps office, Born threw up both hands and said, "Hallelujah! I never thought I'd survive this day! Do you know what just happened, Al? Do you have *any idea* what just happened?"

"Well, I don't think he got much of value out of that," Gifford answered. "I thought he'd ask a whole lot more questions."

"You were a superb witness, Al. They got zilch from you," Ted Born told him. "I still can't believe it happened. He must have been in a hurry and had something else on his mind and the video didn't work and he never came back and asked you the right questions. He didn't pursue. He didn't follow through. I think Alton is a better lawyer than that, but today he botched it."

"What does it mean for the case?" Gifford asked.

"It means we're in a much better position to get summary judgment," Born said. "Kelly's sweat theory, bizarre as it is, might have been enough to get the case to the jury and avoid summary judgment if there was any proper foundation for it. The foundation would have to be that there was in fact a lot of human touching. Without proof of touching - which the plaintiffs don't have - there's no support for sweat as a contaminant. In other words, if you concede that microscopic particles of sweat can be a contaminant, which I don't concede, but if you do concede it for argument's sake, that's not enough unless you also show that the manufacturing processes involved enough touching of tire components to put some sweat on them. After this deposition, Fox can't do that."

"What do you suppose Fred Bates thought about that performance?" Gifford asked.

"I'm sure Fred realized Alton was fumbling around a lot and was disorganized, but I'm not sure Fred really understood the significance of what happened. If he had understood it, he surely would have had a quick side conference with Alton at the end to remind him to delve more into the touching."

Born's face suddenly sobered. "Of course, if we don't get summary judgment, we're still in trouble, because at the trial they could call you or some other Universal employee to the witness stand and there they could ask you, in front of the jury, the questions they failed to ask you today. In that case, this would be a Pyrrhic victory. Actually, I've never thought we had much of a chance for summary judgment, even though the Kelly depo went well. Until now. Now, after your deposition, I'm beginning to let myself think maybe we really have a chance. Better not get carried away, though."

When Ted Born got back to his office and shared with Dave Thompson the news from Al Gifford's deposition, Thompson became as excited as Born had been earlier. This had come just in time to fortify Universal's summary judgment motion before it would be taken under submission by the Judge.

"There are two things we need to emphasize in this last crack we'll have at summary judgment, that we haven't stressed earlier," Born said. "First, there is the lack of evidence sweat was a problem in the manufacture of the ruptured tire. We were afraid to say much about that in our original submission because, of course, we didn't know at the time what evidence would come out. Now we can really hammer it. Second, on the failure to warn issue, we've emphasized that Kelly - their expert - says the only relevant warning would relate to vibration, which all the plaintiffs say did not occur. That ought to be good enough to eliminate the warning issue, but I've just thought of something else that also should help: Sam Johnson testified he never read the warnings which are in fact molded into the tire. If that's so, how could *any* warning help, if you're simply not going to read the warnings?"

"Yeah. That should be added," Thompson agreed.

"We've got a chance to escape the fiery furnace after all. You know, Ted, I go from the bottom of the dark valley to top of the high mountain and then I fall back to the floor of the valley. I'm getting bruised in the process, all beat up. Is this the way it's always going to be with litigation?" Thompson asked, with a faint smile of resignation.

"Somewhat," answered Born, "but this is worse than most. Right now, though, you ought to be on top of the mountain, because we've got a better chance of getting that summary judgment than I ever thought possible. Besides, it's almost Christmas. Merry Christmas!"

"Merry Christmas, Ted." Dave Thompson almost was facing Born head-on as they shook hands. The body language, at least, was showing definite signs of improvement.

In Atlanta, Brad Mansfield and Chet Bernhardt were making last minute arrangements before their Christmas break. They had decided to do some control tests with exemplar vans at a testing site in Ohio, hopefully to prove that a van comparable to the Logos was controllable in the event of a left rear blowout at highway speeds. They also had retrieved from the Tergano archives some test videos showing exemplars of the Logos crashing into a concrete wall at various speeds. In those archival tests, the single latch on the back seat did not break upon impact."

"How do we force the blowout?" Bernhardt asked.

"Sometimes with dynamite. Sometimes with a slicing device activated by the driver. When you make the arrangements, ask them what they would recommend,"

Mansfield answered.

"I haven't explored all the options yet," Bernhardt said, "but they did mention dynamite is not allowed on the testing grounds in Ohio. If we do tests in Phoenix County, I would think we'd need some kind of permit from local authorities for dynamite use. Can you imagine trying to get that approval from the County Council or the Sheriff's office in Phoenix County?"

Mansfield laughed. "No. I can't quite visualize that. Well, it's almost Christmas. We can finalize the arrangements next week." Reaching into his coat pocket, Mansfield pulled out a check and handed it to Bernhardt. "Here's your year-end bonus. Merry Christmas!"

"Mer-r-r-y Christmas!" said Chet Bernhardt, as he vigorously pumped Mansfield's hand.

In Columbia, Fred Bates was talking to Jack Ripps. "Next year could be the greatest year of our practice, Jack," Bates was saying. "We've got the franchise case on appeal. If we win it, and surely we will, we'll get forty per cent of more than eight million bucks, growing every day with interest during appeal. That's going to be over three million dollars for us. We should hear from that appeal sometime in the spring."

"Then we've got this *Johnson case*," Ripps added.

"Oh, yeah. I haven't forgotten that one," Bates said. "How could I? Could be the greatest of them all."

The telephone rang. "Yes, Bess," Bates said as he rolled his eyes. "The case is still scheduled for trial in February... Yeah. Everything's going fine... Well, yes, they've got this motion for summary judgment, but I'm not worried 'bout that. Just one of those things defense lawyers do to muddy up the water. They gotta do that to earn their fee. Might get sued for malpractice... . What's that? Oh, that's just a legal word. Don't worry about 'malpractice.' It ain't got nothing to do with your case.... Don't you worry about a thing, Bess. This case is in good shape. Merry Christmas." Bates hung up the phone and shook his head.

"Fred, you ought to tell your secretary not to put her through to you. That's what I do. I talk to the woman as little as possible," Ripps grinned, despairingly.

"Look, Jack. This is a BIG CASE, an important case. We almost lost control of it once to those other jackleg lawyers. I'm not going to take any more chances. Then, again, I'm not sure it's worth ten million dollars, or more, to have to put up with Bess Johnson. Maybe we need to get Sam Johnson to intervene, tell her to lay off the telephone calls, or I'm going to snip her line with my wire clips," Bates laughed.

"Fred, do you think there's any chance Judge Andrews would grant summary judgment?" Ripps asked.

"Well, Tergano has only asked for partial summary judgment, as to the seat latch claim. So, whatever happens there, Tergano's still going to remain in the case as a defendant and will go to trial in February - worst case scenario. But they've got deep pockets, and we can comfortably retire on a recovery from Tergano alone. As for Universal, I do have a little concern about that.

Those lawyers are kicking and throwing punches. But I figure Judge Andrews will be afraid of reversal. I think he'll say, `What the hell. If I've got to try this case as to Tergano, I'll go ahead and try it as to both parties.' That way he figures he'll keep his options open and can always grant a judgment notwithstanding the verdict if the jury sides with us against Universal. That's what he's probably thinking now. But you know what will happen? I've seen it too many times. When that jury brings in a verdict in our favor, he'll chicken out. He won't want to go against the verdict of a jury. And he'll rationalize all kinds of reasons why he should let the jury verdict stand, you know, he'll notice that the proof at trial was better than the evidence when he was considering summary judgment. Yeah, he'll let it stand."

"I wish I had your confidence in what Judge Andrews will do," Ripps said. "I wish I felt as good about the Judge as I do the jury."

"Relax, Jack. It's okay. I know Judge Andrews like a book. He'll chicken out. He'll let it go to the jury, and he'll let the jury verdict stand. Now let's get out of this place. I've got some good, smooth bourbon at home and some bitters and cool, clear branch water. I need some real serious Christmas cheer, and ain't nothin' gonna' stop me. Merry Christmas!"

"Merry Christmas, Fred, and a real happy new year to both of us, and Alton too."

CHAPTER TWENTY-TWO

GET SET

The first week in January found Chet Bernhardt standing in falling snow at the testing grounds in Ohio. "Damn this white stuff!" Bernhardt was saying to himself. "Wasn't meant for a Georgia boy to have to put up with this stuff," he smiled at the irony of his situation, visualizing Brad Mansfield enjoying crisp, clear weather in Atlanta. A Tergano official, who in the past had arranged and testified concerning test crashes and blowouts, John Frey, was there with him.

Unfortunately, in ten days each party would have to serve on all other parties their trial witness list and exhibit list, and Bernhardt had no time leeway for completing simulated tests if he was to be in a position to file his lists when due. The work would have to be done this week, like it or not. He had mounted a video camera in the test van, focused on the steering wheel and the front windshield, the idea being to show simultaneously the speedometer, the steering wheel and the travel lane marked off on this large expanse of asphalt paving. At the moment of an induced blowout, the camera would hopefully show the vehicular speed, the one-finger ease of steering wheel control and the minimal deviation from straight-line travel. A second video camera was mounted on the side of the van, focused on the deflation device, a cutting instrument wired to a control within the van operable by the driver, which on command would make a giant slice into the left rear tire, causing instant deflation. John Frey had not seemed concerned that the driver's involvement in inducing blowout might invalidate the test. "We do it this way all the time," he assured Bernhardt. Bernhardt was afraid the snow might obscure the view of the road from within the van. Windshield wipers would help, but he was unsure whether they would totally solve the problem. His other concern was that the snow might make the asphalt on the testing ground slick, causing a possible skid - the last thing he wanted to memorialize on film.

Bernhardt was not familiar with judging the skid characteristics of asphalt, but the testing coordinators assured him the surface layer of the asphalt contained no crushed limestone aggregate, the ingredient which can cause asphalt slickness. It was uncertain whether the snow would lessen in the course of the day, so Bernhardt made the decision to go forward now. As final preparations were underway for the initial test, he stood looking at the tire. It was not precisely the same type tire as had been on the crumpled Logos. Bernhardt had not been able on short notice to find such tires. "Must've discontinued production," he thought. He had chosen a three-ply, somewhat more rugged, tire for the test. What does it matter, he thought. Once a tire is deflated, a tire's a tire. What the hell!

The van was ready for the first test. John Frey got in to drive it, so he could testify later. He was strapped with special safety harnesses, then signaled he was ready. An advance vehicle would precede the test van and would videotape the van from its front. Other cameras were set up on the sides and rear. "Ready? Everybody ready? Cameras ready? Okay, GO!" said the coordinator. The van took off, gained speed, leveled off and then there was a loud bang. The van swerved very slightly to the left but maintained a generally straight course.

Frey got out of the van. "How'd it go, John?" Bernhardt asked.

"Afraid I made a slight boo-boo, Chet. I can't explain it. I've done this same test run dozens of times before, but this time somehow the bang startled me, and I grabbed the steering wheel with both hands. Usually, I like to show how the steering wheel can be controlled with just one fin- ger. Can we ditch that one and start all over?" Frey asked.

Bernhardt was frowning but trying to be polite. "I'm afraid not, John. They'd crucify you if we did that. They'll ask you whether our videos depict every test run, whether there was any editing or anything. You'd have to be honest, and if you admitted there was a first test that we destroyed, there'd be hell to pay. The plaintiffs would have a field day, and before they were through, the jury would believe the worst, that the van went out of control to the left. It would validate plaintiffs' theory. Actually, you controlled it fine. It hardly varied at all from a straight path. You just used two hands, which is not all that bad. Best thing we can do is make some more test runs and let's hope it'll be easier on these new runs to use just a finger to control the van. Let's do some more runs now."

Farther south in Greenville, Ted Born and Dave Thompson were meeting with Phyllis Maxwell. Thompson had reluctantly just given a preview of his opening statement. "Dave, I wanted to stand up and clap. That was super!" Born exclaimed.

"It was good, Dave," said Maxwell. She knew Thompson was leery of her advice, and she chose her words carefully. "One of the things you might wish to do is to tell the jury a little more about yourself, to personalize yourself to them. Aren't you from a small town in North Carolina? Maybe you could start off by saying something like this: 'Phoenix County reminds me a lot of the place where I grew up. I'm from a small town in North Carolina. I thought how much alike your home is to my home.' When you say something like that, it establishes you as standing on common ground with the jurors, reminds them that you share a lot with them, makes them more receptive."

Maxwell continued, "Your poise was excellent. In fact, it amazes me that a lawyer with only a little more than a year of practice has so much poise. Your delivery was good, your eye contact was good. Your message was clear and well organized. It might be good if you used a poster with a check list on it of all the features of the tire you want to talk about, so as to reinforce your verbal message with a visual aid. Of course, the tire itself is an excellent visual aid, especially the way you used it."

Dave Thompson was nodding as she spoke. "Hard to argue with those suggestions. I'll incorporate them for the mock trial," he said to himself.

They reviewed photographs and exhibits and picked out some to be blown up and mounted on large poster boards, about three feet by six feet. "Don't try to use more than about eight blowups. Jurors really cannot very well absorb more than about eight. The trick is to be sure the ones you pick are the best eight," Maxwell said.

Born rang for Nita Langley and asked her to get the blowups ready in time for use at the mock trial. "I'm sorry I don't have my closing argument prepared yet. I intended to get you to critique me today, too, but I'm not ready," Born said. "That doesn't mean I haven't been thinking a lot about it. Seems to me we have to do three main things: show the jury it was a well-made tire, show them the tire was abused by the owners, and then provide them with the explanation of why it ruptured. I don't think I can explain or need to explain why the car veered to the left and went off the road—I think I *know* why, I think it was either the panic or inattention of Bess Johnson, but it won't work for me to try to blame her. I think I'd better just leave that alone."

"I think you're right, Ted," Maxwell said.

"One more thing I have to do. Somehow, I have to reach through to them and make them want to rise above their prejudices and natural feelings, I've got to make them want to do something noble. I know that has a preachy, Sunday School smack to it, and I sure can't be blunt and obvious and say `I want you to be noble!' They'd laugh and think I was ridiculous. I have to make them want to do something noble without saying it."

"That's hard to do, Ted," Thompson volunteered. "You have to be real careful, have to hit it just right."

"I agree," Maxwell said. "Well, try it out at the mock trial, and we'll tell you what we think."

Thompson excused himself, leaving Maxwell and Born in the conference room. "He's an extraordinary young lawyer," Born said. "When he first said that stuff about extemporaneous speaking, and all that, I almost laughed at his naivete. Then he gives a performance like the one we just heard, and he's beginning to make a believer out of an old skeptic like me."

"Dave is so transparently innocent, so transparently good, so likeable, it comes through. And, as I said, his poise and delivery were good. Yes, he is. He's extraordinary," Phyllis Maxwell said.

In addition to getting ready for the mock trial a week hence, Born and Thompson concentrated much of their available time on their witness list and exhibit list, which had to be served on opposing counsel by mid-January. They carefully reviewed the depositions and the potential witnesses in order to compile their witness list, including their expert witnesses. This involved the preparation of a summary of Universal's proposed expert testimony. There were two categories of expert testimony for Universal, the technical tire testimony and the medical testimony. Universal would designate Bob Tegrit as its tire expert and Bill Edmonds as its expert metallurgist, as well as Phil Lynam who did the chemical analysis on the sticky tire sealant found on the innerliner. Born and Thompson decided to list some medical and rehab experts also, relating to Jimason Anchrum's condition. They had no intention of using their own medical experts but listed them as potential witnesses primarily to prevent the plaintiffs from going overboard with unreasonable medical claims which could not be rebutted. As long as plaintiffs' medical experts stuck to the facts and conclusions as set out in their depositions, Universal would not introduce any medical evidence of its own.

First, Born reasoned, Universal ought to focus on the condition of the tire, not the condition of injured parties. Second, Universal would have to win the case on the liability question. "We're doomed if we have to defend on the basis of how bad the death and injuries are," Born thought. Still, Universal had to be ready with some kind of medical rebuttal if the plaintiffs claimed injuries far worse than they really were.

In addition to the witness list, the defendants had to furnish an exhibit list, requiring a careful review of every one of the thousands of documents in this case to be sure no important documents were omitted.

Compiling a witness list and exhibit list was a problem for all parties, but for no one was it more difficult than for the plaintiffs. It is a blessing and curse for plaintiffs, Bates thought to himself, that they must proceed *first* with their case at trial. It helps mightily to get in the first shot, but it also puts a lot of pressure on plaintiffs where, unlike defendants, there was no option regarding medical testimony; it was one of the most significant parts of Bates' case. Yet it would be hard to get medical doctors to come to an out-of-the-way rural place like Phoenix County to give testimony. Some of the plaintiffs' experts were in Louisville, for instance, and they had no desire to kill a day or two of their practice to come to Groveton. It was not just a matter of a fee. It was a function of other commitments to patients, like surgery, some of it emergency surgery. In addition, some physicians, probably most of them, were hostile to plaintiff lawyers because of medical malpractice suits being brought against them by the plaintiffs' bar. There would be little desire to co-operate. Subpoenas could be used, up to a point, but the last thing any lawyer wants to do is to irritate a much-needed expert witness by subpoenaing him when he does not want to come. The quality of the testimony might well suffer in such event.

The plaintiffs would list as potential experts every

paramedic, every physician, every psychologist, every therapist, every nurse and every rehabilitation specialist who ever attended any of the plaintiffs after the accident, plus the coroner. But they knew most of these would not be testifying in person but rather secondhand, through the reading of their depositions. The hope was, Bates told himself, the jury won't really need much expert testimony and won't care whether it's live. Once they see Jimason, that's all the medicals they'll need. The jury would surely be ready to award big dollars just by looking at Jimason.

CHAPTER TWENTY-THREE

THE MOCK TRIAL

Ted Born and Dave Thompson picked up Bert Sayre at the Atlanta airport late Friday afternoon and drove to Milledgeville for the mock trial, which would begin the next day. The mock jury pool would be drawn from Hancock County, Georgia, where the demographics were nearly identical to those of Phoenix County, South Carolina, but Jury Science had not been able to find a suitable facility in Hancock for the mock trial. Hence, Milledgeville in adjacent Baldwin County.

Milledgeville was a comfortable Southern town best known in Georgia civics textbooks as the former Georgia state capital, before the railroads built Atlanta and caused a shift of the seat of government to that city. Milledgeville still seemed largely frozen in time. Surveying the town on this first visit, Born thought how much it reminded him of rural South Carolina, hence a good place to have this mock trial.

It was a cold day with a dreary gray cloud cover, a lot like snow weather without the snow. The trio checked into the motel, got their room assignments, and retired briefly to freshen up. They were the advance party, arriving early to check with Dick Santos to see that preparations were proceeding smoothly. They had to step gingerly to avoid tripping over cables on the floor and on the outside corridor as they went to their rooms. Born emerged quickly from his room and began looking for Santos. He had but to follow the cable and found Santos in a meeting room making arrangements for the big show. Santos greeted Born warmly and began showing him around the meeting room - the cameras, the lectern and microphone, the seats for jurors in the "audience."

Santos was taking Born back to show him the individual juror rooms when Thompson and Sayre appeared. Santos took the trio with him to an outside corridor, defined by wrought iron railing opposite a row of rooms. "We have this entire wing of nine rooms for the mock jury," Santos explained. "As you requested, Ted, we'll divide the big group of jurors, after they've heard everything in the meeting room, into four panels of roughly eight per panel. We have four rooms along here - every alternate room - set aside for the deliberations of the jury panels. The in-between rooms will be monitoring areas where you can see and hear on closed circuit TV exactly what is being said and done in the jury room next door, so we have eight rooms here - four for the panels and four for monitoring. The ninth room is a control room where we'll be controlling the equipment and where we'll have snacks and soft drinks and so forth. Also, you can watch what's happening in the meeting room from that ninth room, when you are not in the meeting room performing."

"Do we divide up and take one room apiece after the jury is broken down into the four panels?" Thompson asked.

"I recommend you choose a room and watch it long enough to get the flavor of what that particular panel is thinking, the dynamics of the debate, and all that. Then, if you want to, you can move around and look at any of the other monitors in the other rooms. Don't worry about disturbing the mock jurors. The curtains will be completely closed so they won't see you walking from room to room along this outside corridor. By the way, we will have a staff person assigned to each jury panel to keep it on track in case they start killing time talking about sports, or in case they start arguing loudly among themselves or have some question. We're short one staff person, though. I wonder if Dr. Maxwell would do that for one panel?"

"I'm sure she'd be glad to," Born said. "You know she's the one who's been writing, and will be reading, the narrative summary which will be laid out to the mock jurors between the opening and closing arguments. She was still working on that last time I heard, trying to get it within the time constraints and be sure it's balanced."

Looking toward the parking lot, Born saw a car pull up. "There's the bad guy," laughed Born, referring to Carl Heimat who would play plaintiffs' counsel. "Are you Fred Bates?" Born asked.

Heimat grinned, "Yeah. And this is Brad Mansfield," he said, referring to Tim Archer who had come with him.

Others began arriving, Nita Langley, Phyllis Maxwell, some of Santos' staff not involved in the cable laying and camera installations. At six o'clock there was an organizational meeting where all the ground rules would be explained. Then they went to dinner at a restaurant down the road. Ted Born did not enjoy dinner. He kept wanting to leave, to work more on his closing argument that night.

Even when Born got back to his motel room, he kept getting interrupted. Everyone seemed to need to ask him a question about this or that. At one a.m. Born went to bed, still not feeling good about his closing argument.

The next morning, the defense team watched as the mock jurors started arriving, wondering what this was all about, why they were there. There was a strange blank look on the faces of most of the mock jury. Strange, Born thought to himself, somehow these people I've never seen, in this city I've never visited, have converged on this motel as we have, and all of us are wondering in our own way what is going to happen here.

Thirty-four persons eventually arrived and were qualified for mock jury service. Twenty-seven were African Americans, seven Caucasians. "Can't tell a lot about the rest of the demographics, but the race factor

matches pretty well with Phoenix County," Born thought.
Dick Santos talked to the group first, gave them a minimal explanation of what was happening, and had each of
them fill out a detailed personal biographical form.

Soon, it was time for the opening statements. Dick
Santos and his staff, and Phyllis Maxwell, remained in
the meeting room with the mock jurors. Maxwell wanted
to be able to observe the jurors first-hand as the various
lawyers made their opening statements or closing arguments. The defense team watched the proceedings by
remote video from the control room, except as they went,
one by one, to make their presentations. Carl Heimat was
first, for the plaintiffs.

Heimat's theme was "Why did she have to die?"
focusing on the death of Sarena Miller. He showed a photograph of a young healthy Sarena, smiling, full of life,
and a second photograph made by the Coroner. "Why
did she have to die?" Heimat said throughout his opening statement, as his refrain, its effectiveness reinforced
by repetition. He always had an answer: because a big,
rich company didn't take the care to make good tires,
because another big, rich company didn't design a safe
vehicle. The ultimate answer Heimat gave the jury was
that Sarena Miller didn't have to die, Jimason Anchrum
didn't have to suffer brain injuries and have part of his
brain cut out, if only these big, rich, indifferent companies had had an incentive to build good, safe products.

The jury could give Universal and Tergano that incentive, so that in the future the little girls and little boys

of the world would be safe and could grow up and live full lives rather than have their futures snapped like a dry stick. His side would prove, he said, that the tire should have held together as long as there was any tread, that the van should not have veered uncontrollably to the left, and he gave them a preview of what he proposed the plaintiffs would prove. He closed by asking again, "Why did Sarena have to die? Why did Jimason have to have brain damage? The answer, ladies and gentlemen, is that it didn't have to happen. No, if Universal and Tergano had cared half as much about human life as they cared about profits, Sarena would still be here, Jimason would still have a normal, happy future. It didn't have to happen."

The defense team was silent, eyes glued to the video monitor. Thompson wiped the cold sweat from his brow and shook his head. Born was staring at the cheap reproduction of sunflowers framed on the wall. Finally, Born broke the silence. "He did just what I wanted him to do, and how I hated him for it! He said it too convincingly. The real plaintiffs' lawyers will never do that good a job." Heimat rejoined the group.

"Son of a bitch!" Tim Archer said to him, smiling. Born and Thompson and the others joined in a chorus of "Good job, Carl!"

The mock jury was filling out the first of their series of questionnaires on each speaker. A camera in the meeting room panned the jurors as they sat grimly in their chairs, silently filling out the questionnaire.

"You're up next, Tim. Are you ready?" Born asked.

"I'm ready," Tim answered and left, headed for the meeting room.

Tim began by acknowledging his sympathy for the families and emphasizing that his company, Tergano, was entirely separate from Universal which made the tire which blew out. He never directly blamed Universal for the death and injuries but he strongly implied that, if anyone was responsible, it was Universal whose tire started the sequence which led to the deaths.

At Archer's oblique references to Universal's tire, Born said aloud, "We've promised not to point fingers at each other. I don't think Tergano's lawyers would really say anything like that."

"Don't kid yourself, Ted," said Carl Heimat, who was also watching Archer intently on the monitor. "They'll give you that comfort stuff ahead of time, but they'll knife you in a minute at trial, if they think they will get one dime's worth out of it."

"I guess I have to be alert for that possibility, so I'm glad Tim's doing just what he's doing. But I hope they have better sense than to do that. It truly wouldn't help anyone but the plaintiffs," Born said. Dave Thompson paced back and forth, nervously watching the monitor, knowing he would be next.

Archer denied there was anything wrong with the van's design, and he defended it as best as he could. Born thought Archer was doing a fine job, especially considering the fact there had been no discovery of the defendants' experts, and so no clue as to how Tergano would mount its defense. Archer closed by saying the accident could have been caused by a lot of things, possibly including the distraction of the driver. But he predicted there would not be any credible evidence the van's design had anything to do with the wreck.

The group crowded around the video monitor watched as Tim Archer left the lectern and headed back to the control room. Again, the TV camera panned the meeting room as the mock jurors filled out their second questionnaire, indicating their reactions to the case, and to Archer's performance. "It might be my imagination - or wishful thinking" Born thought to himself, "but our jury doesn't seem quite as grim."

"Great job, Tim," Born said, grinning, as Tim Archer entered the monitoring room, "but I didn't know you were going to trash Universal."

"That's the way I'm afraid it's going to be, Ted, I think you'd better be prepared," said Tim very seriously.

"I hope you're wrong," Born said, "but I guess you've got a point that I need to be forewarned and ready."

Dick Santos appeared at the door and summoned Dave Thompson, who started to go with Santos. "Are you forgetting your notes?" asked Heimat, noticing that Thompson was leaving empty-handed.

"I don't have any, not going to use notes," Thompson replied, turning back slightly to speak to Heimat, but continuing on through the door.

Heimat raised his eyebrows slightly and gestured doubtfully with open palms. "I've had a preview, Carl;

you don't have to worry," Born told him.

All eyes were on the monitor as Thompson stepped to the lectern. The camera panned the audience in the meeting room at that moment. It was only a flash, a split-second glance, but there was clearly an air of expectancy on the faces of the mock jurors as Thompson began to speak.

Dave Thompson spoke very slowly, very deliberately. He had indeed incorporated Dr. Maxwell's advice about his small-town origins. He used a giant pad of paper resting on an easel, turning to a clean sheet slowly and deliberately. There he jotted down a word or two to summarize each point as he made it. He held up the tire and turned it in his hands as he talked about it, like it was a museum masterpiece. It was an old tire, he said, nearly six years old, with nearly sixty thousand miles of wear on it. He pointed to the thin, worn tread as he pronounced it a worn-out tire. Everything wears out after a while, he said. Furthermore, the owner, Sam Johnson, had not taken good care of the tire. He hadn't kept the air pressure high enough, hadn't balanced the tire, hadn't rotated it, had sprayed that fix-o-flat gooey stuff in it. And then the tire hit a road hazard that caused it to rupture.

Born was glad Thompson had used the word "rupture." They had talked about it and had decided that word sounded a lot better than "blowout." Thompson expressed his sympathy to the family but said Universal's tire was not at fault. It had been a good tire, well made, otherwise it would not have lasted so long. Everybody knew, he told the crowd, that things eventually wear out. The soles of your shoes wear out, it's just not as dangerous as when you let a tire wear out and keep riding on it.

Thompson warned that the plaintiffs would try to say sweat on the hands of some unknown worker, years ago, caused it. "We just ask you to use your common sense, ladies and gentlemen when you hear them blame it on six-year-old sweat. And I ask you to do the right thing. Just as we all want people to judge us by the content of our character, Universal just asks you to judge it by the quality of this fine, long-lasting tire that just eventually wore out as any good tire will when driven to the end. Thank you, ladies and gentlemen."

As Thompson left the lectern, the camera panned the audience once again. It was unmistakable that Thompson's message had been heard. It was hard to say exactly how the faces of the mock jurors looked. They were still sober, no grins or smiles, but there was something positive there which had been missing before. "Dave did not have to use any attribution for his remarks about judging people by the content of their character. Most of the audience would readily recognize the allusion drawn from Dr. King's `I have a dream' speech, judging people not by the color of their skin but by the content of their character. Brilliant. Absolutely brilliant."

Bert Sayre looked at Ted Born and said, "Ted, I never doubted, did I?" Born smiled. Everyone in the control room seemed to fall all over Dave Thompson when he entered. Nita Langley was nearest the door as he entered, threw her arms around him and told him it was beautiful. "Super!" "Terrific job!" "Simply wonderful," came at Thompson from all directions. He smiled his winning, self-effacing smile. Bert Sayre smiled admiringly and congratulated him. And then he looked at Ted Born, who at first seemed almost speechless. He wanted to gather Thompson into his arms and embrace him. He analyzed it in a split second, decided it might break down those last barriers faster than Thompson would be ready for. He took Thompson's hand and shook it in a strong, long grasp, put the left hand on Thompson's right shoulder gently and said, "I don't have words for it, Dave. It was unbelievably good. I'm proud of you. Just relax and enjoy your lunch more than any of us will. You're the only one of us lawyers who can really relax, because the rest of us have to perform this afternoon. You were magnificent!"

Dave Thompson just looked at him, pressed his lips together, then parted them slightly to say a simple, "Thank you, Ted." Born noticed Thompson's eyes were watery. He also noticed that Thompson was facing him head on.

Box lunches arrived just as Dr. Maxwell began to read the summary of the evidence to the mock jury. Born took his box lunch and retired to his bedroom. He would need to return at one fifteen, after a lunch break for the jury, to deliver his closing argument.

Born ate his lunch quickly and silently. He stood up and looked at himself in the mirror. His head bore thinning hair, slightly receding hairline, but really plenty of hair, lucky in that respect. The hair was beginning to be gray around the temples, and there were some isolated white strands in other places, but still, it wasn't bad for a man with twenty-five years of law practice. He had washed his hair that morning and it was limp, had always had a tendency to fall down over his right eye when freshly washed. He reached for his wife's hair spray, which he had secretly appropriated for the trip, carefully reordered the falling strands, and sprayed lightly.

He did not like the double chin he was developing, but for the moment - at least - it was beyond help. No magic spray for that problem. He looked at his shirt, tie and suit, all chosen very deliberately for this occasion. His shirt was pale blue, so pale it was almost white. Born knew psychological studies had shown African-American jurors do not generally react positively to white men in white shirts. Dave Thompson had worn a white shirt, but, then, he could have worn anything.

It was not easy to find *really* pale blue shirts. There were plenty of those electric blue types, but they would be as wrong as a white shirt. He could not do anything or wear anything which might be distracting to jurors, cause them to notice *him* and miss his message. It had to be really pale blue, and he had managed to find a few he thought were right.

The tie, too, had to be red or maroon, definitely not Chinese red or tomato red, but maroon or dark red, without any garish designs on it. This, too, was based on psychological studies. Men who wore red ties, of the right type, were perceived by jurors to have maximum credibility, all other factors being equal. Born knew he had to have everything going for him with the jury. He had found a maroon tie with small white polka dots. It went well with the pale blue shirt.

For his suit, Born wore a very light gray faint plaid spring-and-fall weight wool suit, with muted hints of red and blue lines in the delicate plaid. It was really lighter weight than was appropriate for a February trial, but it was the right color and, after all, Born would not be out in the weather much. Never wear sinister-looking dark suits, always suits light-colored and uplifting, was the wisdom of careful trial lawyers.

He was not happy that he had gained a few pounds during the Thanksgiving and Christmas holidays, but he'd try to work that off in the next thirty days, before trial, he thought. He wished he could make those pounds disappear in minutes, rather than days. Another one of those things that was not to be.

All this concern about appearance, he thought, won't mean much unless I do well, really well. It's just a thin margin that might make a small difference. The important thing is what I say and how I say it. For a moment, a thought crossed his mind that he might not do well at all, that Dave Thompson, an eighteen-month associate lawyer might do a better job today than he, a twenty-five-plus year veteran. He quickly put that thought aside. He had no time to consider it, for one thing. For another, he knew only that he must do his best.

Born reviewed his notes, recopied them onto a small

index card with just a few key words, rose from his chair, took one more look at himself in the mirror, then returned to the control room where the Universal team was beginning to reassemble.

Dick Santos at length came into the room. "Here's what I suggest we do," he said. "Usually, of course, the plaintiffs' lawyer has first crack in closing argument, then comes back for rebuttal. We just don't have time for that, especially with the mock jurors' filling out the questionnaires after each presentation. So, I suggest we go with the Tergano closing argument first, followed by the Universal closing, and then ending with plaintiffs' full closing argument. Not only will this save time, but it should yield a conservative result, because the jury will have heard a full thirty-five minutes of plaintiffs' arguments just before they retire for deliberations. To the extent this skews the results, it skews them in favor of plaintiffs, and this helps guard against one of the worst disservices that can come from a mock trial: an overly optimistic result."

"Okay. Let's go with it," Born concurred.

Tim Archer went first as the surrogate lawyer for Tergano, repeating forcefully some of the points he had made earlier, stressing the logic of the positioning of the center of gravity for better and more even traction on a four-wheel drive vehicle, pointing to studies done by plaintiffs' expert Wrack Kelly that drivers rarely remember correctly just how they reacted behind the wheel in emergency situations. He argued there was no latch system for seats good enough to withstand all crashes, and, anyway, the children had already flown forward before the back seat folded down. He again reminded the jurors that the accident occurred with a blown out Universal tire and that Tergano was an entirely separate company from Universal. He closed by quoting his grandfather who had always told him, he said, to be guided by two things, common sense and honesty. "Common sense tells us there was nothing wrong with the design of this van, and honesty to ourselves requires a verdict for Tergano."

It was now Born's turn. He did not wait for anyone to summon him to the meeting room and to the lectern. He left and had a vague, surreal impression of passing Tim Archer on the corridor. The men seemed to move toward each other in slow motion, shook hands, and passed. Born waited at the back entrance to the meeting room as the mock jurors completed the questionnaire on Archer's closing argument. Dr. Maxwell was standing near the door and he motioned to her. They stood just on the outside of the door as Born asked one last question: should he keep his coat buttoned or leave it open?

He was fairly confident of what she would say, but he was secretly hoping she would advise him otherwise. He thought buttoned jackets looked more professional. Besides, it would help conceal those holiday penalties inflicted on his midriff. Maxwell knew he was well aware of the answer, even before she answered with a counter-question: "What kind of impression are you trying to make, openness or closedness? A buttoned jacket is the equivalent of arms folded tightly across the chest. An open jacket is the equivalent of open, accepting arms."

"I'll let it hang open," Born sighed with resignation.

Born stepped to the lectern, a little nervous at first. He said, "Good afternoon," to which the audience responded likewise. He introduced himself, thanked the jurors for their attention and expressed his personal sorrow for the tragedy and his personal sympathy to the families of the plaintiffs. He reminded them they had set off on a search for truth, that sympathy was normal and natural, but justice was on a higher plane, there was something God-like about justice. He invited them to be more than sympathetic human beings but to partake of this God-like quality which is the foundation of justice.

He walked them through this search for truth, suggested they should not take his word nor the word of any lawyer, but should ask and answer for themselves the critical questions. Born then went through a series of carefully worded questions which scarcely could be answered other than in Universal's favor, questions about the condition of the tire, the abuse it had sustained and the road hazard it hit.

Then he turned to plaintiff's "sweat theory" which tire expert Wrack Kelly had posited. Born dealt with this theory in a way that sounded serious but left the definite impression that the "sweat theory" was pure hokum. In fact, he had chosen the words "sweat theory" carefully to connote something less than fact, a "theory," oversimplifying it with the single word "sweat." Born emphasized that Kelly admitted the tire had ruptured from impact, that it was old and, in Kelly's words, "well worn," but Kelly had refused to accept these admitted facts at face value. Instead, Kelly had reached out somewhere in space to come up with this farfetched "sweat theory" for which there was no evidence, blaming some poor unknown worker - like you or me, Born said - for touching and tainting the tire six years ago, and this taint has been suppressed for all these years until it rose up and did its horrible deed. How credible was that theory? No, Kelly had not wanted to accept the plain, uncomplicated, honest truth.

Born reminded them that, in their search for truth, the jurors would not find credible answers in the theories of Mr. Kelly, that they would find the truth in their own reasoned analysis of key questions with clear, straightforward answers. "Thank you for the courage to seek truth, to do justice," Born said, "until both truth and justice flow freely in this courtroom, like a mighty river."

Born could feel the electricity of minds in the audience engaging with his mind, silent voices jointing in unison with his voice. There was a rhythm and a cadence in Born's words that produced an exhilarating, harmonic reaction.

When Born returned to the control room, he was met with profuse congratulations and a few "Bravos," a little less effusive for him, an older lawyer, than for Thompson earlier in the day. However, Born was not concerned about comparisons. He was only glad that he apparently had made the case for Universal with sufficient force and effect to get meaningful feedback from the mock jurors.

"I have a hard time dealing with the `sweat theory'," Carl Heimat said. "Ted makes it sound so ridiculous." Nevertheless, it was Heimat's turn to close as the plaintiffs' surrogate lawyer. He reminded the audience of the question he had posed that morning, "Why did she have to die?" He said the evidence had supplied the answers. It was because of unconscionable, unforgivable, callous neglect by the two defendants. After reviewing his major points, he especially defended Kelly's "sweat theory," explaining that there are industries where cleanliness is very important and where contamination can have very serious consequences. It was entirely reasonable to sup-pose that it took six years for an originally small pocket of contamination to degrade a tire to the point where it ruptured.

"The managements of these defendants sit off in far-away places and they pretend to hear, see and do no evil," Heimat said.

"Okay, here he goes with his `send them a message' argument," said Born who had been watching intently.

"If you just award a few hundred thousands of dollars or even a few million dollars to the plaintiffs in this case, that'll be such a drop in the bucket the word won't get beyond this courtroom door. No, ladies and gentlemen, if you want to accomplish something today so no more Sarena Millers have to die, so no more Jimason Anchrums have to live with avoidable brain damage, you need to award a verdict big enough so it will be heard in the financial centers of this country and around the world.

Send them a message they can hear, a message they can't avoid listening to, that the citizens of Phoenix County will not tolerate unsafe consumer products. Countless lives in the future may be saved if you do your job properly, and send this message loud and clear, so they'll hear you. We ask that you award plaintiffs seventeen million dollars. I know you want to perform your duty as jurors to accomplish something positive. A verdict in that amount will do it. Anything less will not. Won't you tell them what you think, to make changes happen, so the next Sarena will live - and our Sarena Miller will not have died in vain? Thank you."

There had been considerable discussion about the magnitude of hypothetical punitive damages which should be requested at the mock trial. Born thought he and Heimat had been conservative in selecting a fairly arbitrary seventeen-million-dollar figure. They deliberately chose a figure they perceived to be lower than Bates would probably request, because they did not want some jurors to be "turned off" by a really large number, like a hundred million or more, which could adversely affect their feelings about liability as well as damages. It should not be absurdly low, nor absurdly high, in terms of the climate of the day in Phoenix County.

The mock jurors were now filling out their last questionnaire as Heimat returned to the control room. Dr. Maxwell was right behind him. "All of you have done an excellent job. The positions have been well stated, forcefully stated, and you should get high quality deliberations from the jury. Carl," she said looking at Carl Heimat, "I could see you getting through to them. It's going to be interesting to see what they do."

Dick Santos came in and told the group the mock jurors would be assembling after a ten-minute break. "This is the highest quality presentation all the way across the board I think I've seen. I'd have a hard time predicting what those jurors are thinking. We'll soon see."

Phyllis Maxwell moved next to Born and said quietly, almost in a whisper intended only for his ears, "You gave a truly great argument. Your sincerity came through. I think those jurors really knew how deeply you believed what you were saying. You got through to them, but I have a feeling Carl moved them back, at least part of the way. One thing I want to mention before I forget it, Ted. I really hope you won't ask those Phoenix County jurors at the real trial to be 'God-like'!"

"You thought that was a little too much?" Born grinned.

"Yeah. Just a little too much."

The mock jurors were beginning to go to their assigned rooms. There were nine jurors in rooms 201 and 203 and eight in each of rooms 205 and 207. Room 205 was the only room which had solely African American jurors, and Born decided to take his initial station in adjacent room 206 to monitor that group. As he watched, the deliberations began with small talk, which quickly ended as the jurors got down to business. A man in his early thirties ventured he didn't see that either defendant did anything wrong. A woman agreed with him. One or two asked some questions about the tire, then the van, but there was little support for liability. To Born's delight, this African-American jury wasn't buying the "sweat the-ory" nor the center-of-gravity steering theory. They were still talking when Born decided he had to see what was happening in the other rooms.

As Born left room 206, he saw Tim Archer who was in the process of switching rooms also. "Go over to 204, Ted. There's a humdinger going on in 203 which you can see."

He went into room 204 and found Dr. Maxwell carefully monitoring the jurors next door. "Glad you came, Ted. Some interesting dynamics going on over here. The young woman, about thirtyish, I'd say, is dominating the discussion. At first there were some who were skeptical about the plaintiffs' case, especially that older white woman and the older black man, but this younger woman keeps grabbing the floor, and she's got some education and is articulate. There was no credibility for the 'sweat theory' in the beginning, but she's turning it around. Just listen to her."

At that moment, the dominating woman was telling about her experience working in a defense plant in the Atlanta area and how careful the employees were supposed to be to keep their hands clean and avoid contamination. "She's created instant credibility for the 'sweat theory,' that's what can happen in a jury room when you have one very dominant person," explained Dr. Maxwell. "If it's any consolation, Ted, I don't have any doubt she is someone we would have struck from the jury in a real trial. Of course, we didn't have the opportunity to strike any mock jurors," Maxwell added. The deliberations were continuing, and there were at least two jurors who were resisting, but it was looking as if the woman with the defense plant experience was eventually going to win out.

"I can't stand it," Born said. "I want to be everywhere at once. I've got to go check on the other rooms." By now a fruitbasket-turnover atmosphere had overcome the lawyers. Born, Thompson, Loman, Heimat, and Archer literally raced from room to room, trying to get a feel for what was happening overall. Born ran into Thompson - almost literally - as Thompson emerged from room 202. "They've already found for us in 201!" Thompson said excitedly. "They're still in there talking, but they've taken a vote and we won unanimously after about twenty minutes."

"Looks like we're also winning in room 205, but losing in 203. There's an articulate dominating woman juror in 203 who's carrying the day for the plaintiffs. Interesting that none of the jurors seem to make any big distinction between Universal and Tergano. We seem to stand or fall together, both innocent or both guilty. Maybe I'll go next to 207, it's the only one I don't know anything about."

Thompson joined Born in room 208, to monitor room 207. Carl Heimat was already in there. "This one is sort of split," said Heimat. The defendants have the edge six-to-two, but the two who are for the plaintiffs are still hanging in there. The jurors were being very polite to each other, no raised voices.

One man among the room 207 jurors was saying,

"Nearly sixty thousand miles, six years old, and they didn't take care of it. What do you expect? Why do you think it was a bad tire?" he asked the pro-plaintiff jurors. The two holdouts had no good answers. They just thought tires ought not to have blowouts or, if they did, the tire maker ought to pay anyone who was injured.

"Of course, we didn't have any jury instructions," Born said. "It's conceivable they would have helped in a situation like this. I'm always doubtful how much the jurors really listen to those instructions, but sometimes they give the majority some ammunition to win over a vocal minority."

Tim Archer and Rusty Loman came in the door, "The score is two-to-one for the defendants," said Archer. The group in 203 who found for the plaintiffs is now deliberating about damages. How's it going in here?"

"Leaning our way, but not yet decided," said Thompson.

Dick Santos came in. "It's clear the jurors are impressed with the age and mileage and poor maintenance of the tire. It's also pretty clear Universal and Tergano are going to win together or lose together. There's also been a lot of interest in a couple of things we didn't talk about very much, like seat belts and the existence or non-existence of warranties on the tires. Despite some defense verdicts, it's clear there's strong sympathy for the plaintiffs. Is this one still going?"

"Yes," Born answered. "Looks like they're going to end up on our side, but there are some stubborn allies of the opposition in there."

"Well, let's let them deliberate a little longer, while the group in 203 continues dealing with damages. We've been asking a lot of `what if' questions to the jurors who have finished. You know, `what if the evidence had been so-and-so, would this have changed your opinion?' Mostly, they're saying none of the additional facts or issues we've brought up would have changed their minds."

About an hour later, around five-thirty in the afternoon, the mock jurors had been paid, and all except a few stragglers talking in the motel parking lot had left for home. The lawyers and staff were having a brief review of the day's events. "We ended up with three defense verdicts and one plaintiff verdict," said Santos. "That's good and hopeful. But the one jury that found against your side awarded the plaintiffs every penny they asked for, the full seventeen million dollars. One juror in that group wanted to award *seventy* million dollars."

"Did it surprise you that three of the four verdicts, with these kinds of jurors, were for the defendants?" Thompson asked.

"Frankly, yes," Santos said. "We'll know a lot more when we compile the questionnaires. At this point, I think we've already learned a lot, but we'll immediately send you duplicates of the videotapes of the presentations and deliberations so you can view them as and when you can. We'll have the results of the questionnaire compiled and will come and go over that information within a week. I think that's where the nitty gritty is."

It was a long drive back to Greenville from
Milledgeville, but it seemed short to Born and Thompson
who returned together, after dropping Bert Sayre off at
the Atlanta airport. Their adrenalin was up, a sense of
heady exuberance engulfed them. They talked about the
more memorable of the jurors, especially the dominant
woman in room 203. There was no sense of direction to
their conversation. Both of them were floating on something light as air as they steered their way northeast to
Greenville. They were riding high on the results of the
day, not at all discouraged, though respectfully sobered,
by the one adverse verdict for the full amount requested.
They had expected four bad verdicts like that at the out-
set, and it was spectacular that there was only one loss
against three wins.

"Dave, I'm almost afraid to say this. It can't be true.
It can't be real. I can't let myself believe it, but tonight I
feel something I've never felt before, and I'm going to say
it, and then I'm not going to let myself voice it - or even
think it - again. What I want to say - I'm not sure even
now I should - is *this case might be winnable*. Don't ever let
that surface again! I know it can't really be true. I know
Hancock County, Georgia, for all the superficial similar-
ity, is not Phoenix County, South Carolina. So just forget
I said it. But I just *had* to say it. I'm too excited not to, but
don't let me get carried away." Born was suffering with
the pain of holding back the joy he was feeling but which
he did not believe could really be legitimate. A vapor, he
thought. The euphoria will vanish in thin air.

"Twelve God-fearing jurors, that's what I said. Then doubt came into my mind, and I didn't believe enough in us, I didn't believe enough in our case, or that right would prevail," Thompson said reflectively. "You're absolutely right. It wasn't Phoenix County. But, then, some things ought to be universal."

"Yeah. For Universal Tire Company, for us and for our case," said Born. "I'm starting back to work tomorrow afternoon. I'm going to start by looking at pictures of Sarena and Jimason, and my feet will be back on the ground pretty quick."

CHAPTER TWENTY-FOUR

READING THE TEA LEAVES

Days later, the mock jury team had assembled in the large north conference room at the law firm where the slide projector was set up. Dick Santos had a stack of reports he had prepared analyzing the results of the mock trial, but he had decided to distribute them *after* his slide show. "These are the tea leaves," Santos said, "as we read them."

Born and Thompson wanted to understand the results of their day in Milledgeville, but they were also fidgety, knowing it was less than three weeks to trial and reams of "to do" items confronted them.

Santos first compared the demographics of the group which reported for mock jury duty against the demographics for Phoenix County. "Unbelievably close!" Born thought, as Santos flashed up the comparative figures for sex, age, race, marital status, income, political party (88% Democrat), and education.

The screen then traced the ebbs and flows of juror opinion with the various lawyer presentations, as reflected on the individual questionnaires. On a scale of one (weak desire) to nine (strong desire), the jurors' composite desire to compensate plaintiffs went from a high of 7.0 immediately after plaintiffs' opening statement to a low of 4.9 after defendants' closing arguments, then back up to 5.4 after plaintiffs' closing argument. Santos had matrices of figures showing degrees of commitment to plaintiffs and to each defendant, with fairly dramatic swings throughout the presentations. The bottom line was that, at the end of all presentations and just prior to deliberations, there was a near statistical dead heat between plaintiffs and defen-dants based on degrees of commitment. Disregarding the intensity of commitment, fifty-three per cent of mock ju-rors said they would have voted for plaintiffs at that point and forty-seven per cent would have voted for defendants. Despite a numerical majority favoring plaintiffs, most of the mock jurors, pre-deliberation, did not find the tire to be defective. Thompson asked if sympathy had made the difference in those apparently contradictory findings, and Santos said it must have.

Santos explained that the jury deliberations had converted a dead heat into largely pro-defense verdicts because some strong leadership among the jurors tended to favor and be more committed to the defendants. "This is an excellent example of the dynamics of the deliberative process in the jury room," Santos said.

Somewhat disturbing to the Universal lawyers was the fact jurors tended to see a slightly stronger plaintiffs' case against Universal than against Tergano. The difference was small, and the overwhelming conclusion which emerged was that jurors had tended to be for both defendants or against both defendants. Yet a substantial majority considered the case to be mainly about a tire failure, with little blame to the van manufacturer. Born whispered to Thompson, "That's something we need to change at the trial."

In assessing the degree of anti-corporation sentiment among the mock jurors, Jury Science had found it to be moderate, probably considerably different from what could be expected in Phoenix County. However, there was very strong sympathy for the plaintiffs.

No substantial support was found for the "sweat theory." On a scale of zero to one hundred per cent, there was only a twenty-eight per cent composite belief, pre-deliberations, that human sweat could have been the source of the tire's problems. Nevertheless, forty-five per cent "agreed" or "strongly agreed" that the tire failure was premature and was caused by some kind of manufac-turing defect. On the other hand, an identical forty-five per cent "agreed" or "strongly agreed" that a foreign object destroyed a tire which was in no way defective. An even larger seventy per cent thought the tire was near the end of its useful life, making it more vulnerable to road hazards.

As to failure to warn, about forty per cent thought Universal should have given some kind of warning, more so than was given. "That could be more dangerous than the 'sweat theory'," Born thought. There was a slight majority of jurors who assigned some blame to the Sheriff. They thought he should have known it would not be safe to drive a vehicle with the existing set of tires on it, in-cluding the tire that later ruptured. Most jurors agreed there had been poor maintenance of the tire. Few seemed ready to blame the accident on Bess Johnson's driving.

The worn condition of the tire was one of Universal's strongest defenses, the mock jurors found, but there was also considerable frequency in the mention of seat belts, or rather the passengers' failure to wear them.

On the positive side for Universal, there were basic beliefs of jurors in general that most accidents are caused by human error, rather than defective products, and that tire manufacturers invest enormous amounts of money to design improved tires. On the negative side, most be-lieved big companies try to cover-up dangerous aspects of their products and that families of fatal accident victims deserve compensation.

Before discussing recommendations for defending the tire at trial, Santos gave the four participating lawyers their "report cards" from the jury. On a scale of one to nine, every lawyer received a composite score in excess of seven in each of the five categories on which they were graded, an unusually strong group of presentations, according to

Santos. Dave Thompson outscored every other lawyer in the categories of "poise" and "preparation," while Born outscored all other lawyers in "honesty," "organization" and "clarity." The Universal presentations were rated superior to the others in every single aspect of case ratings: interest, organization, clarity and simplicity. Born and Thompson felt these figures indicated they were on the right track, and Born was especially relieved, because he felt he had not done his best at the mock trial and could improve for the real trial.

"Where do you go from here?" Santos posited. "First, I think you are already doing a lot of correct things, and you should mostly refine and perfect what you are already doing. The worn condition of the tire, its age, its heavy usage, the abuse and lack of maintenance, the road hazard - all these points help tremendously. We need to find ways to re-enforce these points visually and in words. Ted, I thought for example you used good imagery when you said the tire had traveled more than twice the way around the world. To make that imagery more visual, we could do a poster showing the earth with a big arrow circling it more than two times. Another poster could list all the major features of the tire, age, mileage, lack of maintenance and so forth, perhaps with a picture of the worn-out tire. Other posters could show tread depth, wear and tear - that kind of thing."

"Second," Santos continued, "you need to take some extraordinary steps to get the best set of jurors with the fairest set of attitudes you can get. Here are some of our findings about jurors that you need to bear in mind:

- Married jurors were more likely to find for the defense than separated, divorced or widowed jurors.

- Jurors with prior jury experience tended to favor plaintiffs.

- Those familiar with road hazard insurance tended to favor the defense.

- The poorest jurors, those with annual incomes less than $20,000 were disproportionately favorable to plaintiffs.

- Males were somewhat more likely to favor the defense than females; divorced, separated or widowed females had an especially strong inclination to vote for plaintiffs.

- Those who work with or around vehicles or rely on them for a livelihood or are car enthusiasts tended to favor the defense, while those who have had a bad experience with a tire retailer or who work in factories where contamination is a problem tend to be pro-plaintiff."

"Race deserves special comment," Santos said. "In one sense it might not matter much because it is unlikely you will get even one white juror in Phoenix County, from what I understand. In the mock trial, the number of white jurors was not large enough for us to be able to draw statistically significant conclusions. But I point out that, going into deliberations, six of the seven white jurors favored the defense. On the other hand, a majority of black jurors favored the plaintiffs going into deliberations. Consistent, I guess, with intuitive expectations."

"Dick, let me stop you there," Born interrupted. "Our studies of the big verdict cases in Phoenix County in the past convince us that one of the critical problems is the inability to get accurate information from jurors when they are quizzed on voir dire examination. What good is it going to do us to know that those with automotive experience tend to favor the defense, if we can't get reliable information out of the jury pool?"

"Good question, and I've got a couple of ideas," Santos responded. "You have to have some help from the judge - I don't know whether you can get it - but, for example, you could try to get written answers to jury questionnaires, like we used at the mock trial, only simpler, because the Judge would never allow a long questionnaire, I don't think. Also, you could try to get individual juror voir dire. In other words, instead of asking questions of a whole courtroom full of jurors, see if the Judge will let you interview them one-on-one. If he'll let you do one of these things, but not both, I'd definitely go for the one-on-one voir dire. You're much more likely to get truthful answers if you look each one individually in the eye as you ask each question. That should be particularly true in Phoenix County, where there may be some real fear of retaliation by the Sheriff. Maybe the Judge will understand that."

"How would you handle the questionnaires, Dick?" Born asked, perplexed with the mechanics of an idea which otherwise fascinated him with its potential promise. "Suppose the Judge asks me how all three sets of lawyers for the parties could make use of these questionnaires at the same time. There'd just be one set of them. Plus, how in the world would we have time to analyze the results well enough in the short time we'll have - maybe fifteen minutes, probably not more than an hour - before the Judge makes us start striking jurors. We might possibly have a hundred of these questionnaires to wade through."

"You would have to volunteer to make copies of each filled out questionnaire for all other counsel, and you'd have to set up some high-speed copiers and staff them to get the copies made very fast. You'd have to convince the Judge to let you have a long lunch break or a couple of hours whenever you get the papers filled in. Then you would have a separate 'quick-score sheet' for every questionnaire to use in scoring. We would assign plus or minus points to each of, maybe ten or twelve key indicator questions. You would split up the Universal set of questionnaires among a group of scorers and would run through them, scoring the potential jurors with their pro-plaintiff or pro-defense scores. In making your individual strikes, you might not have time to go back and look at the individual questionnaires, but you could use the score sheets to help you rank the jurors in the order of those you would most want to strike, down through those you would most like to retain."

"A wonderful idea, Dick, but I heard an awful lot of 'ifs' in there: *if* the Judge would allow questionnaires, *if* we could install high-speed copiers in Groveton, *if* we could staff them to get the copies made and distributed to plaintiffs' and Tergano's counsel, *if* we could come up with a reliable and simple scoring sheet, *if* we could get the Judge to give us enough time to do the scoring. Rusty, what do you think our chances are that Judge Andrews would agree to all that?"

"I'd say it's very doubtful. To my knowledge, he's never done anything like that before," replied Loman. "One thing's for sure: if there's any serious intention to try these ideas, we would have to make a special installation of copiers. It'd take two weeks to copy those questionnaires on that little dinky courthouse copier. The one in my office is a little better, but it's not up to this job either. And of course, you'd have to do it blind, not knowing ahead of time whether the Judge would allow it, you'd have to install and then hope. If he doesn't let us do it - and it's very doubtful he will - you'd have thrown some money down the drain."

"I can see he's probably going to be hesitant to do it just because it's new, he's never done it before, but this is an important case. Do you know any other reason why he might not want to do it, Rusty?" Dave Thompson asked.

"Oh, he's going to be concerned about setting a precedent and might have to do it in future cases, and, of course, it does cause some delays, I don't see how you can get around that," Rusty Loman answered.

"We don't have much time, but I think it would make a tremendous difference if we could do it. It's just a bare chance, I know, but there's so much riding on jury selection, I'd take my chances. Bert, how about you?" Born asked.

"I think it's worth the chance," Bert Sayre answered. "Renting one or two high-speed copiers for a few days shouldn't be *that* expensive. Is your office wired to handle the copiers, Rusty?"

"If they run on regular 60-cycle 110-volt electricity, it's wired. If it's the 220-volt wiring, I'm not sure. We'll check," Loman answered.

"How about this one-on-one voir dire? I'm sure he's never done that either, has he, Rusty?" Born asked.

"No, not to my knowledge. I guess it won't hurt to ask," Loman answered.

"Phyllis and Dick," Born said, "We'll need your help with the voir dire questions. I've been working on them, but I would like each of you to give it some thought and give me any ideas you have. I'd also like both of you to work on questionnaire forms -no, that won't work. You draft up a questionnaire form, Dick. Then fax it to Dr. Maxwell and me, and we'll all work to refine it. Okay?"

"Sure," Santos agreed.

"There's something else here I want to say before we break up," Santos continued. "You've got to have the right message, you've got to communicate it effectively, you have to have an open-minded jury, and you have to make them conscious of the role of personal responsibility without hitting them on the head with it. In other words, you shouldn't have to pay - no matter how bad the injuries are, even death - unless you, Universal, have done something wrong. They need to be convinced that people bear personal responsibility for their actions. There's no way you can make people maintain their tires properly, no way you can keep road hazards from cropping up. People aren't entitled to money from Universal just because a tire blew out, terrible consequences notwithstanding."

"I hear you," Born said. "Let's get organized now. Nita, can you and Mrs. Shelby see about the high-speed copiers? Work with Rusty and his office to get that done. Dave, you and I need to settle on our visual aids. We already have some, but we got some more good ideas today. Also, I can see we're going to have to file motions to allow the questionnaires and the one-on-one voir dire. I'm working right now on another motion *in limine* to minimize prejudicial actions of Bates and his crowd. We're just three weeks from trial. There's an enormous amount still to be done."

"If it helps," Nita Langley said, "you should know I've made arrangements to rent a van to transport these big posters and our boxes of files and all that. I've made reservations at a place in Columbia which should have reasonable accommodations. I'm renting a special suite to use as a 'war room' in Columbia, and we'll have another 'war room' in Rusty's office, which he's kindly allowed us to set up. We'll have a complete set of all files in Columbia and also in Groveton at Rusty's office. Then we'll have still a third set in the van, so it will be with us wherever we may be, say, if we were to come back to Greenville on weekends or whatever."

"Sounds excellent, Nita," Born commended her. "I have the 'trial notebook' you made for me. I presume you made one for everybody."

"That's right," Langley smiled competently. "Each lawyer's trial notebook contains depositions or deposition summaries of every witness that particular lawyer will be examining or cross-examining, plus copies of key exhibits, the pre-trial order, pending motions and everything else I thought he might need."

"Wonderful, Nita. You and Mrs. Shelby have done a great job putting all this together. Dick, how soon can you get us a draft of the questionnaire?" Born inquired pointedly.

"Can you give us about three days?" Santos requested.

"Three days it is, Dick, but remember, there's not a day of flexibility in that. Phyllis and Dave and I all have to review and get it finalized. Nita, when we do get the questionnaire just the way we want it, we'll need about two hundred copies. I think there may be close to that many potential jurors in the February call."

"Okay, guess that's it," Thompson said. "Let's all get to work. Carl and Tim, thanks for your super contribution to the mock trial. I don't guess you want to join up with us and come to Groveton in February, do you?"

"Not on your life!" they said nearly in unison. "Of course, we'll be glad to help if you need us to do anything up here. We know the facts of the case now, and we can help if you need some research or something," Carl Heimat volunteered.

"I appreciate that, Carl. What I need most, right now, is more time, a new jury, a new venue and maybe a new case. Other than that, I can't think of much! But I might, later. Thanks again." To himself Born said, "Well, Ted, this is the homestretch. But I'm not so sure I'll like the homecoming."

CHAPTER TWENTY-FIVE

FALSE ALARM

"It's snowing, Dave! Did you know that?" Ted Born was relieved to find Dave Thompson still in his downstairs office at nine o'clock Saturday evening. Born had been in his office upstairs, working separately on his part of the case, and thought Thompson might have already left for the evening. The plan had been to return to the office early the following morning, on Sunday, meet with Nita Langley and Marta Shelby and load up the van for the trip to Columbia, getting everything settled for the trial beginning Monday morning.

"Really? Yeah, I see, sure is," Thompson replied.

"Tell you what," Born suggested. "I don't know how bad this is going to be, but you know Greenville with its hills and curvy streets. When it *does* snow here, the place is totally shut down unless you've got four-wheel drive, which I don't. I think we'd better start loading up, so we can at least get the critical stuff to the east of the hills before we get cut off by the snow. Can you meet me in the workroom and let's get started?"

"Be right there," Thompson answered.

The two lawyers began grabbing boxes and taking them out to the elevator lobby. They were both anxious about the good-looking posters and visual aids and stacked them carefully near the elevator. They looked out the window, and the snow seemed to be thickening. "I think we've got enough to get us started if we get cut off from the office," Born said. "We can leave the rest and, if we can't get to it before then, maybe it'll clear up enough to have someone drive the rest down on Monday. I think we'd better get out of here while we can still get out. Okay?"

"Let's go," Thompson said, wondering to himself if Born was overreacting.

As they drove from the building with loaded cars - good ballast for traction, they had both thought - the snow seemed lighter. "This may be a false alarm," Born told himself, "but I've found myself immobilized before by snow, can't take a chance with the trial of a lifetime at stake. After all, February is the worst month for snow."

It did indeed prove to be a false alarm. By the time Born and Thompson got to their respective homes, the flurries had almost entirely stopped. "I wonder what this augers for the trial," Born thought. He smiled to himself as he got out of his car at home, remembering how superstitious most trial lawyers are. He had once litigated a case against a lawyer who believed it was bad luck to change his suit or shirt during the course of a trial. That trial had lasted two weeks, and by the end, the opposing lawyer was bedraggled and wilty. Hadn't done much good either. It had been one of Born's memorable wins.

Ted Born went into the house to Lydia, surprised but happy to see him. "I didn't expect you so early, but I'm glad," she said.

"No, I thought I'd be there 'til after midnight again, God knows I had enough work I needed to do, but the snow scared me home. Anybody else here?" he asked, reaching out a hand to her.

"No, William is not home yet. He's down the street working with some of his friends on computers. His hours seem to get later and later, but this is Saturday night and he's a teenager. I guess it's to be expected," Lydia said. Born of course knew their daughter Rebecca was at college, in the last semester of her senior year.

"I love you, and I feel like we've been separated, living under some malicious decree to stay away from each other," Born said.

"How much do you think I love you?" she answered, half smiling, half concerned.

"Enough to put up with me a little longer, I hope?"

"It's not always going to be this way, Lydia," Born said, "when this case is over, I'm going to change some things. I'll delegate more work. I might even think seriously of early retirement, go up to Maine and plant ourselves among the birches and maples. Then we'll have some time for us, and when I'm not writing the great American novel - or maybe when *we're* not writing the great American novel - we'll have breakfast and lunch and dinner together, and we'll go places, just the two of us, and we'll do things together. I really don't want to be anywhere or with anyone but you. I don't get lonely, never bored, I don't have any other needs, any other desires, but you."

"What would your mistress say?" Lydia asked. Born drew back and frowned. Lydia smiled, "Your jealous mistress, what would she say?"

Born got the point and smiled back, "I'd tell her it's time for a change. I'd tell her I have fond memories of more than thirty years of outrageous, flirtatious, intimate relationship with the law, but now I've got to go back to my wife - not altogether repentantly, but back for a joyous reunion with a private life I've had too little of. I'd say, forgive me, Lydia, forgive me and take me back, receive and hold me. I'll look back to memories, but like a stint in the Army, I'll never go back again."

Tears were coming from Lydia's eyes, "Someday there'll be a time for us, like you say. It won't be tomorrow or next week, or even next year, in the way you say. I know that. I accept that. But there is a special space in this stream of time, in this anonymity of place and people and things - and frenzy - a space we seize for ourselves, when we can be together, and the world can't intrude."

She paused, looked into Born's eyes, embraced tightly,

Sunday morning came with bright sunshine and clear blue skies, mocking the snow flurries of the previous evening, seeming so remote in Sunday sunlight. Many connected with the trial would be converging on beachhead Columbia today, then on to Groveton Monday. Born had hoped to the last minute he would not have to make this trip, that he would receive a last-minute telephone reprieve from the Judge's office saying he was granting the summary judgment. The call never came, but Born still indulged the barest unrealistic hope Judge Andrews would announce the good news Monday morning and send them home. He would happily forgive the Judge for allowing Universal to go through all the logistical trauma of setting up three war rooms, installing high-speed copiers and computer modems, and doing all the other preparation that had to be done, all would be forgiven if the Judge would just save Universal from the day of jury verdict. It was not likely, he knew. Surely, the Judge would not let them go so far in trial preparation if he was going to rule for Universal Monday morning. Then, again, Born wondered if judges in general have any idea what is involved in getting ready to try a big, important lawsuit. Could be this Judge was sensitive to the lawyers' plight, Born hoped, and would deliver the saving message Monday. Born was convinced Universal was entitled to summary judgment, but getting it was something else.

On Sunday afternoon, the Universal and Tergano teams met with Phyllis Maxwell to go over the jury list which had just been released the preceding Friday. Loman had been spending a lot of time over the weekend checking out the list, and especially those he did not know, as had Gillespy. It was obvious Loman's information was better than Gillespy's. The lawyers carefully struck through names of potential jurors they definitely did not want and ranked the others on a scale of one to five, with "one" being most desirable for the defendants. "Not a real good crop," Loman said, "but I've seen worse. Some of the real bad ones probably won't show up, and we might can strike some others for cause before using up any peremptory strikes."

Born expressed the thought there would *never* be a time when defendants would get a Phoenix County jury venire they really liked, that this group was probably as good as any. He felt February was a better time to try the case than August, all other things being equal, because he felt the communication grapevine might not operate as well in cold weather, when people tended to stay indoors and did not visit and socialize as much. It was all moot. Here they were, here was the jury pool, and now was the time for trial, like it or not.

After a lengthy session with the jury list, the group broke up and went their separate ways. Everyone had a great deal of last-minute work, but the pressure was really bad for Dave Thompson, for he would be first up with his opening statement, after Bates' opening, and - if plaintiffs called witnesses in the order Born and Thompson predicted - he would also be the first at bat on the cross-examinations. Of course, everyone expected it would take most of Monday morning to "qualify" the jury venire, then there would be the striking of the jury, and almost certainly a preliminary conference of lawyers with the Judge, all before there would be any opening statements. Still, it was likely there would be opening statements the next day and possibly as many as two witnesses, particularly if they were shorter witnesses. There would be no further time to prepare between now and then, except this very Sunday night.

As for Born, he had filed more than twenty motions *in limine*, still not ruled on by the Judge. Born had to review those motions and organize his thoughts. He knew the motion to allow the questionnaire might be debated heavily, and he had to be ready to do battle on that one. It was always possible Bates might employ some "creative" order of witnesses, and he had to be ready to cross-examine anyone Bates might call to the witness stand. He worked late into the night. At about one o'clock in the morning, Born felt like getting a breath of fresh air, went outside and walked around his wing of the motel. He noticed the light was still on in Dave Thompson's room. "Maybe I should knock on the door," he thought, "suggest he get a good night's sleep, so he'll look and feel fresh tomorrow." He shook his head. It would seem patronizing, at least meddling. "I wouldn't like it if somebody told me I should go to bed." One thing was clear to Born, had been clear for a long time: Dave Thompson was a totally committed lawyer.

Caravans of cars and vans left Columbia early Monday morning and headed for Groveton. Born and Thompson arrived at Rusty Loman's office about eight-twenty. Groveton was more crowded than Born had ever seen it. "Did you see that big double-wide trailer down the side street?" Loman asked. Born and Thompson indicated they had not seen it yet. "That's Bates' and Ripps' head-quarters, rolled it in and set it up this morning, made quite a stir," Loman said. "Sleep okay?"

Thompson shook his head sheepishly, "Only got about an hour's sleep, too much to do, too edgy, I guess."

Phyllis Maxwell pulled up, found a parking space with some difficulty, and came inside. "Phyllis, I want you to come over and take a look at the jurors and watch them during jury qualification. I'm not sure whether we can have you with us during the crucial time when we're striking the jury. It all depends on how we come out on my motion *in limine* to prevent the plaintiffs from making disparaging remarks, in front of the jurors, about our use of a jury consultant. The Judge hasn't ruled yet, but if he doesn't rein in the plaintiffs, it could be very damaging to us. You can imagine what Fred Bates might ask the jury pool on voir dire, `Do any of you know Dr. Phyllis Maxwell who is sitting over there psychoanalyzing you for Universal's lawyers?' Jurors might be incensed, might not understand at all. We need a `no comment' rule. But we don't know what the Judge will do. Better get what-ever thoughts you can give us after watching the jurors during qualification, because we might have to whisk you out of the courtroom before we get to the voir dire and striking stage."

As the jurors, and all the lawyers and their staffs and witnesses, for all of the half dozen cases on the trial docket, continued to arrive, the town square was becoming increasingly congested and parking places hard to come by. There was ferment and activity like Born and Thompson had never seen in the tiny town.

The Universal team made its way through the milling groups on the sidewalks, in the streets, on the Courthouse grounds, up to the second floor courtroom of the old Courthouse. It looked strange to see the usually empty, cavernous courtroom packed with jurors and lawyers, with groups standing all around in the aisles and in the back of the courtroom.

Then the Judge began speaking to the jury venire, going through the slow but necessary steps of explaining about jury duty, its responsibilities, and about the rules for qualification and disqualification, the eyes of all the lawyers - and of Dr. Phyllis Maxwell - were studying the faces of jurors. In a surprise move, the Judge said he was going to try something new today, he would have the jurors sit alphabetically as the Clerk called their names. "Bingo!" thought Brad Mansfield. "That was one of my motions, to have the jurors seated alphabetically." A good omen, he hoped.

As Rusty Loman had predicted, a fair number of persons on the venire did not actually report for jury duty. The Judge gave their names to the Deputy Sheriff who was directed to bring them in, if they could be found. Others were released at their request because of age, hearing or sight impairments, change of residence, or other problems.

When he had finished qualifying the jury, Judge Andrews called the lawyers in the *Johnson* case up to the bench and handed them an Order he had just signed that morning. "Read this Order, and think about your case. See if this doesn't simplify it so we can shorten the trial. I'm going to organize the grand jury next and then we'll talk about the amount of time you'll need for trial. I'll call you back, and we'll talk further after you've had time to think about it."

The lawyers took the copies of the Judge's Order and quickly scanned it en route back to their seats in the courtroom. No one seemed especially elated with the Order. The plaintiffs' lawyers seemed relatively impassive as they read it, while the defense lawyers took small comfort in it. The Order had granted a partial summary judgment for Universal on the failure-to-warn issue, also a partial summary judgment for Tergano on the back seatlatch issue, and - as expected - granted a summary judgment as to Citizens per the tacit agreement between Bates and Mansfield. From the defense standpoint, the ruling helped, of course, but the subjects eliminated through summary judgment in some ways could be considered secondary issues. Both defendants were left still exposed to big damages on the main defective manufacture/defective design theories. Born read carefully the part of the Order which suggested the Court almost granted Universal a summary judgment on all issues. "Almost but not quite," Born said to himself, "like losing the World Series by one run." Defense counsel decided to go outside and discuss this development.

There was a consensus among defense counsel that the ruling was a step in the right direction, but that it would do little to shorten the time for trial. "You're talking about shaving fifteen minutes here, fifteen minutes there, from just a few witnesses," Gillespy opined. "We'll still have to go into the facts of the accident, the injuries, death and medical testimony, the same experts - shortened a bit, but not much. I think we're going to need a good week and a half, anyway, and that's what I would have said even before the ruling." Everyone agreed. They went back into the courtroom.

The Judge had just finished the preliminary organizational instructions for the grand jury, telling them they would meet in secret, without a judge being present, to investigate and ferret out criminal activity and to bring criminal charges as they saw fit. The Circuit Clerk was instructed by the Judge to draw twenty-three juror names from a box the Clerk held in her hands. One after another the names were called. Born and Thompson looked at each other in amazement. "Can this be possible?" Thompson asked incredulously. "Nine of the first ten jurors called were white!"

When the twenty-three names had been drawn, thirteen were white. Yet there had been only twenty-six white jurors out of 164 total. "Let me check the percentages. Now fifteen per cent of the whole jury pool were white, and fifty-seven per cent of the grand jury pulled, supposedly randomly, from that pool, were white! What's the statistical probability of that happening?" Born asked in disbelief.

"I don't know off-hand," Thompson said, "but I was a statistics major and I can tell you it's mighty small. I tell you something else. If it was turned around and there were only twenty-six African-American jurors and a white Clerk pulled half of them out to serve on the grand jury, I'd smell a rat. And I still do here."

"I've been figuring, and it works out this way: the percentage of white jurors left for civil duty will now fall from fifteen per cent down to nine per cent. With strikes... ."

"Yeah. With strikes," said Thompson, "there aren't going to be any white jurors on our case. This sews it up. You know, it might seem strange, but I want to see some white jurors on the jury as bad as you do. There's something going on. This just isn't right."

When the grand jury was completely organized and given its charge, the selected jurors left the courtroom and Judge Andrews summoned the *Johnson* case counsel to the bench. "My question to you lawyers is: can you complete the trial of this case in one week? I'm hoping my Order I gave you simplified your cases enough so that would be possible."

Defense counsel looked at plaintiffs' counsel. Plaintiffs' counsel looked at each other. Defense counsel looked at each other. A round of "I don't think so, Your Honor," echoed from spokesmen for each party.

"Well, we're going to have to finish it in a week if we try it now. I have too many cases on the docket to finish during two weeks I've allotted. I thought more would settle, but they didn't. Now, you are first on the docket and you're entitled to have your case tried first. But there are some reasons we have to try some of these other cases this term and, if any case gives, it has to be your case. If you can't assure me you'll be finished this week, I'm going to continue the case and give it a special setting in June. So, make up your mind."

Bates and the other plaintiffs' counsel were whispering among themselves. "May we have a moment, Your Honor, to talk it through? Just five minutes?"

"Yes sir, come back when you're ready," the Judge said. "But come back soon," he added.

Bates and his team went out the front of the Courthouse, onto the large second-floor landing overlooking the square. The defense lawyers went out the back door and stood on the bridge between the Courthouse and Annex as they talked.

Fred Bates looked at Jack Ripps and Alton Fox and said, "How in hell can we try this case in five days? One day's already half gone."

"It'll take a good week to get on our case, with the fact witnesses, the medical evidence and expert witnesses," Jack Ripps predicted. "Even that may be optimistic. Ted Born is capable of asking a lot of questions on cross-examination. Then there are two sets of defendants and they'll at least have experts and possibly some fact witnesses. Then there will be a charge conference, jury charges and jury deliberations. I don't see finishing it in less than a week and a half, at best. What do you think, Alton?"

"I hate to pass up this great looking jury, as I know you do, but I don't want us to break our necks and show our hands and then have the Judge send us home. Looks like we don't have a lot of choice anyway. On the bright side, the Court might relieve us of our waiver of taking depositions of their expert witnesses, if we have this delay. There'd be a plus there. June would be just a four-month delay, not too bad," Fox reasoned.

"All right," Bates summed up, "We're all in agreement it can't realistically be tried in a week, and we ought to just go in and say that. Right?" All agreed.

Meanwhile, the defense lawyers were talking. "I would have been upset if this had happened before that grand jury was set up, but the grand jury decimated the ranks of white jurors so much, I'm now a little bit relieved. It's bad to have this dud occur after all our preparation, and the war rooms and copiers and computer modems and everything else we broke our necks to do, just to be here. But there are worse things than duds," Born observed.

"Yeah," agreed Brad Mansfield, "like TNT exploding in your face. As long as we can leave here today without losing, well, there's something to be said for that. No way can this case be tried in a week, though. It's just not an option, whether we like it or not."

"Of course, we might be giving up an advantage," Born reminded them. "Right now, they've never deposed our experts. With a delay, they might try to do that. I think I'll try to get the Judge to freeze everything just as it is between now and June, no more discovery, no new experts, nothing like that."

"We can try," Gillespy said.

The defense lawyers reentered the courtroom first, the plaintiffs' lawyers a few minutes later. It would be plaintiffs' place to respond first to the one-week trial proposition, and Fred Bates told the Court plaintiffs would like to be as expeditious as possible but realistically did not believe the case could be tried in a period shorter than a week and a half. Born concurred, but requested, in the event of a continuance, all theories, expert designations and discovery be frozen to avoid expanding the case. Fox said plaintiffs were willing to agree not to change anything about the case in terms of new theories or new experts, but he would like to take depositions of defense experts, since plaintiffs had waived that right only as a quid pro quo for a February trial date.

Judge Andrews agreed the case would be "frozen" until trial in June, except for the depositions of defendants' experts, provided these depositions were taken by April 1.

The lawyers moved away from the bench and started leaving the courtroom, Marta Shelby intercepted Born and asked, "What happened?"

"I'm not sure I know *all* of what happened. The whole morning was pretty strange. First, there was the grand jury they organized, incredibly mostly white, leaving the remaining jurors almost entirely African-American. Then the Judge suddenly, with no warning, decided we had to complete this case in a week. We could've all told him months ago that wasn't possible. I fought this February trial date, but once I got ready for it, I was ready. Now he's going to make us go back and wait. And heaven only knows how much money we had to spend just to be ready. I'm afraid we'll have to do it all over. But I guess we can look at it this way, we've had two practice runs - the mock trial and now this. The third time's got to be the charm. Let's just say this was a false alarm."

"Will we be just marking time on this case?" Shelby asked.

"It's possible. In fact, it's mostly supposed to be that way, but don't count on it."

Bert Sayre came up. "What do you make of it?" he asked.

"It could have been worse," Born said. "We might have had to try the case before a jury drawn from that group."

CHAPTER TWENTY-SIX

BATES WINS A BIG ONE

It did not take plaintiffs long to contact defense counsel to schedule depositions for Universal's experts, and Tergano's John Frey and an automotive design expert, Jim Bochard, were to be deposed in the same time frame.

The new bit of evidence from Tegrit's deposition was his testimony that the tire was so badly worn it was *illegal* to be driven on the highways of South Carolina. Applying a South Carolina statute, Tegrit said the tire would be illegal if the tread in two adjacent tread grooves, measured at any three equi-distant points around the crown of the tire, had less than 2/32nds of an inch in tread depth. Tegrit had brought with him a tread depth indicator gauge with a large glass dial and offered to demonstrate, but Alton Fox said it would not be necessary. Ted Born was relieved.

The measurements were very close to the 2/32nds mark at one place, and a slight error in placement of the gauge could have given an embarrassing result. Tegrit also verified that the hole made by the still unremoved and unrepaired nail did indeed leak air. He confirmed a road hazard was the coup de grace for the tire.

For his part, Bill Edmonds conceded he was no tire expert, but he knew all about tensile fractures and shear fractures in wire rope, and provided a dissertation about them in his patient, fatherly manner.

The depositions of Universal's experts went so well that Born was inspired to file a renewed motion for summary judgment. Keep chipping away, he thought. He had at least gotten a partial summary judgment on his first effort, and the Judge had said in his Order that he was almost persuaded to grant a total summary judgment. Perhaps the strength of the depositions of Bob Tegrit and Bill Edmonds, which had not yet been taken at the time the last motion was under submission, would put the case "over the top," convince Judge Andrews a full summary judgment should be granted this time. Born and Thompson filed the renewed motion and supporting brief, knowing that in all likelihood there would be no ruling until near the trial date in June, if then.

In his haste to get ready for the February trial, Born had not taken the time to familiarize himself with Tergano's videotapes, which he had felt would not directly impact Universal, but as he sat in the depositions of the Tergano experts he became fascinated with some of them. He sat watching the videotapes of an exemplar van crashing into a concrete wall. The terrain was flat, the van traveling at forty-five mph. When it hit the wall, the back end rose a good two-and-a-half to three-and-a-half feet into the air, then came crashing to the ground.

Born consulted his engineering training and realized the back end would rise even more if the van crashed while going downhill.

Born began to wonder whether there had really been *no blowout* on the road, that Bess Johnson simply lost control of the van, ran off the road, hit a tree. The rear end was then thrown up in the air about three feet and came crashing to earth with the weight of the van on it. If the left rear tire happened to come down on a root or jagged stone or rock, it could have ruptured the tire and caused the tensile and shear fractures. Then, when the State Trooper saw the tire, he would have naturally assumed it blew out on the road. Bess Johnson, who had already proved herself to be a perjurer, would say that she heard a loud pop, indicating a blowout.

He cross-examined himself and decided not to make a major issue out of it. For one thing, he could never prove the theory, and it was neither as solid or straightforward as the old tire/worn-out tire/road hazard approach which had gone over well with the mock jurors. The jury might not hold Born's new theory in any higher regard than the mock jury had held Kelly's "sweat theory". Furthermore, Born had his own doubts. How did one explain all the shiny wires protruding at the point of rupture? He could explain it only in terms of a delayed rupture, a case where the road hazard does the fatal damage and then the wire gets "polished" for a while before the actual rupture took place. Too many questions, too risky. Still, Born was fas-cinated with the image of the rear end of the van being lifted high at the time of impact and then crashing back down to earth. He would always wonder.

The days moved on, and in April Alton Fox wrote a letter to all counsel, but mainly directed to Universal's lawyers, that plaintiffs intended to use a metallurgist, a Dr. Roy Acosta, as a rebuttal witness. Fox wrote, "Dr. Acosta is a rebuttal witness, not a primary witness. Therefore, plaintiffs had no obligation to disclose him. However, as a courtesy to opposing counsel, we are advis-ing of our intention to call Dr. Acosta as an expert witness on rebuttal, and we proffer him for deposition."

Born and Thompson quickly filed a motion to pre-clude the testimony of Acosta, pointing out that metal-lurgical testimony is standard evidence in tire rupture cases, that this testimony was properly a part of plaintiffs' case-in-chief, not rebuttal. Plaintiffs should not be able to circumvent the Court's prohibition against new experts by the facile expediency of denominating Dr. Acosta a "rebuttal expert."

Nevertheless, there was uncertainty as to how the Court would rule on Universal's motion. Accordingly, Born availed himself of the opportunity to take Acosta's deposition. It was obvious Acosta, despite his doctorate in metallurgy, knew little about wires. His background had involved exotic metals used in certain medical and high-tech applications. Most of what he knew about wires, he had learned at Fox's behest from reading a metallurgical encyclopedia and looking at pictures in the encyclopedia.

Acosta stated very positively that fatigue fractures could be forty-five degrees to the longitudinal run of the wire, as well as a straight-across ninety degrees. To back up this bizarre statement, Acosta showed a picture from the encyclopedia. "But this is a helical spring, Dr. Acosta, don't you understand that the twist, the torsion, makes a taut spring break differently from a simple wire?" Born asked.

Acosta was flustered but recovered enough to say the slight twist in a wire rope was the equivalent.

Most importantly, Acosta had clipped wires from the tire and had examined them under an electron microscope. There were two problems with this procedure. First, the parties had previously agreed, and the Court had ordered, that there be no destructive testing. Second, while Acosta had marked general locations on the tire where he had done his clipping, he was unable to say which clipped wire came from which locations, thus destroying the context necessary for evaluating his results.

"Didn't Mr. Fox tell you there was to be no destruc-tive testing?" Born asked.

"Not at first," Acosta replied. "I asked him if I could clip the wires, and he told me it would be all right. Then he called me back the next day and told me I shouldn't do it. But by that time, it was too late. I had already cut the wires."

Born was amazed that Fox would have permitted the cutting of the wires which were such a key part of the evidence. This was the same Alton Fox who had gotten so upset earlier in the case when Universal's expert had dismounted the tire from its rim. Born went back into his correspondence file and found Fox's letter admonishing Born that there was to be no destructive testing. In researching the case law, Born found that the courts had dealt very severely with parties guilty of unauthorized destructive testing.

Armed with his precedents, Born filed a motion for a default judgment as a sanction for unauthorized destructive testing or, alternatively, to preclude Acosta from testifying. Born did not really expect Judge Andrews to grant a default judgment, but he hoped Acosta's testimony would be prohibited. Ultimately, Judge Andrews did preclude Acosta from testifying, both because of the Court's instructions against new expert witnesses and as a sanction for unauthorized destructive testing.

Time moved forward toward June. Still, Judge Andrews had not ruled on any of Universal's or Tergano's motions *in limine,* and the lawyers were in the dark as to what would and what would not be permitted on various potentially contentious issues at trial. This time the case had been given a special solo setting for trial; there would be nothing else to complicate trial or jury selection, no grand jury to be organized, no other litigations vying for time on a crowded trial term. The special setting was both good and bad, Born considered: good that the complications would be removed, bad that jury tampering would be easier. Anyone inclined to jury tampering would know that fewer potential jurors would be called to service and there was only a single case on which any jurors would serve, greatly simplifying the possibility of making effective, highly targeted advance contacts with the jurors.

Born wondered if he had allowed himself to become paranoid about the prospect of jury tampering. Groveton seemed so peaceful, the people so friendly. The town, and Phoenix County, no longer seemed coldly hostile, the way he had perceived it on his first encounter. He could even imagine himself living there, very happily.

Fred Bates had once lived there but he could not imagine ever living there again. He was ready to retire, but it would not be in Groveton. No, he would retire to the shore, where he could watch sunrises across rolling waves. Bates had discovered a latent love of travel once he hit it rich in the *Driscoll* case, and he had done a good bit of searching out fabled corners of the globe. He had especially wanted to see the Riviera and was amazed that its beaches were of rocks and pebbles. "You even have to wear flip-flops to keep from bruising your feet *after* you get in the water!" Bates complained. Bates said he would take an American "Red-neck Riviera" any day, any time, over the original one. It would be hard to argue with Bates about that, looking just at the beaches and ignoring Cezanne and Matisse, perched villages like Eze filled with bougainvillea hanging in suspense over a Prussian blue Mediterranean, Provencal churches, the music festival at Aix, the Corniches, that is to say, ignoring the essential character of the Côte d'Azur.

While Bates was ready for retirement, retirement was not quite ready for Bates. There was the *Johnson* case in June, and hopefully any day now there would be a decision on the appeal of the franchise case. Two more big wins, or really a big win in either case, would fix him up for life with no more worries.

Bates and Ripps had talked about the juror situation at the June trial. It was a dream to have a client like Sam Johnson in a case like this. His position and popularity should carry the day, and the Clerk of the Court would have some influence. Then, too, this was Phoenix County. The jury situation should take care of itself.

Ripps was willing to accede to Bates' judgment, as Bates was lead counsel and he had brought in big verdicts in the past, but Ripps was more aggressive in some respects and urged Sam and Bess and Doretta and the Millers to talk up the case in the community, whenever they could.

Then came the Friday before trial. Ripps was in Bates' office as the telephone rang. "Yes, ma'am, this is Fred Bates.... Tell me that again, I want to hear it again.... Hallelujah! You've just made my day. Thank y-o-u-u-u!" Bates looked at Ripps. "Our net worth just went up, Jack! We won! We won the appeal of the damn, screwy, crazy nothing case, the franchise case. That was the lady in the

South Carolina Supreme Court's Clerk's Office telling me the jury verdict has been affirmed, and an opinion will be released today. Didn't cut the award a dime. With interest could be worth over nine million! Boy, I'd started sweatin' that one. It had dragged on; I was afraid there was a problem. God, we're good! Shake my hand."

Jack Ripps was all grins, shook hands, and said, "This calls for a celebration. Got some Champagne in the bar that's been on hold, just waitin' for this, real French Champagne. Let's see, they call it "Mowette et Shandon.""

"Jack, when you gon' get some culture? Its `Moet et Chandon,' that's where they invented Champagne, I've been to their wine cellars. They've got people who turn those bottles a quarter of a turn a day, do that for eight years before it's ready. Sure hope this is ready. Cheers!" Bates said with appropriate celebratory gusto.

They invited the office staff in and passed the Champagne around. "Plenty for everybody," Ripps said. Then, looking at Bates behind his desk, Ripps said, "Fred, you gonna have to get another picture made of a new check in about three weeks, soon as the rehearing is denied. Add it to your collection."

"Wish Alton was here," Bates said. "I'd like to share a glass with him, although he doesn't get a big cut of the franchise case, but, hell, it's still a lot of money for him, even so. He's trying to get some work done on this *Johnson* case. Damn! Now I wish we didn't have it coming up on Monday. This is sweet, like to enjoy it without the 'minor' distraction of a lawsuit Monday. Matter of fact, I might just live dangerously, take off some this weekend. Now as I know I've won this one, I don't feel as much pressure from the *Johnson* case."

"Truth of it is," Ripps said, "there's not that much to do. It's going to take all morning to organize the jury, half the afternoon to strike our jury, and then there're opening statements—I know yours is ready. Then we'll probably have a couple of minor witnesses to top off the first day. I don't see why we have to be hermits. If one look at Jimason don't win this case for us, I dunno what will. Three cheers, everybody. Cheer One! (Drink) Cheer Two! (Drink) Cheer Three! (Drink)."

"The more of this Champagne I drink, the more I agree with you, Jack," Bates said. Fred Bates' office by now had become crowded with convivial celebrators. He was still behind his desk, returning toasts and exulting in victory and the congratulations heaped upon him. It was a subtle thing, but Bates - not Ripps - was the focal point of the gathering, not just because it was his imposing office or because of his more senior age. It was mainly because everyone knew Fred Bates was the real trial lawyer, the one who carried this case, as he had carried many others. Bates loved it, drenching himself, immersing himself, in one of life's few great moments.

Bates was laughing and telling witty stories to the apparent enjoyment of all present, fluted Champagne glass in hand. He looked at the door, did a double take, looked again. There in the doorway was a large husky figure in uniform, with a Sheriff's badge shining on the front of his shirt. It was Sam Johnson.

"Sorry if I'm interruptin' the party, Mr. Fred, but you said you wanted me to come by at ten-thirty this morning," Johnson said.

Bates thought to himself, "Why the hell did I want him here this morning? Testimony? What?" But he said to Johnson, "Sam, we do need to see you, be with you in just a minute in the conference room across the hall, but first, have some Champagne. We just won that franchise case on appeal. That's one man who's gonna make a helluva lot more money on a lawsuit than he ever would've made selling hamburgers. You can go back and tell Bess and Doretta and Ben they hired the right lawyers for this case. 'Cause we're winners."

"I'm on duty, Mr. Fred, 'fraid I cain't drink," the Sheriff replied.

"I thought you had gone to the night shift, Sam," Jack Ripps said.

"I did, but swapped out today, because I had to come here and see you. I could do that on my Sheriff's time, official business, you know, as I was a witness to the circumstances of the accident in my official capacity as Sheriff. I couldn't do it, though, on my private delivery time," Johnson explained.

Bates and Ripps reluctantly left the breaking-up celebration and went with Sam Johnson to the conference room. "Jack, who was the lawyer used to shoot off a cannon from the office window every time he won a case?

Can't think of his name. Maybe I should do that. Where would we get the cannon? Got any extra cannons on the Courthouse grounds in Groveton, Sam?" Bates laughed.

When they were seated in the conference room, Bates, still trying to remember why he, or Jack, or whoever it was, asked the Sheriff to come by that morning, said, "Sam, since you're the one who is really the spokesman for your niece and the others and you're the one who made sure we got the case, I wanted you to come by so we could show you how much work we've done and how well prepared we are."

"Yeah, I can see you're workin' hard," Johnson said, eyeing the Champagne glasses.

"Now, Sam, you know we've already prepared this case once, and now we've prepared it again. You wouldn't begrudge us a little toast for this big win, would you? We worked hard on that case, and really you should be reassured we know what we're doing."

"Just so you win. That's all the reassurance I - we - need. You know my neck's on the line, just don't leave me out there," Johnson said seriously.

"Sam, we're ready, and we're gonna work all weekend to get even more ready. In fact," at this point Ripps looked at Bates as Ripps continued, "To be sure we have the peace and quiet we need, we're going to each leave here, cloister ourselves away at our homes and work all weekend. It's gonna' go like clockwork, smooth and reg'lar."

"Who's gon' be your first witness?" the Sheriff asked.

Bates and Ripps looked at each other and frowned slightly. "Who's our first witness, Jack?" Bates asked.

Ripps looked put upon. "Isn't it that guy who was following Bess when the accident happened? What's his name? Or did we decide to call the prior owner of the van?"

"No, we'll have to read his deposition. He lives too far away to subpoena. Look, that's one of the things we'll finalize this weekend, Sam. I'm pretty sure it's the fellow who was driving behind, the eye-witness," Bates said.

"When do I testify?" Johnson asked.

"You're kind of near the top, maybe the third witness," Bates advised. "Might get to you Monday afternoon, more likely Tuesday. See, Monday is mainly going to be jury organization and selection. Could take a little more time than usual. I've agreed to this questionnaire procedure. All the potential jurors will fill out questionnaires. We do that sometimes in other courts and I find it pretty useful. Andrews has never done it here. Anyway, we're not going to get much done on Monday. We've got to get in some good blows in the opening statement. Then one or two minor witnesses. The real testimony starts Tuesday."

"Now, listen, Sam," Bates continued. "There's one thing I really want you to do. Be sure someone walks with Jimason everywhere he goes, holds his hand, leads him around like a robot. The jury's gotta' think he hasn't got sense enough to go to the bathroom by himself. Don't let him talk or giggle. He just needs to look 'out of it', you know, like a damned robot. That's the best testimony he can give, the best anybody can give, and he never has to say a word. Understand? I've told Doretta and Bess that, but I don't know whether it registered. They'll listen to you. Make sure they get it and do it up just right."

"I'll make sure about that. I got another question. Should I wear my uniform?" Johnson asked.

"Glad you asked that, Sam," Ripps said, "I just about forgot to tell you. No, you don't wear your uniform. The jury's gon' know you're the Sheriff. But psychologically they'll feel sorrier for you if they're not constantly reminded that you're a powerful authority figure. Definitely no uniform. Your human, just-plain-folks, side needs to come out at the trial."

"Anything else you want me for?" Johnson asked.

Bates and Ripps looked at each other. "Can't think of anything, Sam. Keep your fingers crossed," Bates said.

"Mr. Fred," Johnson said soberly, looking Bates directly in the eyes, "I came to you because I didn't want to have to depend on crossed fingers. You deliver, and I know how you deliver, and I expect you to deliver this time. We need to win this. We've *got* to win this."

"It's under control, we feel good about it. Soon as the jury list is ready, you pick it up in the Clerk's Office. It's usually ready about one o'clock the Friday afternoon before trial. Look at it real hard, then bring a copy over to us. We'll look at it hard, too," Bates promised.

"We just need to win. That's all I say. Well, I'll have everybody there by eight o'clock Monday morning. Call me if you need anything," Johnson offered.

"Sure, Sam. You can depend on it. Have a good weekend, Sam," Ripps said. The Sheriff left.

"Fred, what's he expecting of us, besides winning, I mean?" Ripps looked at Bates over an empty glass still clutched lightly.

"We've never promised him a damn thing, except to use our lawyer skills as best we can. He brought us this case because he owed us one. Now I'd say we're even. We don't owe him nothin'. Let's take a clean shot at this case. If we do a half-way decent job, we'll win. We've got a child's death, we've got brain damage, we've got the Sheriff and the Clerk of the Court on our side, and this is Phoenix County. I repeat, Jack, this is Phoenix County. We can't lose this case in this county, and we'd be insane to take idiotic chances. We'd be god-damned insane!"

"Makes sense, Fred, makes real good sense. If we don't win the case when the jury first sees Jimason - which in itself should do the job - we'll win it when Ivy League, patent lawyer, Ted Born gets up there to make the opening statement. I just can't wait to see the expression on them jurors' faces."

"Let's go cloister ourselves away now and do our homework," Bates said with a wink.

"I'll toast that," Ripps replied smiling.

CHAPTER TWENTY-SEVEN

TO STRIKE THE JURY

The Universal and Tergano lawyers had worked all Sunday afternoon and early evening on the jury list. Nita Langley checked the list against the data bank she had built up, but her prodigious compilation was over-shadowed by Rusty Loman with his personal knowledge of the jurors. Trip Gillespy now and then was able to add information.

Dick Santos, who had originally been employed to arrange the mock trial, was playing an additional role as jury consultant, Dr. Phyllis Maxwell being out of the country. Santos was to provide insights into the jury pool based on input from Loman, Langley and Gillespy. Rusty Loman had comments about almost every potential juror. Unfortunately, the most frequent comment, jotted in the margins of the jury list, was "Don't Want," usually accompanied by specific and compelling reasons which he detailed orally at the meeting.

In addition to those who were objection-able for other reasons, there were not less than fifteen jurors with the surname "Miller" or "Johnson," and even one "Anchrum." Some of these jurors were kin to some of the plaintiffs, but the group could not verify kinship in every instance that Sunday afternoon. Further, one juror was recognized as being Doretta Anchrum's boyfriend. Another was a co-worker with Sam Johnson in the delivery business; still another was employed in the Sheriff's Department. Some were known to be close personal friends of the Clerk of the Court - not grounds for a "strike for cause," but suggesting possibly a peremptory strike. The jury list was scrutinized in meticulous detail, and as the review progressed, expressions on faces were glum, and got glummer.

Santos offered observations which were only marginally helpful. Everyone realized his main value would be in analyzing the answers to the questionnaire and in reading body language after personally seeing the jurors.

"Just about looks hopeless," said Brad Mansfield. "Worst looking jury pool from a defense standpoint I think I've ever seen."

"Be ready with your *Batson* challenge," Loman recommended, "because Fred Bates will strike every white person from the jury." Loman was referring to a U.S. Supreme Court decision in *Batson v. Kentucky*, which held that, when minority racial groups are struck from juries disproportionately so as to reduce their representation among those finally selected for jury service, the side striking the minority jurors has the burden of demonstrating a bona fide race-neutral reason for the strikes. Otherwise, the struck minority members are seated with the jury. *Batson* originally was applied to protect minority African Americans from being struck so as to leave all-white jurors, but *reverse Batson* challenges had also been used to insure that white members were not arbitrarily and systematically struck to produce all-African-American juries. It was really a *reverse Batson* challenge Loman was suggesting.

"We already have the challenge ready," Thompson said. "Looks like the jury pool is at least four- or five-to-one African-American, so there's a good possibility we will need it.

The group talked for a while about the juror questionnaire. Bates had agreed to it, and so had the Judge, provided all case-specific questions were deleted. It was all right, Judge Andrews had said, to ask some background questions about the jurors and their attitudes, but nothing relating to the facts of the case should be asked in the questionnaires. Too much danger of jurors' talking among themselves about the case before the final trial jury was ever empaneled, he had said. Case-specific questions should be asked only on voir dire examination of the jury, where a lawyer for each party could ask questions just prior to commencing the striking of the jury.

As for the voir dire examination, the Judge had indicated he would give considerable leeway on questioning and would not rush the process. He had hinted he might allow some new approaches to help the lawyers get more accurate and complete answers to voir dire questions, but he would not go so far as to allow one-on-one questioning, as Born had requested. The defense counsel agreed among themselves to challenge the jurors, on voir dire, to prove they could be fair.

One troublesome factor was that Judge Andrews had not yet ruled on any of the numerous motions *in limine* filed by both Universal and Tergano. The uncertainties on the *in-limine* issues were ameliorated somewhat by compromises Bates and Mansfield had worked out, such as, Bates would not make racial references or accuse the defendants of racism, they would not refer to the defendants as "big corporations" or refer to the out-of-state location of their headquarters. Very importantly, Bates agreed his side would not use at trial the Coroner's photograph of the deceased Sarena Miller. All these things would probably have been improper and unduly prejudicial in any event, but now the parties knew they would not have confrontations over these issues during the trial.

As dawn broke the next morning, scattering streaks of pink and gold and gray on the eastern horizon, Ted Born was lugging his trial notebook and two large briefcases to his car. Before getting in, he paused, his eyes closed and his lips moved, then he raised his head and looked across a noisy interstate highway to an on-rushing, light-flooding daybreak beyond. The day did not seem as foreboding as he had expected. It was not the first time he had encountered dawn on a day of trial, far from it, but this case was in a class of its own, seeming up to now surrounded by portents of doom. Only, today, the reality was not quite as ominous as its forecast, not when the day was heralded by a sunrise like this one.

Born drove around to the motel entrance where Theo Burton was waiting for him. Burton had succeeded Al Gifford as the quality supervisor at the plant where the tire had been manufactured, and now he too had retired. Born had been looking for a person other than Gifford to appear as Universal's employee representative at the trial, someone to sit at the table with Universal's counsel to provide advice on technical issues relating to tire making as they might come up in the testimony.

Gifford's deposition had gone extremely well, from Universal's point of view, with no admissions of significant touching of tire components by workers' hands. If possible, Born wanted to keep it that way. His plan was to surprise plaintiffs by bringing as the Universal trial representative someone different from Gifford. Since Gifford was the only Universal employee on plaintiffs' pre-designated witness list - from which all of plaintiffs' witnesses had to come - plaintiffs would be stuck with Gifford's innocuous deposition, if Gifford did not show up in person to be questioned "live." The substitution of Burton in place of Gifford as Universal's trial representative would insure that Gifford did not show up in person.

At least, it should theoretically work that way. There was always the possibility Fox could plead with the Judge to allow an exception to the rule limiting plaintiffs' witnesses to those named on the pre-designated list, saying he had thought Gifford would be there in person as Universal's rep. Fox might ask the Judge to make an exception allowing Fox to call Universal's actual trial representative as a witness.

Born was betting Fox might never make such a request. It would be risky for Fox to call a witness whose deposition had never been taken, when the tenor of the possible testimony was totally unknown to him. Even if Fox was brave enough to risk the testimony of an unknown witness, the Judge might not agree to make any exception to the general rule restricting witnesses to those named on the prefiled witness list. The strategy ultimately might not work for Born, but there was no downside to trying. On the other hand, if it *did* work, the props would be knocked out from under Wrack Kelly's "sweat theory."

"Morning, Theo. Sleep all right?" Born asked.

"Yeah. Slept fine. Nice motel. Nice continental breakfast," Burton responded as he buckled himself into Born's car for the drive to Groveton.

Theo Burton was a distinguished-looking African American, slender build, about five feet eleven, neat understated mustache, and horn-rimmed glasses. His hair was still mostly black with significant white highlights. Importantly, Burton obviously liked people and was friendly in a reserved, low-key manner. Born had listened

to him tell of his rise from menial positions in the plant
to one of the most important positions, always keeping his
positive outlook and quiet optimism. He himself was obviously very intelligent. He had two sons, one a medical
doctor, the other a Ph.D. in chemistry. A great personal
success story, Born had thought when he heard it.

They arrived at Rusty Loman's office to find they had
been preceded by Marta Shelby and Nita Langley who
were busily unloading essential items from the van, taking
care to keep covers over the posters and visual aids lest
the opposition get a preview of them. Born instinctively
stopped and wanted to offer to help them bring some of
it inside. Then he remembered both his hands were already amply encumbered and, anyway, he had too many
other immediate demands on his time this important first
morning of trial.

Loman greeted Born and Burton as they entered
Loman's office. Loman assured Born all systems were
operating perfectly, waving his hand at the large copier
with collator, the extra computer with modem, the additional dedicated telephone line for the modem. Tables
and chairs had been set up for Marta Shelby and Nita
Langley, and upstairs there were extra tables and chairs
for the Universal lawyers. It was as if Universal had in-
vaded the office and it had surrendered to the onslaught.
Loman indicated a suitable place to store the large posters
until needed in the courtroom.

Dave Thompson and Bert Sayre arrived, and the law-yers
all began conferring in preparation for the morning's

events. Loman reported that Tergano and the plaintiffs had both rented vacant office space around the square, no double-wide trailer this time. He said he had arranged for lunches to be brought into the office each day of trial, since there was no longer any restaurant in Groveton. If there was no objection, he would offer this service to Tergano's and plaintiffs' lawyers.

At the temporary quarters of plaintiffs' counsel directly across the square, Alton Fox was complaining moderately that he had not been able to reach either Fred Bates or Jack Ripps over the past weekend. He had not even seen the jury list. Bates told him politely he need concern himself only with the tire part of the case; he and Ripps would handle the van aspects of the case and the logistical and tactical aspects of the whole case. Fox wondered where Bates and Ripps had been the past weekend and was assured they had been off to themselves, working on the case.

Bates observed he was sure Judge Andrews would start off with a lawyers' conference before doing anything else, mentioned that the final form of the juror questionnaire would be submitted to the Judge for approval, that motions *in limine* would be considered, that conceivably the Judge could even seriously entertain Universal's renewed motion for summary judgment.

"That questionnaire is something that gives me huge problems, Fred," Ripps said. "You're giving up a possibly critical advantage because you know so much about Phoenix County jurors, and I don't think the defendants do. In fact, I know they don't except for whatever help they've gotten from Rusty Loman. I think you ought to withdraw our agreement on that. It's still not a done deal 'til the Judge approves the final form. This is important, Fred, it could be the difference between winning or losing."

"I agree, Fred," Fox concurred. "I know I'm supposed to keep my mouth shut unless there's a tire issue, but I've got to agree with Jack that the questionnaire was a mistake."

"Well, hell! I've already agreed to the damn questionnaire. Frankly, I had good reason for it. There are a lot of young blacks on the jury lists these days that I really don't know. Sure, I talk it up that I know everybody in Phoenix County, but truth is, I don't anymore. Now, I might have known their mamas or daddies, but I don't know a lot of these young ones anymore, and they don't know me. I'll tell you, it would help me to have a questionnaire. It'd help me place some of the young ones I don't know, connect 'em with family members I've known. I've used these questionnaires before, and I think they're helpful. Besides, with Rusty in the picture, my advantage is narrowed a lot. In fact, he may know more young folks than me, average age on the list has been running like thirty or under. I'm a lot better with the old-timers."

"I dunno, Fred. I think you're leveling the playing field too much, not just for this case, but look at the precedent you may be setting on future cases," Ripps predicted. "They'll all want to use questionnaires from now on. We've got a big advantage most of the time and we're giving it up. You need to object. Even if the Judge overrules you, go ahead and object. Then in the future you can say it was done over your objection and shouldn't have been done."

"Hell, I hate to do that, but I can see your point. If it'll make you two happier, I'll go in and object. I'll have to admit in Court I agreed to the damn thing, as I've already told him I've agreed - and he might've recorded the phone conversation - but I guess I can put an objection on the record."

"What else have we got?" Ripps asked.
"Can't think of anything, except make sure that kid Jimason has someone walking him around everywhere he goes. The more like a robot he looks, the better. Let's go on over to the Courthouse," Bates answered.

At about the same time that Monday morning, the Universal team made its way to the great white building dominating the Square. At Born's request, Loman had set up a third counsel table in the courtroom, which normally contained only a single plaintiffs' table and a single defendants' table. Because of the number of defense lawyers and trial representatives who needed to sit around the tables, a single table would not have been large enough for both Tergano and Universal, hence the third one. When Born and group entered the courtroom, they found Tergano's lawyers had already laid claim to the table farthest from the plaintiffs and farthest from the jury, leaving the middle table to Universal's team.

Born felt instant resentment. Since Tergano was the

first identified defendant on the Complaint, Tergano up to now had generally exercised its prerogative to be heard first, before Universal, on motions and in other presentations. Born was confident, for example, Tergano would want to go first on voir dire examination of the jury later that day, and would want to go first on opening statements and cross-examinations except perhaps for a few special situations. But here, Tergano was psychologically trying to distance itself from the jury and from involvement in the case. "This is Tergano's way of subtly telling the jury this is a tire case, not a van case, pushing Universal into the middle of the room and trying to fade itself into the background," Born thought. He said nothing, however, and was friendly to the Tergano lawyers who were much cooler in return than he had ever known them to be previously, a coolness especially evident when jurors were around. "Looks like Tim Archer knew better than I," Born thought, "looks like our co-defendant is ready to throw us to the wolves if it gets half a chance." He managed to control himself, still said nothing.

Bates and his group entered with briefcases in hand, followed by boxes on hand carts. Born noted that something was missing - the ruptured tire, conspicuously absent. "Probably just didn't want to be bothered with it during jury organization, voir dire, and striking the jury," he thought. Surely it would magically and dramatically appear in time for Bates' opening statement.

The Judge called the lawyers into the jury room, across in the Annex, for a preliminary conference. He announced he was holding all pending motions and would not rule on any of them. As issues arose in the trial relating, for instance, to the subject of motions *in limine*, he would consider those issues in context as they arose. The Judge said he realized this amounted to a denial of Universal's renewed motion for summary judgment but said he preferred to see how the evidence played out, the case might be a candidate for a directed verdict, but he was not quite ready to dispatch it summarily. "He obviously doesn't want to risk making a reversible error, unless he absolutely has to," Born thought. "Still, should judges play it safe and sacrifice a smooth-running trial where the ground rules are known in advance?" At Brad Mansfield's request, the Judge did agree to enter an Order confirming points previously agreed between him and Bates on the Tergano motions *in limine*.

Born pointed out that an issue which would arise very quickly would be the extent to which plaintiffs' counsel could comment on or characterize Dick Santos, Universal's jury consultant. Judge Andrews looked at Bates inquisitively, asking Bates' position. Bates quickly weighed the situation and answered that plaintiffs would confine their references merely to asking if any of the jurors knew Santos. "You're not going to characterize him as a psychologist or anything like that, are you?" Born asked.

"How would you suggest I refer to him?" Bates asked.

"Just refer to him as someone who is 'assisting Universal,'" Born responded.

Bates hesitated a moment as he thought to himself,

"The main thing is, I've got to keep reversible error out of the record. The Supreme Court might find a characterization like 'psychologist' prejudicial and reverse the whole damn case. It's not that important. Better to agree." When Bates agreed to restrict any negative comments about the jury consultant, Born heaved a tremendous sigh of relief. It was an important step, he felt, in getting a fair jury - having the use and advice of an expert jury consultant, without the downside risk of alienating the jury because of such use.

Judge Andrews interjected that the jury consultant must remain beyond the railing separating the lawyers from the spectators - certainly not an ideal situation, but tolerable. The Judge then said, "I understand this jury questionnaire has been agreed to by all the parties and can be distributed to the venire, is that right?"

"We object, Your Honor," said Bates.

Born could scarcely believe what he was hearing. "But, Fred, you and I talked about it, question by question, and you agreed," Born pointed out, wondering if Bates would possibly deny it.

"I'm not saying you weren't justified in believing we would not object to it based on that telephone conversation, but plaintiffs' counsel have conferred about it, and I am making my objection." After brief further discussion the Court ruled the questionnaire would be allowed.

The conference then adjourned, and the Judge and lawyers returned to the courtroom where the job of organizing the jury was about to begin, the time the Judge would explain the nature of jury service and winnow out any who did not meet the requirements. Marta Shelby was in the courtroom, and Born asked her to go get Santos from Rusty Loman's office where he had been waiting until the ground rules had been worked out. "Tell him to come on over, the coast is clear," Born said.

Judge Andrews had the jurors sit alphabetically as the Clerk called the roll, just as he had in February. "What a tremendous help!" Born thought. "It's almost impossible to keep up with who has said what in answer to questions when hands go up all over the courtroom, assuming they are responsive enough to raise their hands."

There had been one hundred three potential jurors on the original list, of which about ten had been excused in advance, unfortunately for the defendants some of them presumptively defense oriented. The names of an additional seven jurors had been added to the original list, resulting in one hundred potential jurors as of the day of trial. At least a dozen of the one hundred did not show up for jury duty, without being excused from duty, generally some of the "worst" jurors from a defense point of view. "That's always the way it is," Santos remarked. Those who are not conscientious and have no sense of personal responsibility - always bad for defendants - tend not to show up. Of course, that doesn't mean all of those in this courtroom have a sense of personal responsibility. It's just that proportionately the worst jurors often don't show up."

The Court began asking the jurors qualifying

questions: whether they were residents of Phoenix County, whether they were U. S. Citizens, could they read and write in the English language, did they have any physical or mental condition which would make it difficult for them to serve, and so forth.

Judge Andrews began by asking the first row of jurors a question, then asked the second row, then the third row, until all rows had been asked. Born sensed that there were jurors who responded to the questions by raising their hands who might not have done so had the question been asked only once to the courtroom as a whole.

By the time the qualifying questions had been asked and answered and the Court had considered the answers, about nine jurors had been excused. This brought the total qualified jurors down to about seventy-nine. The jury pool looked better by this time than it had looked during the review session the day before, but "better" was a relative term for this group, at least from a defense point of view.

Next, the Court distributed the juror questionnaires to all qualified jurors and gave them time to complete the pages. One of the jurors, Tom Ferris, had difficulty filling out his questionnaire and the Judge personally helped him. Judge Andrews told the parties Mr. Ferris could sign his name but could read and write only slightly. No one objected to Ferris' continuing as a qualified juror, although jurors are supposed to be able to read and write.

Judge Andrews' involvement in helping with Ferris' questionnaire delayed the completion of the process as the Clerk would not release any questionnaires for copying until the Ferris set was finished. By then, the time was already twelve twenty. The Court directed the parties and lawyers to return to the courtroom at one thirty after the lunch break to conduct the voir dire examination of jurors.

Born, Thompson and Loman rushed - literally ran - back to Rusty Loman's office, with Nita Langley and Marta Shelby fast on their heels. Shelby and Langley led the assembly line production: unstapling each of the questionnaires, making three stapled copies, restapling the original, checking for readability and continuing throughout the stack of nearly eighty documents, each being nine pages long. As a group of six or eight questionnaires was completed, they would be taken upstairs where lawyers for Tergano and Universal divided up the forms and began racing through the scoresheets to grade each juror.

Meanwhile downstairs, plaintiffs' copies of the questionnaires were being stacked as they came off the assembly line, and Bates sent runners every five or ten minutes to pick up copies.

Born tried to grab a drumstick from a box lunch of fried chicken to eat it with his left hand as he turned pages and scored questionnaires with his right hand. It was hopeless to finish by one thirty, the defense lawyers agreed. Born and Mansfield left to go back to the Courthouse to plead for more time. They saw Jack Ripps out in the square and summoned him to go with them to see the Judge. As they approached the Annex, the three lawyers saw Judge Andrews upstairs on the balcony. "Do you need more time?" he asked. They answered affirmatively. "Then come back at one forty-five," he said.

"Gee, thanks," Born thought. "This Judge hasn't got the foggiest idea what we're up against. Fifteen more minutes! Ridiculous." But the three lawyers raced back to their offices, Mansfield accompanying Born, to work a few minutes longer.

The defense lawyers continued working feverishly and mechanically with the scoring sheets, really having no chance to absorb the contents. However, each scoring sheet was stapled to Universal's copy of the corresponding questionnaire, with the hope that a few moments could be seized later to look more closely. As one forty-five approached, the scoring was still not finished, but Dick Santos volunteered to stay behind and, with the help of Shelby and Langley, complete the scoring and then bring the results to the courtroom.

Even if time turned out to be extremely limited later in the afternoon as jurors were struck, the defense lawyers would have a double-check on the pro-defense/pro-plaintiff index for each juror, both the assessment from Sunday's review and the score sheet from the questionnaire.

When Court reconvened at one forty-five, Judge Andrews signaled Fred Bates the time had come to conduct voir dire examination of the jury on behalf of plaintiffs. "I'm going to keep my questions short and sweet," he told himself. "The more case-specific information that comes out of this questioning, the more the defendants are helped. It's best to keep the info to a minimum." Consequently, Bates took about fifteen minutes to ask a relatively few, canned questions and sat down.

Mansfield was up next. He began by challenging the jurors: "I have heard it said that a corporation cannot get a fair trial in Phoenix County. How many of you believe a corporation *can* get a fair trial in Phoenix County?" Most hands rose. Mansfield continued, "In this case, a child died, and others were seriously injured in an accident. How many of you think a corporation should be found not guilty if that's what the evidence shows, even though some Phoenix County residents have died or been injured in an accident?" About half the hands rose. Mansfield then repeated the question row-by-row, asking those who did not raise their hands to explain, and taking advantage of the opportunity to stress and educate the jury on the necessity of finding wrongdoing before deciding liability or assessing damages. Ultimately, as the proposition was explained, nearly all jurors agreed.

Mansfield continued probing into the manner in which sympathy would impact their decisions. He eventually turned to questions of kinship/friendship with parties and witnesses.

When Mansfield had finished and Born began his voir dire, he continued where Mansfield had left off, delving into the all-important personal relationships and business relationships, including the delicate subject of unmarried cohabitation. Born eventually asked if they were familiar with road hazard insurance and was elated that most of them knew about it. "Excellent," he said to himself, "those who know about road hazard insurance will be aware that even a brand-new tire can be destroyed by a road hazard, precisely why no warranty covers it and insurance must be bought." In closing, he asked whether there was anyone in the courtroom who would think he hadn't gotten a good tire if it lasted six years and held up under nearly sixty thousand miles of travel. Not a single hand was raised. "I take it all of you would consider you had bought a good tire if it gave that kind of service, six years and nearly sixty thousand miles?" Every hand rose.

Born cut short his voir dire because he had been the last of the three lawyers to question the jurors and he could see they were growing tired and restless as the afternoon wore on. Further questions would alienate them, Born thought, definitely not a good idea.

However, the voir dire had been fruitful for the defense, disclosing no less than twenty jurors who by kinship or other relationships to plaintiffs were due to be struck for cause. In addition, Bates was willing to dismiss a few others by mutual consent of defense counsel, including one man whom Bates called a "religious nut," who did not believe any person should judge any other person.

As a result of the strikes for cause and consensual strikes, the jury pool was down to about fifty-six potential jurors. It was not a good defense pool, but it was far better than the overall list the defendants had reviewed on Sunday.

"Would you like for me to give you a group of about thirty to choose from, to choose twelve jurors and two alternates, or would you prefer to strike alternately from the entire pool?" Judge Andrews asked.

"How would the thirty be selected?" Born asked.

"I'd have the Clerk pull their names from a box," the Judge said.

Born's hair nearly stood on end remembering the last time he had seen the Clerk draw names from a box, when the grand jury was drawn in February. Almost visibly shuddering, Born said he would much prefer to strike from the entire group, and the other lawyers went along.

The striking process began, Bates striking and eliminating a juror and then Mansfield and Born alternately getting a strike so that there were equal plaintiff/defense strikes.

Predictably, Bates systematically struck all white jurors. There had been fifteen white jurors in the pool, forty-one African Americans. Bates had a total of twenty-one strikes and the defendants together had twenty-one strikes. This meant Bates could use fifteen of his twenty-one strikes to eliminate all the white jurors. There were white jurors the defense also did not want, but they struck just one white juror, knowing that Bates was determined in any event to strike all whites. The result was that the twelve-person jury so selected was all African-American; one of the two alternates was a white woman.

Born had his *Batson* challenge ready, written motion and brief, and handed the papers to Judge Andrews as

Brad Mansfield joined in the motion. Born pointed out that under *Batson*, systematic striking of minority jurors was presumptively illegal, shifting the burden of proof to the striking lawyer to establish a valid race-neutral reason for each strike. The race-neutral reason could not be merely subjective but would have to be supported by the record. Born argued Bates should state for the record his reasons for the strikes of white jurors.

Bates attempted to state his reasons, but there were three or four for whom he had no race-neutral reasons. He said he personally knew these persons who were either Republicans or were in favor of tort reform. Born responded that mere political affiliation was not a valid ground for a strike, and that Bates' understanding of the jurors' position on tort reform was not a matter of record in the case. Born silently wondered why Bates had not asked the jurors their attitudes about punitive damages or tort reform during voir dire, so as to lay a foundation for an ostensibly race-neutral basis for striking white jurors, who would be likely to favor tort reform - anathema to plaintiff lawyers, like Bates. But no such questions had been asked. Hence, there was no evidence in the record supporting Bates' stated reason for the strikes.

Alton Fox then stepped into the argument and mentioned a post-*Batson* decision of the U. S. Supreme Court which had backtracked on the *Batson* rule, stating the burden of proof under the newer ruling was not on Bates, but on the defendants, to prove Bates acted discriminatorily.

Dave Thompson had an answer. Even though the U.

S. Supreme Court had changed its ruling on burden of proof, the South Carolina courts had not changed their own formulation of the rule, and still followed the original *Batson* decision imposing the burden of proof on the striking party, Bates in this case.

Judge Andrews retired for some thirty minutes to consider the question, returning to announce that, in his opinion, South Carolina would continue to follow the rule placing on Bates the burden of proving race-neutral reasons for the systematic striking of white jurors. "I find that two white jurors, John Salmon and Walter Jones, were struck without an adequate race-neutral reason. I am therefore going to restore them to the eligible pool along with the last two black jurors selected, which will provide a mini-pool of four jurors for further strikes. I will give each side one strike, and the two jurors not struck will be selected as members of the jury."

Bates again struck one of the white jurors, Walter Jones, whom he had previously struck. The defense then struck one of the black jurors who had received low ratings in the Sunday assessments and on the scorecard from noon earlier in the day. The jury selected then comprised eleven African Americans and one white person. There were seven men and five women. More than half had had some type of automotive-related experience, and half of them came from areas of Phoenix County other than where the plaintiffs resided.

Born immediately reasserted the *Batson* challenge, pointing out that, if there was no race-neutral reason for Bates' striking of Walter Jones the first time, there was still no race-neutral basis for striking him the second time. The Court overruled the reasserted motion.

Fred Bates then moved the Court to continue the case until Thursday to allow the plaintiffs to take an emergency interlocutory appeal to the South Carolina Supreme Court to reverse Judge Andrews' decision on the *Batson* challenge. The Court refused the delay and asked the selected jurors to take their places in the jury box. The Judge cautioned the jury in strong language not to discuss the case with anyone, and to report to him any attempt by anyone to talk with them about the case.

"All right. Let's be back in Court tomorrow morning at nine o'clock ready to make opening statements," Judge Andrews directed. "We'll be in recess until that time."

Lawyers, selected jurors and struck jurors, and Dick Santos left the courtroom. The defense lawyers went together to Rusty Loman's office to take measures of the day's happenings.

"I feel like I've been spinning around in a whirlwind," said Born. "We've gotten ourselves a jury, and I have the impression we ought to be happy, that it's about as good as we could've hoped for, but I don't know. We've been so frantic, I feel like we've been choosing jurors by-the-numbers, with Dick Santos' input, and I don't really know who we've chosen. There was no time to go back into the questionnaires."

"While you were arguing the *Batson* challenge, I was putting together the questionnaires and trying to get a sense for the jury," Santos said. "The average age of your jury is about thirty-six, but that's really misleading because you have one who's sixty-six and one who's seventy. Take them out and you have a very young jury. As you know, our case plays better with older jurors. Having said that, I think the jury is nothing short of miraculous considering the original list we were working with yesterday. Your final jury includes just two people that were on our 'Don't want' list, though I grant you there are several others we could do without. It's hard to pick out a natural leader among the group. But, with the automotive experience - which is favorable - the relatively good marital status of most jurors (married jurors tending to be more conservative than unmarried ones), I think you've got a chance."

"You mean we've succeeded in moving from 'impossible' to 'just barely possible'?" Brad Mansfield asked.

Santos smiled, "I guess, realistically, that's about the size of it - which is not to understate a prodigious achievement. I think you could see on the faces of the plaintiffs' lawyers that they no longer see the case as a slam dunk. It's some cause for keeping our chins up."

Meanwhile, Bates was talking with Ripps and Fox about the jury, trying to decide if they should simultaneously attempt an appeal while proceeding with the trial. "I don't like it, but I'm afraid we may be stuck with it. Even if the Supreme Court gave us an emergency hearing on Wednesday, and even if it ruled with us, it would be too late to reconstitute the jury. The jury pool's been sent home, except for the twelve, and two alternates. So, if we were successful, the best we'd get is a continuance, and maybe no trial before next February—I think the August docket is full. I'm not willing to wait."

"I'm afraid we'll spend all this time and energy, and there'll be a mistrial, or we could even lose, and we'll still have to come back and try it all over again or possibly appeal," said Ripps. "I don't feel all that comfortable with this jury, especially with that white guy, Salmon, on the panel. I'm not sure we shouldn't appeal."

"Who's got the time to work up the papers, Jack?" Bates asked. And how long would it take us to get the transcript? Remember, we'd have to have the transcript of all the voir dire questioning as well as the *Batson*. I've got all I can do to get ready for tomorrow and the next day here in the courtroom. So do you, Jack. So does Alton."

"Look, fellows," Fox interjected, "at the risk of stepping out of my proper role, let me remind you the plaintiffs are all black, one of them is the Sheriff of this county, there's a death, there's brain damage, there're other serious injuries, the defendants are two big out-of-state corporations that are household names, and the jury has eleven blacks and one white on it. I'll take those odds any day. If we can't win with those odds, we're damn poor lawyers or they're damned Clarence Darrows. Let's go win this thing."

"I'm in," smiled Bates.

"I guess I'm in," Ripps said resignedly.

CHAPTER TWENTY-EIGHT

THE OPENINGS

Dick Santos had fulfilled his mission and bade fare-well at early breakfast on this second day of trial. It was hard to see him go. He had become an integral part of the Universal team, and his departure provoked an eerie feeling that an ally had deserted. He would leave Born and company to their own devices henceforth and would experience none of the dreaded impact of the inevitable verdict.

It seemed strange to walk into the courtroom that Tuesday morning and find it so empty, so hollow sounding that whispers seemed amplified into loud echoes, sharply contrasting with the previous day. The jury was assembling in the jury room across in the Annex, the Judge had not arrived, and the Universal team found itself alone for a few moments in the Phoenix County halls of justice. "I am more concerned with what can happen outside these walls than inside," Born said to Thompson, who nodded grimly.

It was not long before the Tergano team came in, then the plaintiffs' team. Born and Thompson noted once again that "the" tire was strangely missing. He asked Fox its whereabouts. "Oh, you want the tire now? It's in the trunk of my car," Fox advised.

"I'd like to have it in the courtroom. Could you get it?" Born asked. Fox agreed, left the courtroom and returned a few minutes later with the tire which he placed between two rows of "pews" in the spectators' area of the courtroom, invisible from the jury box.

There were too many individual plaintiffs to sit at counsel's table, and Bates was not sure he wanted them so close at hand anyway. So, on the first row in the spectators' section directly behind the table occupied by plaintiffs' counsel sat Sam Johnson, Bess Johnson, Katyna Johnson, Doretta Anchrum, Jimason Anchrum, and the Millers.

John Frey sat with Tergano's counsel as company representative and Theo Burton sat with Universal's lawyers as the Universal representative. In the spectator section sat Bert Sayre, unsuccessfully trying to be inconspicuous in a nearly empty courtroom. Tergano expected some litigation liaison reps to come later, but none were there on this first Tuesday of trial.

Judge Andrews, nearly always punctual, came into the courtroom, inquired if all jurors had arrived, then asked that they be ushered in to take their seats in the courtroom. The jurors entered the courtroom led by a Sheriff's deputy. Born had made a motion that State Troopers, or someone not connected with Sam Johnson's Sheriff Department be the keeper of the jurors, but the Court had not acted on the motion. Born did not like what he saw but said nothing.

After a few introductory comments, the Court nodded to Fred Bates to begin his opening statement. Bates gathered his legal pad and other papers and went to the lectern where he began addressing the jury.

He used no visual aids, but spoke to the jury about a blow-out, an out-of-control van, and death and injuries. He noted that Sarena Miller would have no life, that Jimason Anchrum would have only a custodial future. He said his side would prove there was contamination that got in the tire while it was being manufactured and that the van had a load design which caused it to go out of control.

After detailing the fateful climax of Bess Johnson's day trip, Fred Bates seemed to be building up to the strong emotional pitch everyone was expecting. "Now, that's what happened to those lovely people. But let's talk about why did it happen. The question is, why will Jimmy" - he sometimes called Jimason "Jimmy" - "why will Jimmy never work meaningfully? Why must Bess Johnson live the rest of her life without teeth?"

Dave Thompson, listening to this argument, and trying to decide how to deal with it, was remembering Carl Heimat's "why did she have to die" arguments at the mock trial. It was beginning to be effective with these jurors, Thompson thought.

But just at this high emotional moment, Bates got legalistic with the jurors. "We contend that it was the joint and concurrent negligence of Tergano Motor Corporation in and about the design of the Logos van four by four and the fault also of Universal Tire Company which made those tires. Now, the Judge will instruct you on the law at the close of this case, but I used the words joint and concurrent negligence, which is like concurrent and combining negligence. The theory of combined and concurrent negligence is this…," and Bates went off into a long explanation about joint and concurrent negligence. Then Bates began telling the jury about the South Carolina Extended Manufacturer's Liability Doctrine.

"He's destroyed the momentum of the emotional buildup with this lawyer talk," Thompson whispered to Born. "I've never made an opening statement before, and I've only heard one other made, but even I can see he lost an opportunity." Born nodded.

Bates continued, "The defendant Universal will tell you the tire had some wear and some age, but here's the fact: a tire is supposed to be designed to hold together and not blow out if there is any tread at all left on it. Only when the tread is gone, and you wear into the carcass should there ever be a problem. There's still lots of tread on this tire and it should have held up." However, Bates did not show the tire to the jury.

Bates argued that well designed vans do not go out of

control when a blowout occurs on a straight road and that control was lost in this case because the center of gravity had been placed too far back, where it acted together with the drag of the deflated tire to pull the van leftward. He promised the jury it would be able to see some of this happening on video tapes made by Tergano itself.

The plaintiffs' lawyer closed by asking the jury to give close attention to the medical testimony which would show the horrible consequences to those who "trustingly used products put into the market by people and companies that had a callous and reckless lack of regard for human life and product safety."

The jury sat attentively but emotionless as Bates concluded his opening statement. A local reporter had come into the courtroom as Bates was finishing his presentation and began taking notes.

"He never showed the tire to the jury!" Born and Thompson said to each other in nearly inaudible synchrony, quickly recognizing an exposed jugular. "You've got to hit that hard, Dave. He didn't want the jury to see the tire with their own eyes, at least not yet. The jury will think Bates wanted to keep it from them - as he did. When you show it to them, you'll get credibility," Born advised. "I was right about one other thing, too, Dave. Carl Heimat did a better job. Not that this was a bad job, just lacked the drama, the electric spark." Thompson nodded. To himself Born noted, "Fred never made the mock orange reference I expected. He may be saving it for the closing argument."

Brad Mansfield gathered his papers and moved to the lectern. He acknowledged it was a tragedy that the accident had occurred leaving "a beautiful, lovely child dead, a really nice young loving boy brain damaged" and others seriously injured. He stressed that the jury's job was to decide "whether or not the tragedy was caused by Tergano Motors, or was it caused by Universal Tire, or was it caused by drivers and roads and things of this sort. Now the plaintiffs sit at this table," gesturing toward Bates, "Universal sits at that table, and we sit for Tergano at the far table. There are *two* defendants in this case, Universal and Tergano. *We are not the same.* We are both called defendants and we both have to share some duties. And, Mr. Born and I might have inadvertently dressed alike today, but we are not the same."

Born looked at Thompson. Loman looked at Born and Thompson. Theo Burton looked at all of them. They smiled knowingly and Born looked down at the table as he slowly shook his head, "Yep. I knew it would happen. They're really telling the jury this is a tire case, if they find anybody guilty, let it be Universal."

Mansfield continued by pointing out Bess Johnson had never driven a van before. It was a tragedy the tire blew out and it was a tragedy Bess Johnson was talking to Doretta Anchrum. "Now he's trying to blame Universal and Bess equally, or so it seems," Born thought. Born had always felt it was risky to blame Bess Johnson too much for the accident, as far as the jury was concerned, though he had little doubt that her driving was in fact the major ingredient of the wreck and injuries.

Mansfield related to the jury the events preceding the accident and suggested that on a clear, straight road, drivers tend to be lulled off their guards and can be startled by a sudden blowout. Born wished he would quit using that word "blowout" and use "rupture", instead, but Born realized it was a part of Mansfield's strategy to suggest that the culprits were Bess Johnson's inattention, coupled with a blowout of a questionable tire. Mansfield did say the van should have been controllable with just one or two fingers on the steering wheel in the event of a blowout, seeming by that remark to stress most strongly Bess Johnson's driving.

"Did Bess freeze when the blowout happened? Did she fail to make a move? I don't know. A lot was happening that day, and I'm not sure we'll ever know exactly why a wreck occurred. Bess and Doretta are going to tell you they recall at some point Bess turned the wheel to the right. But this is a safe vehicle. When you turn it to the right it goes to the right. When you turn it to the left, it goes to the left," Mansfield contended.

Mansfield talked about the plaintiffs' van expert and pointed out that the expert himself owned a Tergano Logos van. "He must not think it's terribly unsafe if he drives one himself." Mansfield ticked off the safety features of the van, dwelling a little longer on seat belts than on any other safety point. Born and Thompson thought it strange for Mansfield to stress seat belts, since he had said he would not mention them and had asked Universal not to mention them. Maybe he thinks he is being subtle, Born thought.

After stressing the safeness of the van, Mansfield closed by saying "It was unfortunate what happened, but it was not our fault. The plaintiffs will be offering their evidence before I get a chance to talk with you again. I'm going to ask you to remember some of the promises I got you to make, when I was asking you questions before you were selected, promises about keeping an open mind. I want you to remember to respect your community and abide by the rules. Thank you for your time. Mr. Born will be speaking to you next about Universal."

The Judge looked at Born, as did the plaintiffs' lawyers. Born nodded toward Thompson. Thompson asked for a few minutes' break "to get set up," which the Court granted.

Born went to retrieve the tire from between the spectator pews as Thompson brought out a large tomato-red poster and several smaller posters. "I could see the jury was getting tired and needed a break," Thompson said to Born and Loman. "I wanted them to be fresh and comfortable when I talked with them.

"Exactly right," said Born. Then, looking at Thompson, Born said "Dave, you are better than either of those two lawyers you just heard. You'll do great. Just remember one thing: when you stand before the jury and look them in the eye, you are not only Dave Thompson. In the jurors' eyes, you are Universal, you *are* the client.

If they have positive feelings about you, they will have a positive impression about Universal. Go get 'em!"

As Thompson was about to begin, Alton Fox asked the Court if counsel could approach the bench. Fox had seen one of Thompson's small posters with wording from the state law having to do with requirements for tire tread depth, and he objected that Thompson should not use that exhibit or make comments about the tread being worn so thin it was illegal. The Judge said he would allow Thompson to use the exhibit, because the Court intended to instruct the jury about the statute anyway. However, he warned Thompson not to say anything in opening statement about the tire being illegal unless he was very sure it could be proved.

At last Thompson was able to proceed. He walked toward the jury and gently set aside the lectern Bates and Mansfield had used. Thompson had no notes or papers in his hands as he stood directly in front of the jury and began with a "Good morning," accompanied by his winsome smile. He introduced himself and those at his table, Born, Loman and Burton, and told the jury that he too was from a small town in North Carolina which was "a lot like Groveton."

Born carefully watched the jury. They were interested, they were listening, they seemed to like Thompson, but nothing more could be learned from their mostly expressionless faces.

He told them he was sorry, sorry about the accident, sorry about the tragic death, sorry about the serious injuries, just sorry about it all. He slowly moved up and down the rail separating the jury from him, trying to avoid a squeaky board he had encountered early on in his presentation.

"You are here today to do something very important, you're here to do justice. I'm not saying justice and sympathy can't work together. Sometimes you can be sympathetic, yet render a just verdict. A lot of times you can't. It is extremely important to take that sympathy and put it aside just a little bit to try to do justice, it's important. We lawyers for Universal Tire are going to do our best to present a case to you that will make your job less difficult. Because, hopefully, when we have presented our case, you will say there is only one result you can reach."

Thompson mentioned a number of facts which no one disputed, largely the fact of the accident, the events leading up to it and the death and injuries.

He agreed there was a Universal tire on the van which ruptured, but he emphasized that the rupture in itself did not make the company liable, that Universal would be liable only if the tire was defective when it left Universal's hands some six years earlier.

Thompson rolled out a brand-new tire, same type as the one that had ruptured, and said, "This is what the tire looked like when it was new. Just look at all that tread. Universal made several hundred thousands of those tires and not once, ladies and gentlemen of the jury, not once did Universal get a complaint of a rupture, not once, out of several hundred thousand. Universal Tire Company is proud of this tire, it's a good tire and it gives good service."

"Now, let's look at the tire that was involved in the accident," Thompson continued, putting down the brand-new tire and picking up the ruptured tire. "The plaintiffs' attorney didn't show you this tire, as you will notice. He talked about a lot of things, but he didn't show you this tire."

Alton Fox rose from his chair and objected. "Your Honor, it's improper to comment on what the Plaintiffs did or didn't do in opening."

Thompson started to respond, but the Judge simply said, "Let's just move on."

"Wow! What a hit!" Born was thinking, "Dave really scored some points there. If Alton's objection did anything, it just made the jury more keenly aware what a telling blow Dave had struck: plaintiffs were so embarrassed to be claiming the tire was defective they didn't want the jury to see it, but by contrast Dave *wanted* them to see it."

"Well, this is the tire, and I am going to tell you some more things about it that plaintiffs' attorney didn't mention," Thompson continued, twisting the same knife deeper into plaintiffs' wounded opening statement. "One thing Mr. Bates didn't tell you is that this tire had nearly sixty thousand miles on it." Then he repeated in his slow, measured cadence, "Sixty thousand miles. How much is sixty thousand miles? Well, in addition to the numbers on the odometer, it's the same as more than twice around the world, with another ten thousand miles to go after the first two trips around the world."

"Another factor is, the tire was nearly six years old," Thompson told the jury, all the while walking up and down along the rail in front of the jury, an arm through the tire's doughnut hole and then bent back to steady the part of the tire resting on his shoulder, occasionally pointing at the tire with his free hand.

He paused to rest the tire in the seat of a nearby chair as he reached for the tomato-red poster. He began to point, one after the other, to various aspects of the tire listed on the poster. "The tire was practically bald in spots, including the area right near the rupture," he noted, picking up the tire again and holding it where the jury could see the worn spots. "How badly worn is the tire overall? It was worn so badly that it was an illegal tire."

Alton Fox, stung once more by a telling point, objected, and the Court simply reminded Thompson to tell the jury what the law is and what he expected the evidence to show. Fox asked to approach the bench for a side-bar conference, and Thompson said aloud so the jury heard him, "Your Honor, I didn't interrupt them during their opening statement. Well, let's approach."

"Score another one!" Born thought. "The jury will not like this older lawyer interrupting this young lawyer whom they obviously like."

To make the effect even better, the Judge told the jury after the side-bar conference: "Ladies and gentlemen, Mr. Thompson will be allowed to finish his statement. I call to your attention that Mr. Thompson will discuss a South Carolina statute, and it will be for you at the appropriate time to decide whether this particular tire violates that statute, and of course Mr. Thompson will have to back up his claims with evidence. That said, Mr. Thompson is free to continue his presentation."

Thompson had walked briefly to the Universal table while the Judge was instructing the jury, "It's going perfectly, Dave, the jury believes you and I think will regard the plaintiffs' lawyers as obstructing you in your trying to give them the facts."

"I got that last one, about `I didn't interrupt you' from Herbert," Thompson grinned, referring to one of the firm's other senior litigators.

Thompson showed the jury his poster with the South Carolina statute on it about tread depth and told the jury this tire had worn so thin it was illegal to use it on the South Carolina highways. He pointed out the nail, still embedded in the tire, obviously well-worn and indicating it had been there a long time. Then Thompson turned the tire so the jury could see the innerliner and the improper plug repair. He also noted the dried, once-sticky gunk on the innerliner from the spray-in tire sealant the owner had used in a vain effort to stop or slow down leaks in the tire.

Thompson continued down the checklist on the large tomato-red poster board, noting lack of rotation, lack of balancing, chronic underinflation, lack of any significant servicing. Then Thompson went back to the top of his list to emphasize that, despite the abuse seen by this tire, it had been a good one lasting nearly sixty thousand miles.

"Well, you may say to yourself, why is Universal Tire

Company here?" Thompson asked, rhetorically. "Why are they sitting at that table? I mean, after all, we have a tire that had six years on it, gave good service for sixty thousand miles."

Born was inwardly applauding, saying to himself, "You've got it, Dave! Involve your jurors in the questions and answers. Show a little righteous indignation for being here at all - not too much, just enough, after all there's brain damage here, and death."

"Why are we here?" Thompson repeated the refrain. And then he answered it, "We are here because this good tire, past the end of its useful life, hit a road hazard which destroyed its internal structure. And plaintiffs' own expert is going to admit this tire impacted a road hazard. Again, why are we here?"

Thompson had a serious but frustrated look on his face as he stood with outstretched arms, palms up, in front of the intently concentrating jurors, repeating his powerful "Why are we here" refrain. "We are here because plaintiffs' lawyers went overseas and got this Mr. Kelly, all the way from Australia, to come tell you something was wrong with this tire. Mainly, he's going to tell you that six years before the accident some tire worker touched this tire with a sweaty hand."

Fox objected that Thompson was mischaracterizing Kelly's testimony. "Overruled," the Court said.

Again, Thompson turned the objection into an advantage. "I apologize about that. I'm sorry. As the Court instructed you, we will have objections from time to time, but we apologize for that."

By now, Fox had made several objections and had been rebuffed on all of them. The jury hopefully was getting the idea that Fox was the one who should be doing the apologizing, and would be coming to Dave Thompson's rescue, Born thought.

Thompson got in one more jab at expert Kelly, warning the jury that Kelly would tell them the tire was defective, even though in an earlier case "where someone else was paying him" Kelly had said any tire that fails from a defect will do so within the first six months.

Then came the conclusion of Thompson's opening: "I can present my client's case as well as God will allow me to do it and so can Mr. Born and Mr. Loman, but only you can do justice. Justice will only be done in this case if Universal is judged by the quality of its product. Justice. Everybody wants to be judged by the contents of their character. All Universal wants is to be judged by the quality of its product. This product, this tire, was good. That's what the evidence is going to show. At the end of the evidence, we are going to come in and we are going to ask you, the overseers of justice, the stewards of justice, to do justice in this case. I want to say thank you."

There was a brief break and Thompson was literally mobbed by both the Universal team and the Tergano team. The reaction was, if anything, more effusive than at the mock trial, only this was the real trial and these were the real lawyers, no stand-ins here. No one outside the tight Universal team had expected Thompson to make the opening statement, and none had expected it to be so effective, so hard-hitting beneath Thompson's warmth. "What a tremendous job!" Brad Mansfield said. "Outstanding," Chet Bernhardt echoed.

"You couldn't have done a finer job, Dave," Ted Born told him.

Even Alton Fox came over to compliment him, while Fred Bates and Jack Ripps conferred grimly at counsel's table.

The break had ended and already Thompson was reaching for his trial notebook, to be ready for cross-examining upcoming witnesses as the evidence was about to begin.

The first witness was Lonnie Gresham, who had been driving behind Bess Johnson for several miles just preceding the accident. He said he saw the Logos "suddenly drop" to the side but did not remember which side dropped. Then the van swerved, first to the right and then to the left. He did not notice the Logos running over any object in the road before he saw it drop. On cross-examination by Chet Bernhardt, he recalled the van seemed to accelerate after it went out of control, and never saw a brake light come on. Rusty Loman questioned Gresham for Universal and brought out that Highway 53 was in bad enough condition it had been resurfaced a short time before trial, leaving the suggestion that perhaps there had been some potholes in the road before the resurfacing.

Sam Johnson took the stand next. He testified he

was the owner of the Logos and told how his niece Bess Johnson had borrowed it. Fred Bates tried to make it appear that Sam regularly checked - at least visually - the air pressure in the tires, something he had been taught at police academy. He claimed he never put a plug in the tire to repair a leak. He testified - to Fred Bates' surprise - that he had never rotated the tires, testimony different from his deposition where he said he had rotated them once. He said he did not remember hitting road hazards during the last thousand miles before the accident. He said neither he, nor anyone to whom he had lent the car, ever noticed or mentioned any shakes, shimmies or vibrations.

On cross examination, Ted Born brought out Sam Johnson's long experience in law enforcement and how vehicular safety was part of his responsibilities. Nevertheless, Johnson confessed he had never heard of tread wear indicators, the little "bridges", 2/32-inch-high, running from tread to tread across the tread grooves, to indicate how close the wear on the treads was approaching the permissible limit of 2/32 inch. Johnson expressed the belief all four tires on the van were worn about equally - which showed he knew little about the condition of any of his tires. He said he was not aware of the nail puncture in the tire.

Born asked, "Did it ever occur to you that relatives and friends and family might be riding in this van with tires in the condition of this one and did you feel any sense of responsibility for what could happen to them riding on such tires?"

Sam Johnson seemed flustered trying to answer, "That's the only time Bess asked to borrow it. To my knowledge, as far as I knew, she was going by herself. I didn't know she was going to ride the other passengers, but, still, as far as talking about relatives and all, as far as I know, it was safe to loan to folks."

The next witness was the State Trooper who investigated the accident, whose deposition was read into the record, since he had resigned and moved beyond the Court's subpoena power. No surprises there. Then came the live testimony of Doretta Anchrum and Bess Johnson, who testified very similarly to their depositions, except Bess now testified she remembered looking at the tires when she stopped for gas, and none of the tires looked low. Bess Johnson revealed she had been reimbursed for lost wages by insurance her Uncle Sam Johnson had on the van, but there was a subrogation claim for reimbursement if Bess won her lawsuit. Chet Bernhardt was first to take Bess Johnson on cross-examination, followed by Dave Thompson. Thompson cringed when Bernhardt asked her how she thought she would look after completion of her dental work: "Then you will have perfect teeth, won't you, or perfect false teeth?"

Bess Johnson answered, "They're false. They can't be perfect to me."

Bernhardt still had not learned his lesson, asking her, "Your smile then will be better than mine, won't it?" Thompson cringed again.

"I sure hope so," she answered. The jurors and lawyers convulsed with momentarily unsmotherable laughter.

How insensitive can you be, Born wondered. Granted, Bess Johnson played loosely with the truth on some important points, but she *did* lose her remaining teeth in the accident, and to suggest she was going to have "perfect" teeth or a better smile than this white lawyer from Atlanta was the height of insensitivity. Score one for the plaintiffs, Born thought. He had seen Thompson's cringes and knew exactly what Dave was thinking. Chet Bernhardt was a nice fellow and a good lawyer, but he had on blinders this time.

Dave Thompson's cross-examination was gentle and polite, but he reminded her she had said in her deposition she didn't notice the tires, whether any were low on air, when she stopped for gas the day of the accident. She simply said it had happened a long time ago and she really couldn't remember, acknowledging that her deposition testimony might have been correct, and she really did not notice the tires. Jack Ripps tried to rehabilitate her testimony about looking at the tires while at the gas station, but he withdrew his questioning when shown the exact wording from her deposition.

Thompson returned to the table and whispered to Born and Loman, "She obviously manufactured that business about her looking at the tires, and someone from their side failed to go back to see what she said in her deposition. That lie boomeranged."

"Yeah, score one for the good guys, might even make up for Chet Bernhardt's blunder," Born said. "Still can't understand why Chet would ask not one, but *two*, questions like that!"

The Court recessed for the day after the conclusion of Bess Johnson's cross-examination.

The plaintiffs' lawyers retired to their rented storefront space on the square. Sam Johnson stopped by with them briefly.

"How'd you think it went today, Mr. Fred?" Johnson asked.

"Oh, I think pretty well, Sam. I gotta say that jury's hard to read, but you have to think of everything that happened today as a skirmish. The war's not really being fought on the witness stand. It's also being fought - and, I think, won - out there where you and the other plaintiffs are sitting, every time somebody takes Jimmy by the hand or elbow and ushers him to the bathroom. It's being won by that empty space next to the Millers, where Sarena is *not sitting*, where she will never sit," Bates answered.

"That black lawyer got the attention of some of those jurors. Don't know how much, or whether they'll swing, but he made 'em listen. I thought you said that fellow Born was going to do the talking," Sam Johnson commented.

"Well, I thought sure he would, Sam. He's experienced, and this young black twerp ain't got experience, and I didn't see how they could take a chance like they did. I gotta admit, though, Sam, you're right. I was impressed. He did a fine job," Bates admitted. "But don't be too concerned about what's happening inside the courtroom rails. When the jury finally has to make a decision, they're going to forget everything that went on, except a few things that no amount of talking can change: Sarena's dead, Jimmy's brain-damaged, you're the Sheriff, they know you, and this is Phoenix County."

"I'm sure you know what you're doing, but I don't hardly know any of those jurors," Sam Johnson said. "Well, I know some of their family members, and Bess says she thinks she went to school with one of them, not a real close friend, but at least she thinks she knows one of 'em. I just want to be sure you know I ain't got this jury in the palms of my hands. We can't necessarily depend on friendship to win this."

"We're doing all we can do, and we'll continue to evaluate the situation as we go along," Ripps said.

"All I want is to be sure we win. I mean be *sure*. My folks are countin' on me, and I'm countin' on you. Don't forget I brought you this case, told everybody it was a sure winner. I don't want to be - no, I'm not gonna' be - the first one to be a loser in a big case here in my own coun-ty." Sam Johnson, the Sheriff, was not smiling. "Well, I'll go and let y'all work. I'll be here at eight o'clock in the morning."

When the Sheriff was gone, Alton Fox looked at Bates and Ripps, "I heard what you said to Sam, and it helped reassure me too. But I didn't think we had a great day today. Fooled the hell out of me when young Thompson got up to make the opening, fooled the hell out of me even more to see what a good job he did. I had to make those objections, but they backfired. I understand we're just dealing with opening salvos, but if this was a boxing match, I'd have to score round one for the defendants, or at least for Universal."

"Relax, Alton, trust me," Bates said.

Across the square in Rusty Loman's office, the defense lawyers had had a similar discussion before going their separate ways. Congratulations after congratulations were being heaped on Dave Thompson for his opening. Overall, the mood was guardedly positive, although nobody was under the misimpression that good performances would necessarily translate into ultimate victory. "One day at a time," Born said. "If we do everything we can, to do a better job than they do every single day of trial, that'll be all we can do. Beyond that, it's out of our hands. Can anybody read that jury?"

Nobody could read the stony-faced jury. It was mostly a very attentive jury. There was one older woman, Jamie Acton, who seemed to nod off some, either that or she was in deep meditation. There were two younger male jurors on the front of the two rows in the jury box, who seemed unimpressed with the whole proceedings. For the most part, the jury was expressionless. Perhaps they were intimidated by the Judge's stern words at every break and every recess, not to talk about this case among themselves until final deliberations and never discuss the case with anyone, even family members, and report to him anyone who attempted to discuss the case with them. They were comforting words to defense counsel, who had requested but not received jury sequestration.

Ted Born decided he would call Carl Heimat and leave a message on his voice mail about the trial, so someone in their Greenville office would know what was happening. Images flashed back in his mind of farewells he and Dave Thompson had received from other lawyers in the firm before setting out to Groveton for the trial. He especially remembered the grim, almost embarrassed look on the face of a partner conducting a litigation group meeting a week earlier. There had been law students present at the meeting who had come to work at the firm as summer associates. "Ted and Dave will be going to Phoenix County for THE trial next week. We wish them good luck," the group leader had said. Born knew what he was thinking: what kind of impression will our firm make on these young summer associates if a client gets hit with one of the biggest judgments ever rendered against a defendant in South Carolina? Many cases went unnoticed, but EVERYBODY knew about *this* case. Everybody was certain we would lose it; the only question would be "how much"?

He called Heimat at eight fifteen that evening and left the following message on his voice mail:

We struck a jury, about as good as we could expect, but still a big problem. Dave gave a super opening statement, wowed everybody including, I think, Fred Bates. We had a half day of testimony this afternoon following the opening statements - mainly Sam Johnson, Doretta Anchrum and Bess Johnson. They read the deposition to the jury of the State Trooper who was at the scene of the accident. It all went better than I expected. There's a long way to go, but so far we've avoided any big mistakes.

CHAPTER TWENTY-NINE

THE DESERT PALACE

When Al Gifford did not show up as Universal's representative at counsel's table in Groveton, plaintiffs tried to subpoena him, but the South Carolina state court subpoena was not valid in Georgia, where Gifford lived, not even under any interstate compacts for subpoena enforcement. To shore up Universal's opposition to the subpoena, Dave Thompson researched the question via modem from his laptop computer at the hotel in Columbia, then had the research printed out on one of the printers in Universal's war room at the motel. The next day, the Judge quashed the subpoena, and plaintiffs would have to rely solely on Gifford's deposition with regard to conditions in the Universal plant, with precious little in that deposition to provide any factual support for

Wrack Kelly's "sweat theory". Nor would plaintiffs find help elsewhere. They would not risk trying to call Theo Burton to the witness stand, having no idea what he might say.

Witnesses had come and gone, and it was now Thursday morning of the first week of trial as proceedings commenced with the reading of Al Gifford's deposition. The Gifford testimony was a largely irrelevant prelude to plaintiffs' star witness against Universal, expert tire witness Wrack Kelly, who immediately followed.

Kelly was in a professorial mode as he began his direct testimony. He had brought with him a small visual aid, approximately 8" X 10", comprising a picture of a tire innerliner with transparencies which could be flipped one-at-a-time over the innerliner to "build up" the tire from its component parts. Kelly was allowed to step down from the witness stand and position himself behind a small table, in front of the jury, on which his visual aid stood. He flipped transparencies and explained how a tire physically consisted of a number of different components, all vulcanized together to form a single tire, so simple looking, yet one of the marvels of modern technology. He returned to the witness stand to complete his testimony.

As he testified under Alton Fox's questioning, Ted Born noticed that Kelly was making less of his "sweat theory" than on his deposition. "This has to be a strategic retreat," Born thought. "My guess is, he realizes he has no evidence of human touching of tire components in the Universal plant and he can't use that unfortunate 'teach-ing videotape' to give credibility to the cockeyed theory, the way he did in the Houston case. Plus, the plaintiffs are probably gun-shy about the 'sweat theory' after all the criticism I piled on it in the summary judgment motion." Born's earlier deposition of Kelly had fairly well locked Kelly into a contamination theory of some kind, but whereas he had emphasized sweat as the likely contami-nant in his deposition, Kelly was now backing away from sweat specifically and vaguely fingered "contamination of some sort."

Born's cross examination of Kelly began about ten-thirty and ended about three o'clock, with a one-hour intervening lunchbreak. When Born finished, Chet Bernhardt asked a few questions about some tests Kelly had made demonstrating that vehicles are readily controllable when blowouts occur on straight roads. Then it was Alton Fox's turn to try to restore some credibility for Kelly on re-direct examination. Fox decided not even to try, just leave it alone.

At the break following Kelly's testimony, Marta Shelby came up to Ted Born and said, "You made him look like a fool. I began to feel sorry for him after the first five minutes when he said there are tires which will last forever and never wear out and you don't need to rotate or balance tires."

"I'm glad it came across that way to you," Born answered. "Before it's over, I think it will be even better because some things he said will tie in with our expert testimony, which is yet to come. And there was something else I don't think the jury consciously picked up on, but which they will remember when I remind them in my closing argument, something affecting his credibility. I want you to listen for it."

Born now found himself surrounded by Thompson, Loman, Burton and the Tergano lawyers. "Great job!" said Thompson, "I really liked that closing shot where you got him to admit he doesn't pay any taxes on his U. S. earnings. But your whole cross-examination was good."

"Real good," said Theo Burton, a man of relatively few words.

"You totally destroyed him," said Rusty Loman. "I don't know how much the jury took in, but surely they see him for what he is, a damned charlatan."

"Classic," said Brad Mansfield, "You must have read everything the guy has ever written and you laid these beautiful traps for him. I wish I had that on videotape."

"Couldn't possibly have done a better job, Ted. It was beautiful," Bernhardt said. "He admitted defects usually come to light within six months, and then when you asked how he squared that with his theory of manufacturing defects surviving for six years in this case, his only explanation was 'I said *usually*'. What a lame excuse. That jury has been inscrutable the whole trial, but even they smiled at that one."

"I like where you got him to admit he had advocated throwing tires away after six years, even if they have plenty of tread on them," Loman said. "He seemed to be conceding these tires had served their useful life before the accident."

"He didn't look at the wires under a microscope. Can you imagine that?" Bert Sayre said, joining the group. "But, when you showed him enlargements of the wires, he had to admit there were clusters of tensile fractures caused by impact. The other thing he hadn't done was check to see if the nail hole and plug repair leaked. Left himself wide open on that one, because he admits serious underinflation can quickly destroy the integrity of a tire."

"The best one," Thompson said, "was when you asked him if he would put the tire on his own car and he said `no'. Then you asked him if he thought the tire was safe for the Johnsons and Anchrums and Millers, and all he would answer is, `It's a bit of an ambiguous question,' and you let it go and didn't give him a chance to explain. Did you see the dirty looks the jury gave him on that one?"

"Actually, I was concentrating so hard on asking the right questions and asking them the right way and avoiding letting him take charge and control the cross-examination, I wasn't specifically conscious of the jury. I mean, I knew they were there, and I saw them out of the corner of my eye, and I thought I'd scored one with that question, but it's all a little bit of a blur to me now. One thing I was glad he admitted was that old and badly worn tires are more susceptible to failure from impacts - six times more vulnerable - than newer tires with plenty of tread. That should help a lot."

"Well, it's not *my* part of the case, of course," Mansfield said, "but he's so vague on contamination, what it is and why he thinks there was some, I think his whole testimony just reduces itself to mish-mash. He even admits the tire would have looked fine to the naked eye when it left the factory six or seven years ago. Seems to me that pretty well takes out any wantonness or any basis for punitive damages except, of course, in the wrongful death action where South Carolina law makes punitives the sole type of recoverable damages, applying a negligence standard for it, as best I can tell."

Nita Langley was all smiles as she finished restacking the exhibits used on Kelly's cross-examination and rearranging the big poster board enlargements. "That was wonderful," Langley said. "I had no idea a patent lawyer could do something like that. In fact, I've never seen or heard of a witness so annihilated, except maybe on TV."

"Thanks, Nita, for your help in reading my mind and pulling the exhibits I needed. Thank all of you for your great support that helped bring this about. Of course, I know we can win a lot of battles and lose the war. Here comes Judge Andrews. Looks like he is going to start up again. We'll talk about it all at the end of the day," Born said.

The remainder of the afternoon was spent reading medical depositions to the jury. All the defense lawyers were surprised at the amount of evidence, especially medical evidence, presented to the jury via reading depositions rather than by live testimony. Not only did the reading seem to bore the jury, but most of the questions had been asked in those depositions by defense counsel and had more of a defense slant than live testimony would have had. Of all the considerable medical evidence in the case, only the family doctor, an occupational therapist, and a child psychologist testified in person. Really the child psychologist testified only as a fact witness, not an expert, because Bates and Ripps had failed to pre-designate him as an expert, and thus he could express only very limited opinions.

Bates had decided he would not call Jimason to the witness stand. He considered Jimason unpredictable and felt that the youth could best be a "witness" by playing the role of robot led around by adults who ushered him everywhere, herding him by his elbow or holding his hand. Born objected to what he described as "testimony without the right of cross-examination," especially the exaggerated performance which had been taking place. The Judge warned the plaintiffs they risked a mistrial if he concluded the plaintiffs were unnecessarily making a "show" of Jimason outside the safeguards of testimony and cross-examination. Ripps said the defendants were callously insensitive to Jimason's need for help. However, after the Judge's warning, plaintiffs eased up somewhat on the hand and elbow holding and occasionally allowed Jimason to walk around unaccompanied.

Katyna testified briefly. She skipped up to the witness stand, pigtails bouncing as she went - all to the dismay of Bates and Ripps who wanted her to appear to be badly hurt. She simply verified she had been in the accident and had suffered a broken leg. The defense did not cross-examine her.

At the end of the day, the defense lawyers as usual went together to Rusty Loman's office, and the plaintiffs' lawyers went to their store-front space.

A transformation had slowly taken place among the defense lawyers. On Monday and on Tuesday morning, the Tergano lawyers had tried to distance themselves from Universal and its lawyers, at least while in the presence of the jury. Increasingly, the distance had narrowed, and Tergano's lawyers had been following Universal's lead on almost every development and move in the courtroom, to the point where they were now practically clinging to Born and Thompson. All the lawyers were very tired. All thought the trial thus far had gone well, but all thought the possibility of actually winning the case was still re-mote. For now, the Universal lawyers had earned a slight breather. Tomorrow would be Tergano's day, as plaintiffs' van expert, Peter Justin, would be testifying for probably most of the day.

"We'll be thinking about you as you burn the mid-night oil, Brad," Born teased. "For me, I'm going to have a nice shower—I feel sticky in this heat, even though I showered this morning - and then I'm going out for a real meal. I've been subsisting mainly off cans of cold soup as I've stayed and worked in my room every night this week. Thank God Rusty has made the arrangements for good lunches to be brought in, or I'd be suffering from beriberi or something. Then, after a nice dinner, I'm coming back and I'm going to go to bed by ten o'clock. It's been so long I've been to bed that early I might not go to sleep, even though I'm dead tired. Anybody want to join me for dinner?" Born asked.

Loman opted out, as he wanted to spend some time with his family in Groveton for a change, and of course Brad Mansfield had to be sure he was ready for Justin's cross-examination. Dave Thompson, as well as Bert Sayre and Theo Burton said they would come. "Do you need me tonight, Brad?" Bernhardt asked Mansfield. "I'll be glad to help if I can, but I know Justin is all yours." Mansfield said he would not need Bernhardt, at least not for a while, just would like for Bernhardt to check in with him after dinner, in case something came to Mansfield's mind they might need to discuss.

"Okay, I'll meet you Universal guys for dinner. When and where do we meet?" asked Chet Bernhardt.

"How about the Desert Palace?" asked Born. "At seven."

By seven o'clock, all five men had arrived at the restaurant and were seated. Born recommended the West Indies salad and a cup of gumbo for starters. "The food is spicy hot - that's why they call this place the Desert Palace even though it's located in a virtual rain forest. It's good, though." Born ordered a couple of bottles of good French Chardonnay. "Bert," he said, "I'm not even going to apologize for ordering the wine. I'm thanking you for indulging us, though. Our meal expense has been pretty modest. How much is a can of cold vegetable soup!"

"You've earned it," Sayre said. "All of you. I think we've definitely out-lawyered them."

"Be sure to put that in your report," Born joked,

referring to the fact Sayre sent an e-mail memo every evening to Universal's headquarters summarizing the day's events. Every time something good happened, Born would grin and say to Bert Sayre, "Put that in your report."

"How do you size up the jury's reactions so far?" Sayre asked, looking first at Born, then at Thompson.

"Don't look at me," Thompson smiled. "Just because I'm black, I can't read that jury any better than y'all can. Every once in a while, something will happen and they'll change their stony faces, but it's hard to say. Can you tell anything about it, Theo?"

"Sure can't. Sure can't. I think we're making some good points. They'd mean something to me, but I don't know about these jurors," Theo Burton answered. "See, I just think people, white or black, have to use their common sense about something like this, but I know so much about tires, and what I don't know is the people, these plaintiffs. So, I'm sort of reversed from the jurors. I know the tires but don't know the people; they know the people but don't know anything about tires, except what they've heard here. I'm afraid being black doesn't give me any answers."

"Being black or African American does create a kind of bond, I think," said Thompson. "We've all had a lot of common experiences and we can look at each other and know we've got a common heritage. It's natural. Like the churches we grew up in, with lots of differences but a lot of the same, and I feel welcome in any of those churches, regardless of the denomination, as long as it's Baptist," he joked. "Maybe it's like, if you see somebody across the room who's wearing a suit like yours or you're driving down the highway - yeah, that's a better analogy - you're driving down the highway and you see somebody in a car just like yours. Well, really, if you are into cars in a big way, you automatically feel a kinship. Or two people meet up in Oregon discover they're both from South Carolina, they're instantly kin. It's like that with us, except more so. It means you're my brother, more than just kin, you're my brother and my sister. It's all the suffering that we share that makes that bond what it is - the brotherhood and sisterhood of a suffering race and in particular a suffering minority race."

Born listened, not wanting to ask any leading questions.

Thompson continued, "This case has been a real experience for me. See, I know I'm African American. That's with me all the time, but for the second time in my life I've felt something crowd out the race consciousness. I feel like a lawyer, and it's crowding out everything else for periods of time - not for very long - but for some periods. I forget everything except I'm a lawyer and our defense is right and just, and that's what makes these weeks and months meaningful."

Burton looked at Thompson and asked, "And the first time?"

"The first time?" Thompson asked aloud, repeating the question, and then remembered what he had said. "Yes, this was the second time. The first time was when I realized that I was first and foremost human, and secondarily African American. Now, you may think that's a strange thing to say, but for a long time in my life I defined myself as black. I don't think I was just being narrow and parochial, because frankly, an awful lot of white people didn't seem to want to let me forget I was black. But I was not going to let anybody else tell me who I am or what I ought to be. I'm human, that's number one, the way you, and you and all of us are human. I had friends in law school who quit being my friends, accused me of a sellout to the white establishment, because I wanted to be a defense lawyer. It hurt, it's still painful to lose friends and imagine what they're thinking about me, but I can't be their kind of man. I can't live their kind of life. I have to live my life for me and be the right kind of person for me."

"I've worked through a lot of those same things," Burton said. "You're black, but you live in a white world, and you don't think you're quite accepted by the whites or trusted by other blacks. But you gotta' do what's right for you. Amen! I agree with you. I guess white folks don't have to work through those things, do they?"

"Strange as it may seem to you, I have gone through something a little like that," Bernhardt said. "Now, I want to say up front it's not like what you've gone through, in fact, I'm sure it really doesn't compare. See, I'm German, German American. I've had to live all my life with the fact that being German has a negative connotation to a lot of Americans. The United States fought the Germans in two World Wars and, to make it really bad, the Germans were responsible for the Holocaust. So, I have a name, Bernhardt, that fairly screams out to the world that I'm German, and there's nothing I can do about the fact I am a German American, third generation. My father fought in World War II against Hitler and all he stood for, but I still feel a personal guilt and I'm especially embarrassed when I introduce myself to someone who is Jewish. I wonder, are they thinking, `This is one of those master-race Germans who wanted to kill all our people, all our faith?' Sometimes I feel like saying to them `I didn't do it' and sometimes I feel like saying, `forgive me.' Ted, are you German?"

Ted Born had been surprised at the philosophical overtones of this dinner conversation. He had intended it as an escape, but there was no escape. "Yes, partly," answered Born. "My father was three-quarters German, my mother English and Scottish. Strangely, I've felt some of the same things you've felt, Chet, only I didn't feel them until I was a young lawyer. My father never talked about being mostly German, although I sort of absorbed the fact by osmosis, I guess, being Lutheran in South Carolina. Still, it was something of a shock to realize on a conscious level that I'm nearly half German. I had some of the same guilt trips you had, Chet, only I was never embarrassed to introduce myself, because hardly anyone realizes the name is German. I've learned there are a lot of names like that, `Braun' became `Brown', `Gruen' became `Green', `Vogel' became `Bird', `Lang' became

`Long,' and hardly anyone realizes these names are associated with a German heritage."

"Must be something in the gumbo," Burton smiled. "I used not to realize there was any difference in whites. You all looked alike to me," he joked. "It's hard for me to believe any white person would have a second thought about being German. Did anybody ever hold you back because you were German? Did anyone ask you to drink at a different water fountain or go to the back of the bus? Did anyone ever tell you, `we don't want any Germans moving into our neighborhood?'"

"No, of course not," Bernhardt said, "and I don't lose any sleep over it, you understand. By the same token, I doubt anyone has said anything like that to you in a long time, either. But I admitted in the beginning it's really not comparable. I just meant that everyone has to come to grips with something about himself in relation to other people and the way they perceive him, that causes internal conflicts. I have to confess I'm proud of some things about being German. I mean, Beethoven was German, and Bach, and Goethe, and Leipnitz and Hegel and Planck and... ."

"And Einstein?" asked Bert Sayre.

"Yeah, definitely Einstein. I'm proud Einstein was Jewish German," Bernhardt said. "I think he's one of us. My only hesitation is, would it offend Jews for me to say that, since he had to flee Nazi Germany? I am so offended myself, so personally wounded and bitter about the insane Holocaust, that I don't feel worthy to claim him, proud as

I am of him. I have to remind myself that the reason many Jews lived in Germany was because Frederick the Great welcomed them, and other Germans welcomed them, at a time most countries shut their doors. The Holocaust can't be a condemnation of something inherent in the German character. Still, I feel a heavy sense of guilt."

The waiter took their orders for the entrees. As soon as he departed, Sayre said, "Ted, Dave just used a phrase I once heard you use, 'the brotherhood of suffering' or something like that. You never did explain what you meant. I'd be interested in whether you and Dave mean the same thing."

"Yeah, the brotherhood of suffering, I belong to that group, all right, and I don't think there are any racial lines dividing that brotherhood. Now there might be more African Americans proportionately, but once you become a member, there's a bond that's based on something a lot deeper than race," Born said.

"We've never talked about this, Ted," observed Thompson. "I did use that term, and I'd be interested in how you see it."

"Well, I'll try to make it short," Born promised. "I was always very poor, growing up. All during world War II we didn't own a car. My father had a run-down little pickup-truck and he'd sometimes take me with him in the truck. I can relate to Bess Johnson in a way, we always had to get rides with other people. Then, when I was five years old, my older brother Aston - who was thirteen at the time and the apple of my parents' eye - was killed when a drunk soldier driving an Army truck side-swiped the running board of a car parked on the street, you know, the old-fashioned running boards. My brother was standing on that running board, his internal organs were crushed, and he died at the hospital that night. My mother cried every day for years after that, unconsolably. I told her I'd try to make up for it, would be like him, take his place. Of course, it was all foolish talk from a child who didn't realize no one could ever take Aston's place, but I didn't know what else to say. It distressed me to see my mother so often in tears."

"When I was ten years old I started working part time, after school and on weekends. It was in violation of the Child Labor Laws and so my employer couldn't write me a paycheck, had to include my pay on somebody else's paycheck, and then I always had to work out and argue about how much of the withholding should be allocated to my share of the pay. I was getting paid twenty-five cents an hour in those days, when the minimum wage was forty cents an hour, and I never earned more than a quarter an hour—no, I take that back— I did get a raise to thirty-five cents an hour when I was in the eleventh or twelfth grade," Born continued. "I got to keep hardly any of the money I earned, either. It all went into the family pot just to try to help make ends meet. I didn't resent that, I was proud to be doing my part, but it did seem like we were treading water."

"My senior year in high school, my mother became terminally ill with cancer, and I watched her waste away and die, painfully, but a tribute to the nobility of the human spirit. Eight days later, my father had a heart attack and died. I was numb from all the body blows life had dealt me, so numb it was hard to feel the pain that was there, it hurt too much to confront it. There was no insurance, just my two older sisters and me. That summer after we lost our parents was one of the truly low points in my life. We were really just three big children trying to cope in a world we didn't understand, a world that could care less about us, for the most part."

"Oh, I remember we had one other thing! There was a field my father had planted with corn before his death. It had a pretty good crop of corn, and we would get up early in the morning, when the corn silks were still wet with dew, and pick ears of corn. There was a neighborhood grocery store where we took the corn and bartered it for milk and bread and maybe a few other items. It helped us survive, a legacy from our parents. Then, I well remember picking the corn one morning and taking it to the store and the storekeeper practically threw us out, said the corn had gotten too old, wasn't tender anymore and he couldn't sell it, don't bring him anymore, he said. We were in despair, but somehow we made it, kept encouraging ourselves."

"Then I'd gotten a scholarship and went off to college in the fall where my scholarship covered my tuition and room, and I worked in a dining hall for my meals. My wonderful sisters would write me letters and would enclose five or ten dollars whenever they could. I had a quick childhood, had to grow up fast, grabbing what little I could snatch from brief interludes among school and work and tragedies. To this day, my life has been defined by work and stress and tension and fighting just to survive. And it doesn't seem to be getting much better. I'm still struggling, still fighting, still striving. But I've never quit believing. I've never lost hope. When it's my turn, I step up to the plate and take my best swing. The odds against me sometimes are overwhelming, near impossible, but I still swing, and I believe and hope. I guess that's why the Almighty sent me this lawsuit. He must enjoy seeing me take swings. Anyway, I'm not going to take a dive."

"I think you've earned a life membership in that brotherhood of suffering," Thompson said. "I never realized you ever went through anything like that."

"And I'm sure you've gone through at least as much and probably much more, that I will never be able to know or appreciate. It's been a part of the human condition almost forever, so I know I am not unique and have no grounds to complain. I've had opportunity, and that's all we have a right to expect. I am embarrassed that I've talked on and on. But here we are sitting at this table, telling sad tales, and talking about brotherhood, and somehow confession is cathartic." He reached out his hand to Dave Thompson. Dave grasped it. Then another hand rested on top of theirs; it was Theo Burton's. Then came Bert Sayre's, and finally Chet Bernhardt's.

The bonding was instantaneous. The joined stack of hands was held together with muscle and tension and emotion. The moment seemed frozen, and it seemed impossible time would ever move forward. Born thought, "This is what St. Peter meant when he said, 'Lord, let us build three tabernacles' to sanctify the moment of the Transfiguration."

Then they saw a waiter standing near them with the main courses. The moment would be saved in memory, but the tabernacles would have to wait.

CHAPTER THIRTY

NEVER PAY A BRIBE

Plaintiffs' expert on the van design, Peter Justin, fared little better than Wrack Kelly. He stuck tenaciously to his opinion that the van had been designed with its center of gravity too far back, and he ventured that a stabilizer bar would have helped with control of the van. His problem was that he had almost no credible credentials to critique vehicular design, except he had an undergraduate engineering degree not involving a single course on *automotive* engineering. He proved unable to make simple mathematical computations, alternately frowning and looking bewildered punching at a hand-held calculator as seconds, then minutes, ticked away. He spent his entire lunch break sitting alone in the courtroom futilely trying to perform a simple two-step calculation. He was stumped as to the meaning of rather basic automotive terminology.

Brad Mansfield also was careful to bring out that Justin himself owned a Logos of about the same vintage as the one Sheriff Johnson owned, that he for years had transported himself and his family in it, a model which he was telling the jury was too unsafe to be on the highways.

Shortly after noon on Friday of the first week, the plaintiffs rested their case. Universal and Tergano both filed motions for directed verdicts at that point. The motions had been basically prepared before the first day of trial, waiting to be used at this time. As the trial had proceeded, both defendants refined them to add new points strengthening their positions.

Universal was particularly hopeful the Judge might grant a directed verdict in its favor. The Judge had written in his February summary judgment ruling that he was almost persuaded to let Universal out of the case at that time, for lack of evidence. He had hinted at it again when Universal filed its renewed motion for summary judgment, and now the trial had gone well for Universal, especially the cross-examination of Wrack Kelly, the tire expert. Born and Thompson and Sayre hoped Judge Andrews would send them home victorious, where they could unpack for good and not have to face the next phase of the trial beginning Monday morning. Maybe the Judge knew all along Universal should be dismissed from the case but was waiting until now to order the dismissal, feeling his Order would stand up better on appeal after the actual trial testimony had come out.

It was not to be. The Judge listened courteously, apparently carefully, then denied the motions. The hearts of all defense counsel dropped in unison. The trial had gone well for the defense so far, and they had allowed themselves to entertain some hope the Judge would put an end to the case as they felt sure was richly deserved. Now they knew there would be no quick end. There would be one more remaining chance for a directed verdict; they could try again at the end of all the evidence, after the still-to-come defense case, and plaintiff's rebuttal. There was a bare chance a directed verdict could still happen, but it was increasingly probable that the case would not end until the twelve men and women in the jury box came out of deliberations to announce a verdict.

The case had now entered a new phase. No longer would defendants be preparing to cross-examine opposing witnesses. Starting first with Tergano Motors, it would be the defense's turn to lead with their own witnesses, which plaintiffs could cross-examine. In one sense, the defendants now had the ball in their hands and were in a position to call the plays and initiate the action. Yet, having the initiative was dangerous and had to be handled with care. One of the lawyers in Born's and Thompson's firm had a saying that, "It is more blessed to cross-examine than to examine," meaning that mistakes do not hurt quite as badly when cross-examining an opposition witness, as the jury is willing to forgive and discount bad results with a basically hostile or adverse witness, but the jury never forgets when your own witness kicks you in the teeth on direct examination.

There was time enough that Friday afternoon for Tergano to put up its first witness, design expert Jim Bochard, who defended the design of the van and had the credentials and obvious competence to make a good witness. He escaped cross-examination relatively unscathed as the day and the week came to a close.

Born and Thompson would return to Greenville for one night's rest, then go back to work all weekend to get ready for the next week. Mansfield and Bernhardt remained in their Columbia motel over the weekend getting ready for Tergano's next witness, John Frey, and for the other events of the coming week.

Meanwhile, the plaintiffs had all met with Bates, Ripps and Fox in their storefront space at the end of the day Friday. Up to now, at Bates' request, Sam Johnson alone had met with counsel briefly at the end of each day as a liaison between counsel and the rest of the plaintiffs. Bates had said he was too busy to have to deal with all the plaintiffs during the weekday, but now the first week had come to an end, plaintiffs had rested their case, and Bates was ready to meet with everybody.

"We think the case is going fine," Bates said. "Our main goal is to get the case to the jury without any errors in it, and we're succeeding in that. The Judge has denied two motions for summary judgment and he's now denied a motion for directed verdict. I also don't see any errors much in the case. There's a little problem, a little inconsistency, in the way the Judge handled the *Batson* challenge, you know, how many white jurors we were going to have to take on the jury. Probably, the Court should have denied the whole motion, but if he was going to grant it, he probably should have put two white jurors back on. So, he split the baby and might have made a mistake, one way or the other, but I'm betting he made the mistake against us."

"The biggest problem we have in this case," Bates theorized, "is the one white juror, John Salmon. But I've won 'em before with white jurors in the box and I can win again. He's a mechanic, I think, a working man, might be sympathetic, or there might be some strong black jurors who can sway him. I'd hate to get a hung jury with him as the holdout."

"Mr. Fred, what do you think about the black jurors?" Sam Johnson asked. "I haven't got any real good vibes."

"Me, neither," Bess Johnson agreed.

"Long as you haven't got any real *bad* vibes, I think we're all right, subject to the white guy on the jury. Main thing is, I don't want any reversible error. You can work hard and win a big verdict and then the Judge can set it aside or the Supreme Court of South Carolina can set it aside, and you've got to essentially start all over, with the delays and everything. That's what we want to avoid," Bates instructed them, like a team coach.

"What bothers me is those jurors don't even look at me, or even say hello, or nothin', when we pass. Looks like one or two of 'em at least would wink at me or do somethin' to say `I'm with you'," Sam Johnson said.

"Amen, brother," Ben Miller spoke up. "I've got a little girl who's dead and looks like I'd see more sympathy than I'm seein'."

"They don't even seem to be payin' no attention when I take Jimason to the bathroom," Doretta complained, "we're goin' to all this trouble to impress 'em about Jimason and they ain't even noticin'."

"Any of y'all know any of the jurors?" Ripps asked.

Most of them shook their heads, but Bess Johnson spoke up, "Seems like I know Estrata McNemar. Seems like she was in school with me. We weren't best friends or nothin' like that, but I know her, and I think she knows me."

"Now, don't get me wrong. We can't tell you to contact anyone on that jury," Ripps continued. "In fact, if anyone ever asks, I'm telling you it would be wrong to contact a juror. Understand? It would be wrong. Of course, this is a helluva important case and you've got to just think about all that money that's out there waitin' for you. Let's say we ask the jury to give you twenty million dollars - we'll talk later about the exact figure - but let's say twenty million dollars. You'd walk home with all that money after splittin' with your lawyers, and what would the jurors get? Nothin'! Oh, they'd get a few dollars a day fee for jury service, just about enough to pay for their gasoline to get here to the Courthouse, but, really, they'd get nothin'. Maybe that's why they've been avoiding eye contact. They probably wonder what's in it for them.

Now, we can't offer to pay them, understand. But it'd be nice if they could know you appreciate what they're going to do for you."

"How're we gonna' do that?" asked Sam Johnson.

"Well, *we* can't take that risk. We're just lawyers. And I don't know how to get across our appreciation. You certainly should never pay or promise anything that would sound like a bribe, even though you don't mean it that way, it's just your way of saying, `thanks'. All I'm sayin' is, a little thanks would make them feel better about themselves and what they're doing, and that good feeling might mean you would carry home gold in pick-up truck loads," Ripps answered.

"What if we tried to express our thanks and someone mistook it for bribery?" asked Bess Johnson.

"Well, you'd be subject to prosecution," Ripps answered. "If it worked, probably nobody would know anything about it, 'cause you wouldn't tell and the jurors wouldn't tell, and who'd ever find out? You'd just enjoy that Hollywood lifestyle and Hollywood style mansion for the rest of your life, with not a worry in the world. You'd be weighin' all those riches against the possibility of prosecution. If it didn't work, it might still never come out. More than likely, the jurors would realize you were under stress, and they probably wouldn't report you to a white Judge. Even if they did, what jury in Phoenix County would ever convict a mother who was stressed out over the tragedies she endured and was just trying to help get some money to compensate for these children, injured and dead? I doubt very much there'd ever be a prosecution at all. You understand, don't you, Bess, I'm just givin' you my professional advice about what might happen. I'm not recommending anything at all, in fact, I'm telling you to never pay a bribe."

"You think those jurors are waiting for us to make a move?" Ben Miller asked.

"It's a possibility," Bates said. "I don't know that for a fact. It could be they're already with us. We just don't know. The Judge has scared them, I'm afraid, with all his talk about 'don't speak to anyone', 'don't even say pleasantries' and I think they're just afraid to act natural. You'd sure feel a lot more comfortable if they could somehow give you a sign of what's going on in their minds. But I'm telling you professionally, as a lawyer, not to pay or promise any bribes."

"Don't you have ways of makin' sure we win?" asked Bess Johnson.

"Bess, our hands are tied, we can only put on the evidence, lay it out for the jury. Whatever you've heard, we can't do any more than that in this case, or in any case. Just think about what we told you," Ripps said.

"Speaking of evidence, I'm not a lawyer, of course, but I didn't think our experts came across too good," Sam Johnson observed with a look at Bates which called for an answer.

"Look, Sam, experts are something you've got to have to protect yourself. It don't matter to that jury what a damned so-called 'expert' says. They're all whores. You know it, and I know it, and the jury knows it, and every guy walking around on the street out there knows it. It's just that our court system pretends experts are important and they pontificate in appellate opinions about whether there was any expert evidence supporting a plaintiff's theory of liability. If there is, the case goes to the jury. If there's not, it might not get to the jury. It's a key to the jury room, the way you make sure your case isn't thrown out before it gets to the jury. Our experts did what we hired 'em to do. They got the judge to deny the motions for summary judgment and the motion for a directed verdict. They did their job. You can be damned sure if they hadn't been here, or if they hadn't been good enough, Judge Andrews would have already thrown this case out.

"What I'm saying is," Bates continued, "Sure, I wish they had been able to bowl over the Judge and jury and everybody else. But you have to remember what those experts had to work with - a six-year-old, sixty-thousand-mile worn out tire, and a van where we had a real struggle to find anything wrong. So, don't be too critical of them, they did the best they could with what they had to work with. The main thing is, because of what they've done, a jury is going to render a verdict in this case. Let me repeat that: *a Phoenix County jury is going to render a verdict in this case!* That's a tremendous step forward, right there. The experts ain't gon' win this case. I'm telling you, Jimason and Sarena are gon' win this case in the jury room. We just had to make sure the jury gets that chance. With a little luck, that jury will send you home richer than anything in your imagination, probably richer than Mrs. Driscoll."

The plaintiff question-and-answer session broke up, and all went home.

On Monday morning, John Frey took the stand for Tergano and explained the tests he had made with the exemplar van in the snowy weather at the Ohio testing grounds. Frey surprised Universal with a casual observation that he had used a different Universal tire than the Surefoot model because the Surefoots had been discontinued. "Not true!" everyone at the Universal table thought silently, looking at each other, and then looking back at Bert Sayre in the spectator area. Thompson whispered to Born, "Is the jury going to get the impression the tire was discontinued because it was a bad tire? We've got to do something about that." They agreed to check with some Universal tire dealers in the Columbia area during the break to verify they still carried the Surefoot, and then prove it to Frey and his lawyers, and get them to retract the statement.

At the first morning break, Thompson verified the Surefoot tires were available locally, and invited the Tergano lawyers and Frey to check it out, but they resisted correcting the testimony. "It'll make it look like we deliberately used a different tire for our tests," Bernhardt said, "and I promise you I checked several places and couldn't find any Surefoots." When confronted with Universal's promise to subpoena local area dealers to testify about availability, Bernhardt reluctantly agreed to the retraction.

Bates took Frey on cross-examination after the break and pointed out how Frey had had to hold the steering wheel with two hands to control it on his first test run. "And you're a great big man, Mr. Frey, and Bess Johnson is a small woman?" Frey responded that he had grasped the steering wheel with both hands only on the first trial run and had been able to control it with two fingers on other runs. "But Bess only had one chance, didn't she...? And you knew it was coming, the blowout, and Bess didn't know it was coming?"

Bates also took the films and tried to get Frey to admit the exemplar van had first headed to the left before Frey managed to get it under control, and that the front right tire was raised off the ground as the left rear tire deflated. Frey acknowledged there was a slight movement to the left, but it was insignificant and easily controlled. He denied the front right tire was lifted off the ground. Bates pointed to the front left tire on a stop-motion still frame on the video monitor, "You mean to tell me, Mr. Frey, that my eyes aren't seeing what they're seeing...? You mean you don't see that right tire coming up off the ground...? Oh, you think that's just a shadow, do you...? You mean to tell me my eyes are deceiving me?"

Frey in each instant denied the front right tire came up off the ground, but Bates' continued insistence that he could see it was an effective strategy; "At best, Frey's testimony is neutral," Born thought. "At worst, it could give some credibility to the way-out theories of Peter Justin." Born and Thompson were concerned about Tergano's case as well as their own, remembering the mock jury results showing the two defendants standing or falling together.

Born briefly cross-examined Frey who acknowledged he had been in error to suggest the Surefoot was no longer being manufactured. Born rolled the new exemplar Surefoot tire up to the stand where Frey was sitting, the same new Surefoot Dave Thompson had shown the jury during his opening statement nearly a week earlier, "Would you like to touch it to see if it's real?" Born asked. The jurors smiled.

Tergano rested its case just before lunch, and Universal would be starting its case immediately after lunch.

Born planned to read the deposition of the chemist who analyzed the tire sealant and identified what it was, and then put Bob Tegrit on the stand. Thompson had let the plaintiffs know he was considering calling Jimason as a defense witness, as well as a therapist who had seen Jimason. However, the Judge had ruled the therapist could not testify because the plaintiffs had not taken her deposition, despite some dispute as to whose fault that was.

The chemist's short deposition was read first. The only problem with the chemist and his deposition, from Universal's point of view, was that he had not come from his out-of-state lab to the Phoenix County area to collect the samples of commercial tire sealant he compared with the sample of gummy substance taken from the tire innerliner. Plaintiffs' lawyers were aware of that problem.

Born expected them to object at the crucial part of his deposition, and Born knew the Judge should and probably would sustain the objection to that portion of his testimony. To Born's amazement, the plaintiffs objected one question too late. Some elaboration about the gathering of the commercial samples was excluded by the objection, but the tie-in of the gummy substance with locally available commercial cans of sealant had already gotten into evidence. It wasn't absolutely vital, Born knew, to establish that point, or even to deal with the gunk on the innerliner, but it helped reinforce the underinflation suffered by the tire, and the leakiness of the tire.

Bob Tegrit came to the witness stand with an air compressor equipped with a cup-like metal piece on the end of the compressor hose. He was obviously prepared to do a demonstration, and plaintiffs' counsel were determined to try to prevent it. After a sidebar conference, Judge Andrews prohibited an actual in-Court demonstration, but said Tegrit could use the compressor to illustrate how he had gone about his out-of-Court testing of the tire.

Tegrit went through the steps in his examination process and analysis of the tire and was warming up very nicely. The jury seemed to be listening to him, maybe even *liking* him. Then Ted Born asked him if he had made any measurements to determine whether the tread was less than 2/32 inch in two adjacent tread grooves measured at three equidistant places around the circumference of the tire. Tegrit said he had done so and proceeded to demonstrate.

Born nearly went into shock as he saw Tegrit reach for the tread depth gauge with the big circular glass-faced dial. It was the gauge Born had been using for his own purposes, the one where he had taken red paint and painted a red arc on the face for the shallow "danger zone" less than 2/32 inch. He had pulled it out and offered to demonstrate it in his deposition, but Fox had not required such demonstration. Since then, including the last time Born and Tegrit had gone over Tegrit's proposed testimony - last night, in fact - they had both agreed Tegrit would use a smaller instrument similar to an air pressure gauge, that could be seen only close-up by one person at a time. They had specifically agreed it would be too risky to use the big round dial, because there was one spot on the tire, one of the six measuring points, where the measurement was fairly close to the 2/32-inch mark, and a slight variation in placement could result in a reading greater than 2/32. Too risky on a gauge with a dial big enough to be read from the jury box.

Yet it was this risky gauge which Tegrit used for his measurements in front of the jury. The first three measurements went well. The fourth was the tough one, and Tegrit fumbled a bit but found the right spot and got the right reading. The last two measurements were easy. Wow! What a relief! The whole case could have blown up in Born's face. Thompson and Born had both stressed that the tire had illegally thin tread and had invested so much in that concept a mistake could have been disastrous.

Mindful of Judge Andrews' earlier ruling, Tegrit then

used the air compressor to illustrate, but not actually demonstrate, how he had been able to prove a leak in the areas of both the nail and the plug repair. Just apply some soapy water on the exterior areas and place the cup at the end of the compressor hose over the nail or plug on the innerliner side, turn on the air compressor at a pressure level less than in a fully inflated tire - say twenty psi - and watch the bubbles on the other side. It even leaked at much lower pressures, like five and ten psi, Tegrit said.

As for contamination, he said that nothing about the tire remotely suggested such a defect. First place, a large chunk of tread would have come off. Second place, the tire would not have survived for six months, let alone six years. Third place, he took issue with Kelly's statement that the blowout destroyed the evidence of contamination. The blowout in case of foreign matter nearly always takes place at a point distant from the location of the foreign matter, and the evidence can usually be found back at the point where the foreign matter is and where the tread separation began.

Tegrit concluded by underscoring the key points: good service and long life for the tire, abuse and misuse of the tire by its owner, worn out illegal tread, road hazard destruction.

After Born finished the direct examination, Fox tried to cross-examine but got nowhere. If anything, Tegrit got stronger and stronger on cross.

"My heart stopped there for a minute, Bob," Born said to him when cross-examination was over.

"I know what you're going to say, Ted. I know we agreed I'd use the small gauge, but I kept practicing this morning and I felt confident I could do it with the big one. And I knew it would be much more convincing if the jury could actually see the gauge dial for themselves. So, I made an executive decision to use the big one. Sorry we didn't have time to talk about it before I took the stand."

"Now that it's behind us and it came out right, I'm delighted," Born said. "It just came as a surprise and I had instant nightmares when I first saw you pull out that gauge. Anyway, you're forgiven. Your testimony went great. Better hang around at least overnight to be sure we don't need you for rebuttal."

Born and Thompson pretended to confer about whether to call Jimason to the witness stand. Actually, in their own thinking they had in fact left the door open slightly, but only slightly, to the possibility of calling Jimason as a witness. There was a fair chance Jimason would come across as being a good deal more normal than plaintiffs had portrayed him. Defense counsel could kindly lead him through some questions he could answer, and his own lawyers could scarcely attack him or imply to his face that he was a robot or sub-normal. On the other hand, the case so far had gone about as well for Universal as one could hope, no big problems at all. When things are going well, do you take chances, and how big? Jimason was totally unpredictable. He could say or do something that could detonate in Universal's figurative face. And would it be wise in any event to focus attention on Jimason - the most sympathetic person among the plaintiffs except possibly the deceased Sarena Miller - just before the jurors retired to the jury room? It did not take Born and Thompson long to decide not to call Jimason as a witness. With that announcement, Universal rested its case.

By now it was late in the day. The Judge asked the lawyers to give him their proposed jury charges to study overnight, as well as any proposed forms for the jury verdicts. They were ready and were handed up. "Will there be any rebuttal?" asked the Judge.

Bates indicated he might have some rebuttal, was not absolutely sure of it, and he would appreciate the Court's giving him the evening to consider the situation. The Judge agreed, provided the lawyers meet with him at eight thirty the following morning for a "charge conference" to iron out the jury charges and jury verdict form.

As the trial recessed for the evening, Born asked Bates whether he was considering rebuttal against Universal, pointing out he would like to know because he was holding Tegrit pending any possible rebuttal. He was vastly relieved when Bates told him, "No, none at all against Universal. We're considering some fairly brief rebuttal relative to Tergano."

The Universal team went back to Rusty Loman's office, with thoughts turning toward the forthcoming closing argument. Rusty had a proposition: "Ted, why don't you and Dave split the closing? I think it would help. You've been in front of those jurors an awful lot lately. Dave was real visible at the beginning, but you've cross-examined major witnesses like Sam Johnson, Wrack Kelly, Peter Justin, some of the medical witnesses, and now today you've put on Bob Tegrit. You've done a great job, too, but Dave has been in the background lately and I wonder if it wouldn't help to let Dave participate in the closing?"

Ted Born was taken aback at the suggestion. From the very beginning he had gone out on a limb to put Dave forward to handle the crucially important opening statement, a very daring move, given Dave Thompson's short tenure as a lawyer and the tremendous importance of this case. Now he was being asked to give up the closing argument, or divide and destroy it, by including Thompson on that one also.

"I hear what you're saying, Rusty," Born responded thoughtfully. "I know I've had the laboring oar in front of the jury for the last few days and maybe I've gotten over-exposed. The problem is, I'm prepared on the closing and Dave isn't, and we've got to make the argument tomorrow, maybe as early as tomorrow morning. Also, the closing argument has to be a unitary whole. I don't see how in the world we can make it a coherent, unitary presentation flowing logically from beginning to end, if we divide it up. I'd like to get Dave out before the jury again, but I don't want us to end up with a jumbled and confused argument which doesn't convey a clear and logical message. I think it's a good suggestion. I need to see if I can figure out a way it could work. Let me think about it, and Dave and I will talk later." Turning to Thompson, he said, "Give me about an hour, Dave, to look at my argument and see whether I think it would be feasible."

"I'm willing to do it or not do it, whatever you think. All I care about is winning the case. Just let me know what you think," Thompson volunteered.

Ted Born and Dave Thompson drove back to their motel in Columbia and went to their separate rooms. Born pulled out his notes and looked them over and thought. "Ted," he said to himself, "the thing that you can't let happen is to allow ego to get tangled up in this. You've got to remember the only thing of any importance is to win, like Dave said. You've got to ask yourself, Ted, are you jealous of this young lawyer, thirty years your junior? Does it bother you that he might steal the limelight and, if you win, he'd be the hero of the case? Are you allowing yourself to feel you've 'earned' the right to make this argument and letting that get in the way of doing what's in your client's best interest? Sure, I know Rusty feels it would help with the jury if they're reminded just before deliberations of this attractive and able African-American lawyer over here in our corner. He's right, too, it probably would help.

"Then, again," he continued reasoning to himself, "is that our winning message? That we have a fine black lawyer on our side? Sure, the world being like it is, I'm a realist and not above letting that fact reinforce our message, but *is that the message*? Should it be allowed to supplant the message we've so carefully cultivated? I had to handle all those experts because that's my forté, developed over a twenty-five year period of practicing law, to destroy opposing so-called experts and keep ours from being destroyed. I can't help that. But our game plan was for Dave to start and for me to finish.

"How, Ted, do you divide up this argument?" he asked himself. "Honestly, you can't. You start out building a mood, building a rapport, and you keep building and building as the argument goes on, and moving the jury with you until they embrace you at the end, if you've done it right. You just can't do that when you break up the argument."

He took a deep breath. "Am I rationalizing? Is it just that I'm trying to justify my preconceived plan, not be flexible enough to take advantage of a good suggestion from Rusty Loman, who's doubtless a lot more objective than I am?"

He looked through his notes another time and shook his head, "There's no way to break this up. Absolutely no way. That's got to be my call. I hope it's the right one. We've got an excellent chance of getting trounced regardless, and I'll never have another chance to change my mind. But I still think it's right. I'll handle the closing by myself. Right or wrong, that's the call."

CHAPTER THIRTY-ONE

THE CLOSINGS

Tuesday of the second week began with a legal skirmish about a plaintiffs-sponsored expert who was proposing to testify in rebuttal that the Tergano van should have been equipped with a stabilizer bar. The Court held this was not proper rebuttal testimony because, as an aspect of overall van safety, plaintiffs should have submitted the proposed testimony during their case-in-chief, the Court ruled.

The plaintiffs had no other rebuttal testimony and rested their case. Universal and Tergano immediately filed motions for a directed verdict at the close of all the evidence, which Judge Andrews politely heard and then denied. By this time, defense counsel had resigned themselves to the fact the Judge simply was not of a mind to save them from the fate of a jury verdict.

Judge Andrews and all the lawyers retired to the jury room in the Annex to work out the charges the Judge would later use in instructing the jury following closing arguments. It was there the plaintiffs made a surprise announcement: They were voluntarily dismissing Sheriff Sam Johnson from the group of plaintiffs they represented. Out of the case completely, for Sam Johnson. Though Johnson's exit was unexpected, Ted Born immediately guessed why Bates had done it. Bates knew he could ask the jury for only a few thousand dollars for Sam, Born thought, because Sam had lost nothing but an old van and had no way to claim punitive damages for mere property loss. Ted whispered to Dave Thompson, "Fred's afraid the contrast between Sam's small claim and the other humongous claims will hurt him, make the jury think the millions he's asking for the others are excessive. He doesn't like the juxtaposition of those numbers, so he's dropped Sam and Sam's claim. I'll tell you, though, you can bet they've all made a pact with Sam so he'll get some money, and my guess is it will not be just thousands of dollars, but hundreds of thousands, even millions, from whatever the others get."

The defense counsel were pleased with the jury charges, though no one had any confidence the jury would be influenced much by them, one way or the other. Bates also pretty clearly thought the jury instructions were largely irrelevant. His main concern seemed to be the avoidance of any reversible error in the instructions, so he was fairly agreeable and reasonable in the charge conference.

It was now time to begin the closing arguments. The morning had mostly been consumed by legal wrangling about the rebuttal witness and in working out the jury charges and verdict form, and there would be time only for Fred Bates' argument before lunch. The Tergano and Universal lawyers would have to make theirs after lunch. The defense counsel were not entirely happy with that schedule. "It gives the jury the entire lunch hour to digest and absorb Bates' arguments and get their attitude set before they hear our side," complained Born to Brad Mansfield. On the other hand, there seemed little alternative. No one, certainly not Mansfield or Born, would want to make their important arguments to hungry jurors with growling stomachs. They shrugged and determined to make the best of it.

The Judge convened the jury in the courtroom and, after a brief explanation to them about closing arguments, he signaled Fred Bates to begin. Bates began with a low, solemn voice that he was standing before the jury - "standing up," he said - for a dead child, a brain-damaged child and three other battered, injured passengers. Without the tire blowout, there would have been no deaths, no injuries. Bates touted Wrack Kelly as "probably the foremost tire expert in the world," crediting Kelly with achievements he never accomplished, then went on to make comments about tires that were embarrassingly off-the-mark. He then said Bob Tegrit had relied on a "mysterious road hazard" of which Bates said there was no evidence. Bates said Tegrit had "invented" the road hazard.

Referring to Tegrit, Bates said, "And he told us, admitted to us, that all tires should be designed in such a manner that they will last, the carcass, that includes the steel belt, will last through one tread life plus a recap. And Mr. Tegrit comes to Phoenix County on Universal's behalf and says, `you Phoenix County folks ought not to have the benefit of one tread life plus a recap, you ought to replace your tires before that time, even if you can't afford it.' Now, I suggest to you if you don't get one full tread life plus a recap out of a set of tires, they haven't been properly manufactured."

Bates said the tire was where the deadly events all started, but the van too was defective, mentioning especially the location of the center of gravity causing rear steerage and the lack of a stabilizer bar. He went into the video films and his perception that the right front tire rose off the pavement in Tergano's Ohio tests when the left rear was suddenly deflated. He talked about the "thousand acres of asphalt" where the testing was done, where the driver was protected from collisions for any lack of control—a protection the van passengers did not have.

If Bess Johnson had had all that asphalt, and if she had known there was going to be a blowout, she might have been able to control the van. But even Mr. Frey, who was driving under those protected conditions, had to grab the steering wheel with both hands and apply main strength of a strong grown man to control it.

Bates then turned to the matter of damages, starting with Doretta Anchrum. "God bless the least injured of the parties involved in this accident," he said. He talked about her "multiple contusions", "pain in the upper left dorsal area", "left arm injured", "right index finger injured," and "abrasions around both knees." This was Bates' way of describing bruises and scratches. Next, he mentioned the "trauma" and the "mental pain and anguish." For Doretta, Bates asked three hundred thousand dollars in damages.

"Hmm, pretty modest for Bates," Born thought. "He must have scaled down his expectations some, maybe as a result of the way the trial has gone."

For Bess Johnson, Bates asked the jury to award one million five hundred thousand dollars, mainly for loss of her teeth but partly for the gashes and some fractures.

"Seems a bit high," thought Born, "I'll bet Bess Johnson was pretty insistent he ask that much. On the other hand, Doretta probably went along with whatever figure Fred mentioned.

But Born - and all defense counsel - really raised their eyebrows when Bates asked two million dollars for the broken leg of Katyna, whom Bates called "Katy".

As Bates began discussing damages for the death of Sarena Miller, his face turned red, he pulled a handkerchief out of his pocket and rubbed his eyes. It was the only time defense counsel could remember seeing Bates with a real linen handkerchief. He took his glasses off, after first trying to rub beneath them, his voice sounded strange, a little like a whimper, a little like a cough. Apparently overcome with emotion for the first time during this trial, Fred Bates managed to compose himself sufficiently to blackboard damages for Sarena's death.

"You cannot compensate Ben and Agnes Miller, the parents, compensatory damages for the loss of their baby," Bates told the jury. "You can't do that under South Carolina law where all lives are valued equally and punitive damages alone can be awarded. What you've got to do is assess damages based on the quantum of wrong that was done by these two defendants, or either, and put that in dollars. Because life is precious, and what a jury does on a wrongful death action in South Carolina, hopefully, makes other manufacturers of products be a little more careful, for the good of all of us.

"You can look at the value of life that we assess - life in general, spring mornings, Christmas day, hurt, pain, tears, laughter, marriage, children. What is a life worth?

"Robert Service used to say it's just a little pain, a little gain, a laugh, a little fame, a little blame, the moonbeams on a stone. That's life. All that's left of Sarena's life is a death certificate that's been admitted in evidence. 'Sarena Miller, died Phoenix County, South Carolina, Highway 53, hospital not applicable, race, sex, age, date of birth, Social Security number, blunt force trauma to chest and abdomen, death,' a piece of paper that's certified."

Then Bates wrote a figure on the board which was

turned toward the jury and away from defense counsel who could not see it at the time. The jury could see it: it said five million dollars.

Bates was building up to Jimason, and his face was getting redder and he used his handkerchief more frequently.

"Now we come to the tragedy. Suffer the little children to come unto me," Bates said. "I'm going to be talking about a once normal boy, didn't make super grades, played a lot of basketball, probably watched -"

At the point, Bates wheeled around and faced the row of plaintiffs right behind him. Jimason Anchrum at the moment was sound asleep, leaning on his mother who had her arms around him. Bates said to the group, motioning toward Jimason, "Can you take him out of the room? Could you take him out? Would you go with him?" In order to comply with Bates' request, Doretta Anchrum shook Jimason gently to wake him up, with the eyes of the jury focused on the child, who was urged to stand up and who then walked sleepily out of the courtroom, accompanied by his mother.

Thompson whispered to Born, "He's been talking about Jimason through this whole trial, and right in front of Jimason. It never bothered him before. Now he's got to cry and make a show before the jury of being considerate of Jimason, so he makes them *wake up* Jimason who otherwise would have slept peacefully through the whole thing."

"Worst contrived stage act I've ever seen," Born agreed. "But will it work with the jury? That's the key question, not what we think about it."

Bates continued, turning again toward the jury, "Would you go with Jimason where he has to go? The mortality tables say he'll live sixty more years. They took out part of his brain. The occupational therapist says he'll never hold a job because his IQ is now so low, that though he might get a job, he can't compete with anybody and can never keep one.

"Now it's tough enough for any kid from Phoenix County to grow up and earn a place, but you all have the right to do it—I can't finish," Bate told the jury with choked voice.

But somehow Fred Bates did finish. "To compensate Jimmy for becoming a vegetable and to live sixty years that way, not able to bathe, loss of quality of life, justice demands - you won't be doing justice by that boy unless you give him ten million dollars.

"Lincoln concluded the Gettysburg Address, that we resolve that the dead shall not have died in vain. You can say that is true with an appropriate verdict in this case. Thank you very much."

He never mentioned the mock orange tree, never used the analogy of the big corporations as today's plantation masters, thought Born. "Maybe he's saving it for rebuttal, when we can't answer him. For the moment, I have a motion to make."

Born requested a side-bar conference of lawyers with

468

the Judge and said, "Universal Tire Company moves for a mistrial based upon the following circumstances: just as Mr. Bates was in his closing argument and he got to the point that he was talking about Jimason Anchrum, he paused, apparently caught up by emotion, and, with tears coming down his face, asked for Jimason to be removed from the courtroom. Jimason was at that time asleep and had to be waked up to be removed in the visible presence of the jury, which was done for dramatic effect and which was extremely prejudicial to this defendant in the timing and manner in which it was done." Brad Mansfield on behalf of Tergano announced he joined in the motion.

Judge Andrews raised his dark, bushy eyebrows and looked over the top of his glasses at Bates. "Mr. Bates?" he asked.

Bates said, "Well, I think the Court is aware I did become emotional and I apologize, I had no control over that. I asked that the child be removed because of my emotion, I didn't want in his presence to discuss his unbearable future. I saw nothing wrong with asking that he be removed from the courtroom. I have had clients that have been removed from the courtrooms in a multitude of cases when statements are to be made about -"

The Judge interrupted, "I don't like it, Mr. Bates. I'm not going to grant a mistrial, but if anything like that happens in the remaining part of your closing argument you can bet you're going to get a mistrial in this case. Do you understand me?"

"Yes, sir," Bates answered.

The Court recessed for lunch. Brad Mansfield got off to himself to refine his closing argument, and so did Ted Born. For the plaintiffs' counsel, there was a contentious session which ended with Fred Bates telling Jack Ripps to handle the rebuttal for plaintiffs. Ripps had been critical of Bates' handling of the closing, and Bates was edgy that he might do something further to irritate the Judge who had given him a stern warning not to try any more questionable tactics, like asking the family to remove Jimason from the courtroom.

When Court reconvened at one thirty that Tuesday afternoon, it was Brad Mansfield's turn at closing argument. He went to the lectern with his notes and began by reminding the jurors of promises they made during voir dire examination. He first reminded them of his question, "Does anybody believe a corporation can't get a fair trial in Phoenix County?", and how nobody felt that way. Mansfield recalled how he had asked them if they could keep an open mind, and everyone said yes. They had all said they would render a fair verdict without being swayed by sympathy, and Mansfield reminded them of that commitment. He urged use of their common sense.

Then Mansfield did something which at first was a great relief to Born. He tried to give the jury perspective about how much money some of Bates' big figures represented. "Do you know what ten million dollars will do? That will produce $700,000 a year and you will still have ten million dollars left." Born suddenly was not quite so glad. He and Mansfield had talked about a way to get the jury to focus on what a million dollars really is. Born was glad, at first, that Mansfield had done this so Born would not have to discuss money with the jury, could deal only with liability issues. But he was not happy Mansfield had chosen as high a figure as ten million dollars for his illustration. While Mansfield went on and said this was not a ten or twenty-million-dollar case, he seemed to concede that it was a million or million and a half case. That kind of approach just invites the jury to split the difference, Born thought.

Mansfield acknowledged the Millers had suffered two years of pain, but then he said, "They have done well, and they will continue to do well. And life is going to go on." Not for Sarena! Born thought, that was not empathetic at all for Mansfield to say. Mansfield went on to say how well Jimason was going to do, and Katyna and Bess and Doretta. Born and Thompson looked at each other, hoping Mansfield would move to some other subject.

Mansfield drew on the testimony of Wrack Kelly - seemed to build him up, Ted Born thought, quoting Bates' description of him as, "the finest tire expert in the world," to the effect one cannot rely on the recollections on those involved in an accident for accurate accounts of what happened. He quoted Kelly as saying that human reaction in case of vehicular emergency is the key factor.

Then Mansfield ticked off Bess Johnson's driving credentials: never driven the van before; never driven *any* van nor truck; had not owned a car in years, since she collided with a cow; never had experienced a blowout;

was not a seasoned driver. He said she was frightened by the blowout, might have turned the steering wheel too far to the left and kept it there too long.

Born was conscious that this buildup of Kelly and the emphasis on Bess Johnson's overreaction to the blowout had the effect of trying to separate Tergano from Universal and effectively said to the jury, if any defendant was at fault, it was the tire manufacturer whose tire blew out and startled Bess Johnson.

Mansfield reviewed some of Bess Johnson's testimony, then tore into Peter Justin's qualifications as an expert, referring to his supposed expertise on vehicle dynamics, handling, steering and suspension as "baloney," calling Justin a "vacant bag expert" who, when you ask him to reach into his bag of experience and education and training will grab and come up with nothing, because there's nothing there.

He then critiqued the expert testimony on the van in detail, comparing Justin's testimony with what Tergano's own experts had said.

Mansfield finished by saying, "What happened out there? Maybe the blow-out was too loud. Maybe Bess was startled. Maybe she wasn't ready. Maybe she wasn't attentive enough. I don't know. But there's been nothing proven against Tergano Motors, and you folks promised me that when you went back into the jury room you would base your verdict on the evidence and not on emotions. I won't have another chance to answer Mr. Bates. And so, if he says something against Tergano

Motors, just ask yourself, `What would Brad Mansfield say in response to that?' I hope you defend me well."

The Court gave the jury a brief break before Universal's closing. During the break, Bates tried to get a ruling prohibiting Born's use of the tomato-red poster on closing, but was unsuccessful when the Court became aware the poster had already been used during the opening statement.

When the jury reassembled, Born started to rise to make his closing argument. Thompson reached over and touched Born on the shoulder. Born turned to Thompson as the latter said to him, "You're a lot older than I am, and you probably already know this, but you have an ability to make people trust you."

"Trust." "Trust." "Trust." The words reverberated in Born's mind. Then he got up, without any notes, pushed the lectern to one side and stood directly in front of the jury, light suit, open front jacket, maroon tie, open palmed hands.

"Good afternoon," Ladies and Gentlemen, he said, looking at the jurors warmly. "Although we have been here for about nine days, I don't know whether you feel that you know me." To himself he thought, "Yes, Ted, you *are* the client. They'd better think well of you, or Universal loses." "I feel that I have come to know you and that we've been working together in a kind of search here. Today is the culmination of that search. It's really the only time in this lawsuit that I've had a chance to come and just talk to you, as one person to one person, about the case."

As Ted Born moved slowly before the jurors, his eyes were mainly trained on them, but he became conscious that all of the Tergano team had moved from their table and were now standing against the side wall of the courtroom behind the jurors. The courtroom seemed to swell with spectators he had not seen before. Despite the crowds, there was a tomblike silence except for Born's words, all eyes riveted on the lawyer standing in front of twelve jurors and two alternates.

"Mr. Bates spent a lot of time, most of his time, talking about pain and suffering and injuries, and not so much about anything wrong that the tire company did. I don't blame him because that's where the strength of his case is. He doesn't have much of a case, and he is stressing the one thing he does have.

"What I want to tell you is that I know something about pain. I know something *personally* about pain, and I think most of you probably do yourselves. I had a brother who was killed in an automobile accident. I had a mother and father who died when I was a teenager in high school and left me without anything, no money, only my faith which has sustained me during the years. I'm not going to cry today in front of you. I didn't cry when my brother died or when my parents died, and I'm not going to cry here, or pretend any undue emotion, although I feel the strongest sympathy for these families." Then, turning to the plaintiffs, still seated on the front spectator row behind their lawyers' table, he looked at them understandingly and said, "I have deep feelings for the Johnsons and the

Anchrums and the Millers, and I can only ask that they be comforted and have the strength that comes from the tenets of faith."

Sayre and Thompson looked at each other and nodded. They did not have to say it to each other, they both were remembering conversations with Ted Born about the brotherhood of suffering. The genuineness of his feelings, the sincerity of his empathy, were beginning to have an impact. The jurors showed an intensity of concentration, a hanging on every word, that had not been evident during the Bates and Mansfield closing arguments.

"We are called here today, not just by a summons that came to you from the Court. You are summoned here today by a still higher calling. You are summoned here today to do justice, and I am going to take up exactly where Mr. Thompson left off in his opening statement when he talked about justice. Justice is fairness, justice is doing the right thing, justice is making the hard choice rather than the easy choice, it's doing right instead of what your impulse and sympathy wants you to do - what you yourself might want to do. Justice is finding the truth and basing your decision on the truth. So, what we're involved in here today is a search for truth. What is the truth about the case?" Born asked. He was carefully tying together the justice theme Dave Thompson had emphasized, with a call to do a noble thing. He took Phyllis Maxwell's advice that he not ask them to be Godlike, he would not be so direct, but still he wanted to inspire them to do something noble.

Born told the jurors they should bring their common sense to bear on their deliberations. Then he turned to the "trust" issue: "Another thing is to ask yourself the question, 'who can you trust, of these witnesses and what they have said, what can you trust?' Trust, I submit to you, is more important than qualifications. You can get the most highly qualified person in the world and, if he is not truthful, if he will say whatever is asked of him by the person on the other side, then that isn't very helpful to you or to the Court."

He next folded the trust theme back into the justice theme and subliminally challenged the jury to do something noble. "When we came in here today, we came into a special place, this place of justice where corporations and others are treated just as fairly as individuals. And you feel as you walk in here the sense of justice that surrounds us.

"I am proud to represent Universal Tire Company because they make good tires. And when I get through walking with you on this search for the truth, I believe you will agree with me that they make good tires and that they made a good tire in this case." Born wanted to assure the jurors Universal had a sense of responsibility and said, "Universal will step up to the plate and take responsibility for what it did do, but I don't believe you or anyone would expect Universal to take the responsibility for what it did not do."

Thompson leaned over and said to Theo Burton, "He's hit empathetic notes with his brotherhood of suffering, he's hit justice, he's hit trust, he's hit personal responsibility - all as he summons them to do something noble. Great beginning!"

Born wanted the jury to know that he would not be able to answer all the questions about the accident, that he only knew the tire had not been defective. At the same time, he wanted the jurors to ask themselves a question he could not put to them directly, out of courtesy to Tergano, a question about the unused seatbelts: "Now, I can't tell you ultimately what caused this, what caused them to go into that tree, I wasn't there. I don't know what might have been done to prevent that accident, or to prevent the injuries that occurred. Maybe there were things that could have been done *to keep those children from flying forward*, maybe other things that could have kept this tragedy from occurring. All I know - and I think you will agree after we've talked about it - is, this is a good tire that had worn out and been abused and then something happened to it. We'll be talking about that 'something'."

Born asked the jurors a series of questions, jotting down each question on a big easel, then talking about the question and writing down the answers he said were inescapable. His first question was whether the tire had given good service. He emphasized the age of the tire, the nearly sixty thousand miles of life, the worn tread. To illustrate the mileage, he took a tape measure and walked over to a good-sized National Geographic Globe, appropriated from his own living room in Greenville, and began extending the tape around the globe, once, twice and gave out of tape before he could get it nearly halfway around again. He pointed out the first set of tires on the van - some *other* company's tires - had only lasted some thirty-nine thousand miles before they had needed to be replaced, while the Universal tires lasted half again as long. Born wrote a "yes" by the question about good service.

Next came the question about abuse, and Ted Born had a field day with the chronic underinflation, lack of rotation, lack of balance, unrepaired nail hole (leaking), improperly repaired plug (also leaking), the worn-out condition of the tread, use of a cheap can of sealant as a solution rather than properly repairing the leaks. "If there's any possible way this tire was not abused or misused, I can't think of what it is. I'm sorry, I wish it had been taken care of. I wish it had been maintained. I wish we lived in a world where people didn't have to take care of their tires. Now, there are some things, if you don't take care of them, it doesn't matter that much, but if you don't take care of a tire that your life is riding on, it's an accident waiting to happen, and that's what happened in this case." He wrote a "yes" next to the question about tire abuse. He reminded the jurors that even Kelly, plaintiffs' expert, said tires should be thrown away after six years of use, even if they had been properly cared for.

The third question was whether the tire was worn out before it ever ruptured, and Born took a shiny penny out of his pocket and used it to show the shallowness of the tread. He emphasized state law declared such tires to be illegal, not to be driven on the highways of South Carolina, because they would be dangerous. "Tires do wear out, and despite what Mr. Kelly says that they make tires that don't wear out, I want you to go and ask your nearest tire dealer to give you some of those tires Mr. Kelly said don't ever wear out. I want you to go and ask that question after this case is over and see if they will say, 'Oh, I have one of those right here on the shelf, that will be so many dollars, please.' I think you will find that, just like the soles on your shoes wear out, tires wear out too, and this one had already worn out." The jury members smiled broadly as they imagined making the trip to the store Born had suggested.

"No, no tire that wasn't really an exceptionally good tire could have possibly taken the abuse and misuse and then worn out all of its usable tread, completing its useful life, no tire could give all this good service, if it hadn't been a remarkably good tire, not just a good tire, but a remarkable, exceptionally good tire; and that's why I'm proud of what Universal Tire Company did in making this tire."

Born dealt next with the cause of the rupture, that the tire impacted a road hazard which finally destroyed it. He pointed out plaintiffs' expert Kelly conceded as much, quarrelling only with the size of the road hazard. He showed the jurors the magnified pictures of the tensile fractures, the "fingerprints" implicating the cause of the rupture. Born put another large "yes" next to the question about the road hazard causing the rupture.

Now it was time to destroy whatever credibility Wrack Kelly might still have with the jury, to tie the argument back into one of the principal themes, "trust".

Born began, "I hesitate to say very much about Mr. Kelly, because I hate not to say something nice, but I just have to give you some examples you need to think about when we talk about `trust', not just common sense, but more importantly trust."

"Do you recall when I was questioning him we took a lunch break and I had a question that was pending to Mr. Kelly as we broke for lunch. He had said something that was a little different from what I remembered him saying in his deposition, and I was there looking through the deposition pages to find the place, and the Judge said, `Why don't we take a lunch break?' Right after lunch I asked Mr. Kelly whether he had discussed the answer to that pending question with Mr. Fox during the lunch break. Well, I knew the answer, because I saw and heard them discussing it as I gathered my things together and went past them, Mr. Fox and Mr. Kelly, on my way back to my table."

"When I asked him whether he and Mr. Fox had discussed the answer during the break, he first said, `Uh, I'm sorry, I don't understand your question.' Then I asked again, `Mr. Kelly, did you talk with Mr. Fox about the answer to the pending question?' And he said, `I don't remember. I can't recall.' Now this is the man they're asking you to trust when he tells you things. This is the man who could not remember what he and Mr. Fox had discussed just one hour earlier."

"So that's the credibility item from his testimony Mr. Born mentioned to me after the cross-examination!" Marta Shelby told herself.

"Mr. Kelly is a man who comes to this Country and makes all this money and then he evades paying his taxes here," Born hammered away. "He doesn't pay taxes, and that's a credibility problem! Our Mr. Tegrit is a Canadian, but he pays his U. S. taxes."

Born pointed out Kelly had testified in an earlier case that contamination usually shows up within six months to two years, if it's a problem, two years being the outer limit. Born related that, when he asked Kelly about this prior testimony, Kelly had admitted, "Yeah, I said that, but I also said *usually*."

"That's what he said, that's how he tries to wiggle out. He said this particular tire was an exception. An exception! Now I'll give him a one-month exception to that two-year outer limit. I might even give him a six-month exception, maybe if I'm really feeling generous I'll give him a one-year exception. But he wants me to give him a four-year exception!"

The jury smiled again. Born could see what he thought were nods of agreement coming from several jurors as he made points in his argument. Signs of juror agreement were still subtle, but he felt sure they were there. They were responding.

He talked more about the issue of trust and the

Kelly credibility gaps. He reminded them that on voir dire they all said a six-year-old, sixty-thousand-mile tire was a good one.

"Universal will step up to the plate and take responsibility for what it did do, and it made a good tire. And I'm sorry, but we can't take responsibility for everything in the world that goes wrong. We can't take responsibility for the fact that the tire was worn out. We can't take responsibility for the fact it's been abused and misused. We can't take responsibility for the fact there was a road hazard out there waiting to be hit by this worn tire. We can't take responsibility for the fact the tire did hit it. We just didn't do any of those things."

"With his voice rising almost for the first time and with his face filled with emotion-charged supplication, he said, "We did not do anything wrong here. And we're in this courtroom having to defend ourselves because our system allows anyone to file a paper in the Clerk's office, called a Complaint, alleging almost anything against anybody, even when there's no basis for it."

Born closed with a plea that they think about what is true and not base their decisions on sympathy and emotion. "Also, do not compromise your principles. Don't trade in that jury room and say, well, if you'll vote for liability, we'll come down a little bit on damages. You ought to decide that liability question first and decide it on its merits. It is a tragedy this tire was on the road. It's a tragedy the accident happened. I'm sorry but it was a good tire when it left the factory. Prove to us, prove to yourselves and prove to the world that justice can be done in this special place, in Phoenix County. I thank you because you have been listening. I know that and I appreciate it."

Ted Born walked deliberately to his chair at the Universal table and took his seat as the Judge announced there would be a five-minute break before plaintiffs' rebuttal. As soon as the Judge rose for the recess, the Universal table was quickly surrounded by those who had heard Born's argument. "Real good, Ted. You brought 'em home!" said Thompson, patting Born on the shoulder.

"You did a great job. I'm so glad I got to hear that. I've never understood what goes on in a jury trial until I got involved in this one," Marta Shelby told him.

"You can go anywhere, try any case anywhere, any time, you and Dave," said Brad Mansfield.

"Thanks, Brad, coming from a pro who goes all over the South trying cases, that's a real compliment which I'll never forget," Born replied. Then he saw a beaming Bert Sayre in the crowd and said with a smile, "Bert, did you hear what Brad said? Be sure to put that in your report!" Sayre smiled and slapped Born on the back.

Rusty Loman said, "Ted, you were so right. It would have been a mistake to split up that argument. It went perfect."

The compliments came from every direction. They were mostly an impressionistic blur. Born felt the exhilaration of running weightlessly on the side of a corniche, with the pounding surf of the sea almost directly beneath.

"O sea! beckoning to embrace me back to yourself as a mother, a primordial mother I have never known, yet know well. This closed county, this hostile town, dreaded as death, is now become home to me as well as my brothers, my sisters, of that jury. I looked into their eyes. We peered at each other's soul, and we found a meeting place which was their hometown, my hometown." Born was not to plunge from the cliff, but he saw and knew the sea, and in his mind he waded into it and found it warm and soothing. He kept running, running, high above the sea, inhaling the breezes from Elysium.

The Judge and jury returned. The plaintiffs, who had been huddled with their lawyers during the break, took their seats as did their counsel. Fred Bates announced that Jack Ripps would give the rebuttal. Ted Born, fast returned from the marathon on Olympus, raised an eyebrow toward Thompson and Loman. They mutually shrugged.

Jack Ripps apologized for having been "in and out" in the case. He said he was sorry Mr. Bates had gotten emotional and was sorry Mr. Born had not cried when his family members died.

He rambled about the tire looking like "a pretty good old tire," used on a weekend vehicle. He said he was not in the habit of measuring his tire tread with pennies and he had no tread depth indicator. He said, "so what" if the tire had given good service, "so what" if it had been abused, he said according to Universal's expert the tire would have failed anyway if it had hit the road hazard.

Born and Thompson were having trouble seeing where

Ripps was going. Could he be arguing that Universal should make tires that could not be destroyed by road hazards? It was never clear to them what his point was. He said something about the rubber being rubbed off the wires and then abruptly said, "I'm not going to waste any more of your time trying to rebut and say things that their expert says different, back and forth. Y'all heard all that. Y'all heard the testimony. You heard some things in oral argument you might not have heard from the stand." After mentioning again Kelly's theory that "separation" caused the blowout, not a road hazard, he moved on to the van part of the case.

Ripps defended Peter Justin and said he had a doctorate degree and "no, he doesn't work for Tergano. I'm sorry we don't have a staff engineer who can come and testify. We tried to provide you with a reasonably good qualified expert that we had, and our expert hasn't been working for Tergano Motors for thirty years."

He talked about Frey's testimony that the van was easily controllable with two fingers. "But we know in the proving grounds in Ohio the blowout scared the fool out of him. Remember when he reached down and grabbed with the second hand? What Bess heard was a pop. Didn't even know what it was. Never experienced one before.

"Dr. Justin testified the vehicle would be safe if they had put, I think a stabilizer bar and lengthened the frame an additional six inches, that would give a person time to react to, what was it, rear axle steer?" Ripps half asked, half told the jury. He argued that rear axle steer was a real problem, and that on Tergano's own films the test vans had all tended to steer leftward after blowout. He implied Frey might not have been truthful about some initial test runs in which the tire deflator failed to work - the implication being that maybe the tire deflator really had worked and maybe Tergano and Frey had concealed the film because it proved the leftward pull of rear axle steerage.

Ripps then turned to the damages plaintiffs were asking the jury to award them. He pointed out that - other than Brad Mansfield's discussion of "how much is ten million dollars" - no defendant had contested the level of damages; nobody had said plaintiffs were asking for too much money.

That is always a good plaintiffs' point, which defendants unfortunately cannot very well prevent, Born thought. "If you argue about damages, plaintiffs will tell the jury the only question is how large the verdict should be."

"I don't agree," Ripps said, "that the Millers have done well and will continue to do well. I don't agree that Jimmy will go back with his mother, brothers and sisters and he will be okay, and I don't agree life will go on for Katy." Born and Thompson looked at each other. Brad Mansfield had asked for that one with his remarks in his closing.

"The defendants are right about one thing," Ripps continued. "They said you have a duty in this courtroom to return a true and fair verdict. Nobody in this courtroom wants that for their clients more than Fred Bates and me. What's the value of Sarena Miller's life? Justice would call for at least five million for her life and ten million for Jimmy's injuries. Punitive damages will deter similar conduct from happening again, prevent other similar defendants from producing defective tires and will protect human life in this state. Thank y'all very much for your time."

Thompson and Born had been whispering as Ripps finished his argument. Thompson quickly rose and asked for a bench conference. "Your Honor, Universal Tire Company moves for a mistrial once again, on the grounds this time that during the closing argument of Mr. Jack Ripps he referred to the punitive damages recoverable for the death of Sarena Miller, as being measured by the value of her life, which is not the correct basis for punitive damages for alleged wrongful death." Tergano's Brad Mansfield joined in the motion.

"Surely he won't grant it," Born thought to himself, almost prayed. "We may lose this case and lose it bad, but I think I know one thing. This case will never again be tried as favorably for us as it has tried this time. We have to protect ourselves by making the motion. It would be malpractice not to make it, but *surely* he won't grant it. I don't want to go through this trial again."

Born need not have worried. Up to now, the Judge had adamantly resisted summary judgments, directed verdicts and motions for mistrials, and his mood had not changed. "I deny the motion, but I will direct the jury to disregard the comment."

The Court then instructed the jury as he had promised, saying in reference to Ripps' offending statement, "It is improper to make such an argument in this Court. So, you will disregard that argument in its entirety; it will be improper for you to consider it."

"Congratulations, Dave," Ted Born whispered, "Jack Ripps just suffered the worst setback a lawyer can have. He just lost his credibility with the jury, and you did it to him. Not a good rebuttal by Ripps to begin with, but to the extent the jury was giving it any credence, all they're going to remember now is that Jack made improper arguments which should be disregarded. They might even think the Judge was referring to Ripps' entire argument. Anyway, I think that'll be the effect." To himself he thought, "I'm surprised the plaintiffs' lawyers never mentioned the symbolism of the mock orange tree. Maybe they didn't know the history, or maybe in the heat of battle they just forgot to bring it up, to stir up passions. It would not have been fair to do it, but I was expecting they would make something of it. Whew!"

"I hope the jurors felt there was a credibility gap," said Dave Thompson. "We need all the help we can get just to level the playing field a little. I noticed Sam Johnson was frowning when the Judge told the jury to disregard what Jack had said. I don't think he's very happy. Bess Johnson's not smiling, either. In fact, none of the plaintiffs look too happy."

Judge Andrews spent the remainder of the afternoon giving instructions to the jury about their duties and instructions about the law that would govern their deliberations. After the jury had been charged, the lawyers had a chance to make their objections and the Judge gave a few clarifying instructions.

It was already past five o'clock in the afternoon, a time when the Court would normally recess for the day. But the Court sent the jury in to the jury room to elect a foreperson and begin deliberations. That done, the Judge released the two alternates from jury service.

The lawyers all stood respectfully as they watched twelve jurors file out of the courtroom, all somber faced, then watched through the back courtroom windows to see them cross the bridge to the Annex to be ushered into the jury room. A Deputy Sheriff closed the door behind them.

CHAPTER THIRTY-TWO

DARK WAS THE NIGHT

To see the door to a jury room, to know that men and women on the other side of it are deciding your fate, is an experience like no other. Floor pacing was invented for such times, aimless motion, going nowhere, filling time when there is nothing more one can do and when it is impossible simply to do nothing.

The courtroom was subdued as lawyers paced and talked with clients and representatives. Nita Langley and Marta Shelby gathered boxes of documents and stacked them on a dolly, then bundled together the huge posters and photographs. The ammunition of legal warfare was similarly being readied for removal by the plaintiffs' and Tergano's staff as this eerie lull in punch-throwing hostilities wore on. "Strange," Ted Born thought, "how just ten days ago, all this mass of papers and files and posters seemed so precious, so vital, and today it's all passé. Whatever could have been done with them, whatever their potential for winning over the jury, it's too late to do more now."

Brad Mansfield and the Tergano house counsel, who had flown in for closing arguments, came into the courtroom through the front door that overlooked the Square. Ted Born had not been aware of their absence. The two headed straight for him.

"Ted, I've got to hand it to you," Mansfield said. "We've been outside talking to the two alternate jurors the Judge just released, and we asked them what they thought. They were one hundred per cent for both defendants. When we asked them why, they repeated your closing argument right down the line. Ted, have you met Nat Howard, he's the in-house group counsel for Tergano, flew in for the arguments today?"

"Good to meet you," Born shook hands.

"Yeah, I had my doubts," said Howard, "whether you had made a mistake arguing all that abuse and misuse of the tire when your expert said the road hazard would have killed a brand-new tire, but looks like you read 'em just right. My hat's off to you, you knew 'em better than I did, and I'm obviously an African American."

Gillespy and Bernhardt had stopped briefly to speak to Dave Thompson, and then the three of them joined Born, Mansfield and Howard.

"I don't know how long these deliberations might

last, but I hope the Judge will keep the jurors here as long as possible," Mansfield said. "Frankly, I'd like to see them stay until nine o'clock tonight, though I doubt the Judge would do that. It scares the hell out of me to see those jurors turned loose tonight. Somebody might try to get to them."

"I totally agree," Thompson said, "but I don't think the Judge is going to want to sit here late tonight."

"I'd like to see them stay here until a verdict is reached, if it takes all night, but there is a negative to that. I'm not sure it's in our interest to have tired, irritated jurors deciding this case. It's probably going to be academic. We really will have to go along with whatever the Judge decides," Born said with resignation.

At about six o'clock, after forty-five minutes of de-liberations, the jury sent out a note to Judge Andrews. "They want to go home," the Judge told the lawyers. "I think I should let them go. It's been a long day."

"That's understandable, Your Honor," said Ted Born, "but the deliberations are so terribly important I would request the Court give the jury extra-strong instructions not to talk with anyone."

"I'll do that. Bring them in." The jurors took their places back in the jury box and the Judge said to them: "You shouldn't allow anyone to talk to you about the case. If anyone approaches you about the case, now it's your obligation to come forward and tell the Court about it. This is y'all's case now, so don't allow anyone to talk to you. Don't allow anyone to talk about the case in your presence or in your hearing. You should only talk about the case among yourselves while you're here in the jury room so that everybody can hear what you're talking about. Don't two of you go off and decide to talk about it outside the jury room. Any deliberations should be done only in the jury room. Please return to the jury room tomorrow morning at nine o'clock to continue your deliberations."

"Strong words," Born said.

"Yeah, I hope they'll be effective," said Mansfield. "Ted, I'm beginning to think we have a chance. I'm still scared of letting those jurors out into the night. I just feel very uneasy."

The defense lawyers left the courtroom together and Born looked at the triangular holding cell in the corner of the courtroom. "You know, I've often wondered about that cage over there," he said to the group. "If we lose, I'll feel like I'm forever imprisoned in that cell in Phoenix County and, in a way, I would be. My whole professional career would be captive to this case."

Bess Johnson and Katyna were dropped off at her house by Sam Johnson. Bess started toward the front door walking just behind her daughter, then stopped in her tracks. "Katyna," she called. Katyna turned. "You go on inside and get yourself somethin' to eat. If the boys ain't already, tell them to get something, too, help yourselves. I ain't hungry, just want to take a little walk. Been sittin' in the Courthouse all day, need to stretch my legs."

CHAPTER THIRTY-TWO

"Okay, mama. See you in a little while. Where you goin'?" asked Katyna.

"It don't matter. Just gon' stretch my legs. I'll be along in a little while," Johnson answered as she motioned Katyna toward the door.

The houses were scattered with lots of space between them in the area where Bess Johnson lived. She could walk and think, without being too conspicuous, and, anyway, it was not unusual for her to be walking. The neighbors would think nothing of it, knowing she did not have a car. She could be private on this walk, all to herself. She needed to think - even more than she pretextually needed to stretch her legs - and there was nothing like a quiet and slow and lonely walk to promote thinking.

She had been jolted today by the closing arguments, where her side seemed to stumble, and then the Judge had told the jury to disregard some of Attorney Ripps' arguments. She had been jolted by the rapport between Attorney Born and the jury. She had been jolted by the look on the jurors' faces as they came in the courtroom that last time before they retired for the night.

Bess had wanted this time to come, had thought about it day and night, the time when a jury would give its verdict. She had become convinced a win was sure, just a matter of getting the case to the jury. Now the time of high expectation had become the time of the Second Terror, almost as frightening for Bess Johnson as the first terror that day in March when it had all started. Was it possible she might not win after all? Was there any way on God's green earth this jury was not going to see her pain and Jimason's brain injury, and poor Sarena's death, and not be moved to tears and compassion and want to do something about it, right this wrong?

"If it was me," she told herself, "I'd want to help my friends. I'd want to help somebody in pain and havin' a hard time, even if they wasn't 'specially my friends. It's the right thing to do. Them big corporations with all that money, wouldn't miss it for a minute, and we ain't got nothin'. I've worked hard all my life, 'til right now, when I'm supposed not to work, even though I want to."

"Oh, Bess, you and your dreams about that Hollywood mansion, the life of the rich and famous. It *really could be*, it really could. It's all up to that jury. I could be rich as Mrs. Driscoll, maybe richer, and Doretta, and Ben and Agnes, all of us.

"I pray to God it'll happen. I've got all this guilt about Sarena and Jimason. I'd feel like I had sorta made it all right if I could get them some money, some big money. Like the preacher says, atonement, I'd feel like I'd atoned."

"I wouldn't have to get *real* rich, just a little rich," she mused, "if only I could get some money for the others. I don't want to be selfish or greedy. I just want to help other people."

Bess Johnson began wondering what the jurors might be thinking. Could they be resentful that they were getting only a pittance while being asked to turn over millions to the plaintiffs? It didn't seem right, just to think about it. They deserved more than they were getting. There just ought to be some way to show appreciation, let them know their good deeds were recognized. But now was the time they really needed to get that message. It might be too late, later on. They might render a bad verdict, just on account of how they don't realize they're appreciated. It wouldn't be bribery, just plain courtesy, plain old appreciation for their hard work, those jurors.

"Just a little appreciation that's all, it'd be well worth it, and we'd all have plenty of money left. Attorney Bates asked for about twenty million; now, if we gave each one of those twelve jurors fifty thousand dollars, that'd be... let's see, that'd be six hundred thousand, right, Bess? Still have more than nineteen million left. Little enough just to show our appreciation."

"I couldn't do that, though, could I? Judge says not to contact, not to talk, call him if anyone attempts to contact," reflected the slowly walking woman who had just turned in her tracks and headed back toward home. "It's not a bribe, of course, just a little appreciation, but somebody might take it wrong. I'd have to be careful. Now, there's one juror there I went to school with, I'm just about sure I went to school with her, Estrata McNemar. I could talk to her. She could pass on the word, could let the jury know we 'ppreciate what they're doing. Of course, it shouldn't all come out of my pocket. I've got the contact, I'd be goin' out on a limb, but the others ought to chip in. After all, it's only fair, they're gettin' more money, lots more than me. They oughta do their fair share."

"It's gettin' late, turning dark. I need to get home and

make some phone calls. No way can that jury go against us, but then again, they might. I didn't like some things I saw. Insurance is what it is, and appreciation and doin' a good deed for others, and doin' right by me too."

"I got dreams, I'm here to tell. I got dreams so big they cain't make no Hollywood movies big enough for 'em. This is it, for me and for Katyna, and for the boys, for Doretta and Jimason, for Ben and Agnes, the minutes is tickin' away, this is the one chance. All them dreams just tied up in what happens tonight. C'mon, dreams. The stars is comin' out. The omens are right."

It was, meantime, a strange evening for the lawyers. For the first time since the case was filed, there was ab-solutely not a single thing they could do about the case. It was of no importance what they knew of the case or of tires and vans. There was no legal research to be done, nor were there motions to file or answer. Feelings of a sudden and violent release from tension came upon them, but there was also a feeling of helplessness, nearly uselessness. Beyond that, the lawyers were consumed with a hand-wringing unease, all because a scattered group of twelve would surely be thinking about this case in the dark of the night. Positions would be jelling among the jurors, and tomorrow, in all probability, there would be a consensus of some sort.

Ted Born made his usual nightly call to Carl Heimat's voice mail: "Carl, the jury has the case now. They got it about five fifteen and stayed out for some forty-five minutes before retiring for the night. I think the closing arguments went about as well as could be expected. In fact, looking back at the trial, I think the whole thing went as well as we could have hoped. At least Bert Sayre told me he thought we 'out-lawyered' them, and he said - win or lose - he had no regrets. I appreciated that. Whether a good lawyerly effort will make any difference is doubtful. As you know, the pattern in the past has been the plaintiffs always win, usually big. They asked the jury this afternoon for about twenty million in this case. They might well get an award for every cent of it. One good sign, which I hesitate to let myself enjoy, is that both of the alternates tell us they would have voted in our favor. Of course, it's possible they were telling the other side at the same time they were going to vote for the *plaintiffs*, but they seemed sincere. Who knows what's going on in the real jurors' minds tonight? I hated to see them break up and go home, with all the past history of jury tampering or suggestions of jury tampering. But what can we do? We've done our best. You know what the worst thing is for me? Not knowing is the worst part. I guess sometime tomorrow we'll get a verdict of some kind. Could be a horror show. I'm nervous, but at least it's not the nervousness of regret, because I think we did a good job. Dave Thompson was super, and Rusty Loman and his staff have given tremendous support, and Nita and Mrs. Shelby - we couldn't have made it without them. Talk to you tomorrow." After dinner in Columbia, Born thumbed through the newspaper without absorbing anything. He turned on television, but it seemed even more trivial than usual, and he clicked it off. Born paced. Then he did some packing, wondered whether he should bother taking some uneaten fruit, bought as snacks for the Universal lawyers, back to Greenville with him, after the verdict came in tomorrow, whatever it might be. Finally, he walked outside.

Born could hear the sounds of the expressway and could see the endless parade of moving white lights flowing down its elevated corridor. Otherwise, there was a stillness in the night. A lone family played about the motel pool. The scent of barbecue persisted in the area of the community outside grill. He walked past the war room, previously a nerve center, strangely abandoned tonight.

As he rounded a corner of the motel on his aimless stroll, Born saw Dave Thompson coming out of his room. "Are you nervous, too?" Dave asked.

"I'm so nervous I can't eat, I can't sleep, I can't read, I can't watch television. All I want to do is run the hands of the clock forward to make it be morning, to go back to Groveton and get the result - whatever it should be, good or bad. The uncertainty is killing me, the worry about what could be happening tonight that we cannot see and will never know. I wish there had been a way to keep that jury there," Ted responded.

"Nothing we can do, I guess," Thompson answered. "At least it's over and we've done the best we could. It might seem tomorrow morning will never get here, but it will. It will. I still can't read that jury, but I feel better than I ever thought I would."

"Win or lose Dave, you've done a wonderful job. No seasoned partner could have done better. One of the things that comes from a draining, emotional experience like this case, is a feeling that we've walked that road together. In walking with you, I've come to appreciate you as one of the most talented lawyers I've ever met, and as a great teammate."

Dave Thompson was moved but said only, "Thanks, Ted, you've been a great mentor. I've learned a lot." Then Thompson looked up at the sky. "It was so clear earlier, now the clouds have moved in, just that glow of the moon behind the clouds. Think it will rain?"

"I hope not. It might be a bad omen." Born laughed hollowly, "I can't help being a little superstitious."

At that moment, juror Estrata McNemar was on the telephone with an unexpected caller. "We're not supposed to be talking, you know," Estrata said. "Well, what're you saying?... Fifty thousand for each juror... Appreciation?... I don't know about that... I think I'd better get off now. You know, we're not supposed to be talking... Yeah, I understand they're hurt bad... I really gotta' go.... No, you know, I'm not sure I remember you from high school. Course, I know who you are now.... I think it's better if we hang up for now. We can talk some more after the trial, maybe."

McNemar hung up the telephone and sat there, thinking. "I better get some fresh air," she said to herself. She walked outside and stood on the porch, in her bathrobe, listening to the tree frogs and crickets, peering out into a heavy night air that seemed especially dark and murky. "All I have to do is vote one way, and I get - all the jurors get - fifty thousand dollars apiece, with no taxes. That's a lot of money. All we have to do is vote that way. Ten minutes' work, maybe an hour's work. Easiest money I ever made in my life. It's so simple. And it sure wouldn't be the first time it's ever happened. Probably nobody would know."

CHAPTER THIRTY-THREE

THE SYSTEM WORKS

It could have been an empty rural train depot with hollow echoes and jaded, spartan look. Men and women soberly began entering the silent tomblike room and took their seats at tables up front, whispering softly. Others came and sat in the rows behind. They could have been passengers waiting for their train to come into a cavernous station on Courthouse Square. They had no notion when the train would come, whence it came, or where it was going. They had all bought tickets to a common but unknown destination and were waiting for the conductor.

It was Wednesday morning, and this was not a train station but a courtroom in Groveton where lawyers and clients had assembled at the appointed hour for the culmination of a multi-months-long journey. The absent conductor was a Judge who was uncharacteristically running late. The Clerk of the Court came into the courtroom and announced that Judge Andrews had called and directed that the jurors simply resume deliberations, that he would be along shortly. The jurors had been milling around the outside of the courtroom, on the Annex corridor or on the bridge between Annex and courtroom. Mostly, they were silent and seemed serious. The Clerk ushered them into the jury room, and once again the door was shut, Deputy Sheriff standing guard.

In a few moments, Judge Andrews arrived, shook hands with the lawyers and exchanged pleasantries. He noticed Fred Bates was not there. "Where's Fred?" he asked.

"He had something he needed to deal with this morning, Judge," answered Jack Ripps. "He said he would trust Alton and me to handle this," Ripps smiled.

The Judge stepped up to his bench and sat down busying himself with paperwork he had brought with him. "I must have mountains of work waiting for me," Ted Born thought. "But I couldn't handle it, even if I had it with me. I can't do anything but think about this case. Totally pointless, nothing I can do, but my adrenalin has me hyper."

Born talked with Theo Burton about Burton's family, an achievement driven family more interesting than most, but Born only half heard what Burton told him. Burton appreciated automobiles and liked to talk about them. In the course of the trial, he had talked with Born and Thompson about the van as much as he had talked about the tire. Now there was more conversation about cars, but Born listened blankly, responded reflexively, for Born's mind was in the jury room with the twelve.

For the first time since the case began, the plaintiffs' and defenses' counsel were cordial to each other, not friendly, but at least cordial.

There was much pacing in the courtroom. Ted Born kept going to the windows and looking across the bridge toward the jury room. On one trip he noticed Sam Johnson had wandered over to talk with his Deputy standing guard just outside the jury room. Born thought Johnson might move on, but then it became clear he had settled in near the jury room. Born was worried and motioned the other lawyers to approach the bench. "Judge, I notice Sam Johnson is standing right outside the jury room with his deputy. I'm very concerned that, if the door to the jury room opens for any reason and the jurors see Sam - the Sheriff and former plaintiff and relative of other plaintiffs - standing right outside, it could have a chilling effect on the deliberations."

"That may be my fault," answered Judge Andrews. "He asked me if he could have a word with the deputy and I said it would be all right. But if he's continuing to post himself there, I'll tell him he needs to move away." The Judge came down from the bench, went over to speak with Sheriff Johnson, and the latter sauntered off.

The minutes ticked on. At approximately ten o'clock, Born was looking through the window toward the jury room when he saw the Deputy turn suddenly toward the door and open it. A juror handed him a note. He took the note, shut the door to the jury room and walked across the bridge to the courtroom where he handed the note to the Judge. Judge Andrews opened the note as the silent courtroom watched. He raised his eyebrows in an indication of surprise as he read the handwritten words on the note: "WE THE JURY HAVE A VERDICT."

"Okay, let's bring them in," said the Judge. "Where's the Court Reporter?"

"Judge, I believe the reporter has gone to get coffee," said Ripps. "We'll send for him."

"Well, we obviously can't receive the verdict without the Court Reporter. I'll appreciate any help in finding him," said the Judge.

Born's heart was beating hard as he knew the moment of truth was approaching. Dave Thompson mainly seemed agitated that the Court Reporter was not there, but he too was nervous. "Why can't that Court Reporter be where he's supposed to be?" Thompson asked - said, really - with nervous irritation.

Born allowed himself a fleeting moment of optimism. "A short deliberation period, like this one, should be a good sign, shouldn't it? If they had found for the plaintiffs, surely they would have needed more time to reach a consensus on damages. No, Ted, you know better than that, you can't tell. They could have simply awarded every penny the plaintiffs asked in thirty seconds - the full twenty million dollars."

After a lawyer's psychological eternity, the Court

Reporter was located and he shuffled up to his court reporting machine, coffee cup in hand. "I'm ready, Judge," he said.

"Then we're all ready. Bring them in," said Judge Andrews. Chet Bernhardt was not in the courtroom, but Brad Mansfield said nothing, not wishing to delay the proceedings further.

The lawyers and clients all stood for the entry of the jury, as a show of respect. The plaintiffs' lawyers were smiling as Alton Fox leaned over and said to Born, "This is the hardest part." Born agreed.

The person in the courtroom who beamed most expectantly was the Clerk, Fred Bates' promoted Clerk, as she stood by her table next to the bench. "Does the Clerk know something we don't know?" Born asked himself. "If she does, that smile on her face, that radiant glow, is bad news for us."

The jury filed in and stood by their chairs in the jury box, inscrutable as ever, looking straight at the Judge and not at any parties. "Please be seated, everybody," said the Judge. Everyone in the courtroom took a seat. "Has the jury reached a verdict?"

"We have, Your Honor," answered a female voice at the left end of the first row.

"Will the foreperson please hand up the verdict forms," the Court directed.

The foreperson, Mrs. Denise Jones, handed up two one-page verdict forms. The defense counsels' hopes soared. A one-page verdict would indicate a defense verdict, a two-page form a plaintiffs' verdict. "It's just one page!" Thompson said excitedly to Born.

Born nodded but continued to suppress any hope. "It can't be good news," he said to himself. "There's no way to win this case. There's got to be a reason it's a one-page plaintiffs' verdict. You can't get your hopes up."

The Judge read from the first form as Born closed his eyes and bowed his head. "WE THE JURY FIND FOR THE DEFENDANT UNIVERSAL TIRE COMPANY AND AGAINST THE PLAINTIFFS."

The smile drained instantly from the Clerk's face.

"We won! We won!" whispered Thompson excitedly to Born whose head remained bowed, though his eyes opened slightly. He allowed himself a weak smile and then turned solemn again.

"WE THE JURY FIND FOR THE DEFENDANT TERGANO MOTOR COMPANY AND AGAINST THE PLAINTIFFS," Judge Andrews read the second verdict form.

"Would you like to have the jury polled?" the Judge asked the plaintiffs' lawyers who looked shaken and sallow.

"Yes, Your Honor," said Ripps, looking piercingly at the jurors.

"I know it's just a formality," Born told himself. "The losers always ask to have the jury polled to see if the verdict really is unanimous, nothing to lose by asking. But I've never seen it make any difference. Still, I can't relax until I know the verdict is nailed down."

The Judge started with the foreperson on the left end,

CHAPTER THIRTY-THREE

"Is that your verdict?"

"Yes."

To the next juror, "Is that your verdict?"

"Yes."

To the third juror, "Is that your verdict?"

"Yes."

To the fourth juror, "Is that your verdict?"

"It was, but now I've got second thoughts," he said. It was juror Eston Gilliland. The entire courtroom was aghast. Ted Born's heart dropped to the pit of his stomach.

"Ladies and Gentlemen, your verdict must be unanimous. I am going to return these verdict forms to you and ask you to continue your deliberations," said the Judge.

Ted Born was distressed beyond words. He and Dave Thompson and Rusty Loman had almost won the case, and not just any case. It would have been the win of the decade, at least. Nobody thought they could do it, certainly not Born. But they had done it - almost. They had been ready to pack up and leave the courtroom in glory, and glory had been snatched right out of their grasp. Release, sweet release, it was almost theirs, and they had earned it, and deserved it, and they had been teased as it vanished in their very grasp.

Born recovered enough to approach the bench and move the Court to enter a judgment for Universal. "The juror stated it *had* been his verdict. Once the jury unanimously reached a verdict and it was read in Court and acknowledged, it was too late for further deliberations. We are entitled to entry of judgment in our favor without further deliberations," Born stated in support of his motion.

"Tergano Motor Company joins in that motion," Brad Mansfield said, just as Chet Bernhardt returned to the courtroom, surprised at what was happening.

"Do you have any law supporting your position?" asked the Judge.

"Not immediately in front of me, Your Honor, but it all makes logical sense," Born answered.

"If you can find some law, I'll be glad to look at it," Judge Andrews offered. "In the meantime, I'm going to let them continue their deliberations."

The lawyers left the bench conference and broke into their own groups. "Did you see that look Jack Ripps gave Eston Gilliland, the juror?" Thompson asked. "Ripps intimidated him into changing his mind."

"That may be," said Born. "But in the meantime, we need to look for some law. Dave, can you and Rusty go back to Rusty's office, get on the phone with Carl Heimat or Tim Archer or somebody and see if they can do some quick research? Dave, try your modem to get to one of the legal databases. Rusty, why don't you look in the Code? I'll stay here and defend the fort in case the jury comes out again, or anything."

Thompson and Loman hurriedly left for Loman's office. Loman began pouring over the Code. Thompson called the GOB office in Greenville and reached John Mann. "I don't believe it!" Mann said. "Are you kidding me? You mean the jury brought back a *defense* verdict in *that* case, and then a juror screwed it up and they've gone back in?... Yeah, I understand you need some precedents to protect that verdict in case a second one comes out different. We'll get right on it.... Give me your telephone number in Groveton.... Got it. Be back soon as I can."

On his way to the library back in Greenville, Mann spread the word, "Ted and Dave got a defense verdict, and then one of the jurors wanted to reconsider. I need to find some law to protect that first verdict."

It was like the Pied Piper as lawyers came out of their offices and followed Mann into the library. There were about twenty lawyers and summer associate law students already working in the library as the entourage burst in, shattering the silence with the announcement, "Ted and Dave got a defense verdict in that Phoenix County case, but a juror wanted to go back and talk some more. He admitted he had agreed to the verdict and the Court received and published it in the courtroom, but then he said he had `second thoughts'. We need crash help, everybody. Can a juror change his mind after once agreeing to a unanimous verdict?" All the lawyers and summer associates were aware of the case and needed no briefing. In fact, there had been the expectation that a loss was certain, and the firm had braced itself for the worst. In groups of two's and three's, the library for a while would be a new off-site war room, some looking at digests, some reading cases, some running down the annotations in the Code.

Meanwhile, the word spread like wildfire within the

firm, on all floors. "Have you heard about the Phoenix County case? They won! But this bizarre thing happened... ." "Incredible! But then... ." Lawyers were talking excitedly in hallways. Secretaries were telling each other. The receptionists were telling sheer strangers who happened to be in the reception area at the time. No one could remember an electric moment like this one, a moment of hope and fear. But hope seemed to dominate because, until now, fear of near certain disaster had been unchallenged among lawyers in the firm. Now the very possibility that one might dare to hope was itself cause for celebration, no matter what might happen in the end. Already there had been a victory of sorts.

The crash research went on in Greenville and Groveton. Unfortunately, the results were not encouraging for Universal. Try as they might to find some helpful law, the only law they found supported the Judge's actions in sending the jury back for further deliberations. The law seemed to be that a juror can have a change of mind at any time before the jury is discharged. There was nothing to do but wait nervously while the jurors remained behind those closed doors.

Ted Born kept watch by the windows where he could see the jury room. Down the open Annex corridor from the jury room, Sheriff Sam Johnson was having a serious discussion with Jack Ripps, as they stood next to each other, arms resting on the outside railing. One could safely assume Johnson was not happy with the verdict and that he was making sure Ripps understood his displeasure. Ripps looked glum, peering vacantly toward the ground below, occasionally gesturing with one hand or the other, avoiding eye contact with Johnson, who was looking directly and intently at the side of Ripps' face as he spoke to Ripps.

Born looked toward the jury room again and noticed the Deputy opening the door and receiving a written slip of paper which he quickly brought to the Judge.

"The jury has a verdict again," said the Judge. "Let's bring them again. Where's the Court reporter?"

Like a repeating bad dream, the Court Reporter was not around. Dave Thompson was really agitated this time. "Why in the world doesn't that Court Reporter stay where he's supposed to be? This is killing me, and we can't do anything - this whole courtroom and all the lawyers and parties are all held up - without that Court Reporter. Always gets out of pocket when you need him," Thompson said with a frown as he went outside to try to find him. Thompson could not find him, and returned to say, "This is the second time this morning. Looks like he would have learned to stay put after the first time."

Eventually, the Court Reporter was located, and the jury was brought in. Again, two single-sheet verdict forms were handed up to the Judge. "You have now handed back to me the same two verdict forms you gave me the last time. I will not read them, but I will simply say they find in favor of each of the defendants and against the plaintiffs. Mr. Ripps, I assume you would like to have the jury polled."

"Yes, Your Honor," answered Ripps.

The jury was polled, and the courtroom held its collective breath as juror Eston Gilliland was asked if it was his verdict. This time, Gilliland said it was his verdict, with no apparent second - or third - thoughts.

The Judge thanked the jury for its service, told them it would be permissible to talk with counsel if they wished but they were under no obligation to do so, discharged the jury and adjourned the Court.

Alton Fox reached over from the plaintiffs' table, congratulated Born and shook hands. Other congratulations followed. Ted Born had intended to speak to the individual plaintiffs, though he was not sure what he would say, but they were gone, silently gone. Soon, too, their lawyers were gone.

Nita Langley was snapping photographs of the happy defense teams. Born said, "Nita, I've been looking at that cage in the back corner since the first day I set foot in this courtroom, and I've looked at it each day of the trial. For me, it's come to be a symbol of the case and the trial and of my situation. Could you take a picture of me in that cage?"

"Yeah, me too," Thompson asked.

"Why don't we take a picture of the five of us, me, Dave, Rusty, Theo and Bert?" Ted Born suggested.

The cage door was swung back and the five of them stepped in. They locked arm-in-arm, grinning joyfully as Langley snapped several pictures. Maybe it was the Elysian air again, the bringer of supreme joy, but Ted

Born's mind was turned to Schiller's gaudy Ode to Joy and he found himself drawn to the words:

Freude, schoener Goetterfunken,
Tochter aus Elysium,... .
Deine Zauber binden wieder,
Was die Mode streng geteilt.
Alle Menschen werden Brueder,
Wo dein sanfter Fluegel
weilt.

The words had been inseparably wedded to the music of Beethoven's Ninth Symphony, and the strains of Beethoven lifted the words as the five reveled in the brotherhood of joy. Ironically, the brotherhood of suffering, on which Born had often reflected in the course of this case, was not the only binding force among people. There was also this brotherhood of joy. Two extremes, a common result. "Joy, thou beautiful, divinely-sprung daughter of Elysium. Your magic binds together that which custom has torn apart. All mankind becomes brothers where your gentle wings spread!"

It was the wings of joy which carried them back toward Rusty Loman's office from the Courthouse. Somewhere en route, Marta Shelby said, "We have a surprise for you waiting in Rusty's office. Nita and I went out and got it last night."

At Rusty Loman's office, Champagne popped and cheese and fruit - especially fresh strawberries - floated in front of their eyes. And there were sweets and all kinds of good things. "I can't believe you went out and got this last night!" Born said. "The odds were overwhelmingly against us."

"We knew you were going to win after the closing arguments," Nita Langley said.

"I wish you had told me!" Born said in amazement at her seemingly naive confidence. "I thought our chances were pretty remote."

"The system worked," Dave Thompson said excitedly. "We should have won, and we did win. Looks like we found twelve God-fearing residents here in Phoenix County."

"Yeah, maybe I was too hard on this county. Maybe you *can* get a fair trial here. Of course, we had to do some extraordinary things to get a fair trial, which no one should have to do, but we won," Born said.

"Do you think the plaintiffs ever thought they might lose?" Thompson asked.

"No. Everything they did through the whole trial broadcast their confidence of winning. And I sure wouldn't have bet against them. How about you, Dave, did you ever think we could win?" Born asked.

"I kept telling myself we *should* win, that we *could* win, but I never could tell what they were thinking, except they did seem to warm up to your closing argument, Ted," Thompson answered.

"You all did a super job," Bert Sayre said.

"Put that in your report," Born said with feigned seriousness. The whole room convulsed. The front door to Loman's office opened, and the Tergano lawyers came in the door with two jurors in tow - the foreperson Denise Jones and Estrata McNemar.

Ted Born's first reaction was embarrassment. The celebration might look to the jurors like gloating, something unseemly in light of the death and the injuries. His second reaction was that he really did not want to talk with jurors. He had a feeling he might learn something he did not want to know. He simply wanted to finish the celebration and get out of Groveton.

But Born and Thompson had hugs for the jurors. Then Born said, "Mrs. Langley and Mrs. Shelby fixed this spread. They had a lot more confidence than I had. Won't you have something?"

"Oh, I knew when I first saw that tire that Universal shouldn't even be here," Jones said. "I still wanted to hear some more about Tergano, but you didn't have anything to worry about."

"You could have fooled me," Born said, "none of us could ever figure out what y'all were thinking. By the way, I feel sorry for the plaintiffs, especially Jimason and the Millers, I wish I could help, but it just wasn't our fault."

"We felt the same way," Jones said. "We felt real sorry for the children and their parents, but we couldn't see how you were at fault."

"How about the juror who wanted to go back and talk some more, Mr. Gilliland, what was that all about?" Born asked.

"Oh, he just wanted to talk more about the

stabilizer bar. Didn't have anything to do with the tire," Jones answered.

"You mean I could have relaxed all that time instead of going crazy?" Born asked. "You mean Universal was safe all the time but there was a possibility you might have stuck it to Tergano?" Born laughed and pointed toward Brad Mansfield who was standing in the circle surrounding the two jurors.

"Yeah, that's about the size of it," Jones answered, also laughing with the whole group. Estrata McNemar had said nothing beyond "Hello" and "Congratulations."

Born thought how strange it was that the mock jurors had thought Tergano's defense was stronger than Universal's and that even in this trial, particularly in the beginning, Tergano had tried to distance itself from Universal. In the end, it had all turned around, with Universal having the stronger case and Tergano being the defendant more likely to lose.

The jurors obviously liked Dave Thompson and took him aside and told him so. Thompson was flattered but embarrassed as he came to Born and told him with broken words - really *didn't* tell him - of the jurors' admiration, laughing and smiling with embarrassment.

The caterer had come with the daily lunches, and the Champagne, fruit and cheese gave way to fried chicken and potato salad and iced tea. The visiting jurors said "Goodbye", then Estrata McNemar turned and said, as she disappeared through the door, "I'm glad you sampled some real Phoenix County justice." At the time, it seemed like a normal statement under the apparent circumstances, what one might expect, nothing unusual.

Born, Thompson and Sayre were walking to their cars after all the back-slappings and reminiscences and cross-compliments and farewells when they encountered Judge Andrews going to his car. The Judge hailed them. "I just wanted to tell you I've enjoyed having you in my courtroom," he said.

"Judge, I just want to thank you for *not* granting our motions for summary judgment and *not* granting our motions for a directed verdict, although I have to tell you that's not the way I felt at the time," Born laughed.

"I know what you mean," said the Judge. "A jury verdict will stand up much better on appeal than a summary judgment or directed verdict."

"Maybe I was wrong, Judge," Born said apologetically. "Despite all my fears, the system worked, at least in this case."

"Yeah, you've got to have faith in the system, or we're all in big trouble," Judge Andrews said.

Dave Thompson moved on to his car, saying he was heading straight for home, and would definitely *not* be stopping at the office. Ted Born and Bert Sayre got in Born's car for the trip to the airport where Born dropped off Sayre.

Then Born drove back to his Greenville office. "Gee, I'm not sure anyone ever called to tell the office we won. I need to go by and let them know." The air was warm and the sky had cleared. But Born's mind still swarmed with overwhelming thoughts and reflections of an experience he could not yet grasp.

He walked into his office and went straight to John Mann to thank him for the crash research effort of the morning. Before he got there, he was stopped by first one lawyer, then a group gathered, and lawyers and secretaries came to greet and congratulate Born from all directions, blocking traffic in the firm. They had indeed found out the result, and it had been announced on the PA system. Mike Jackson saw him at a distance and made a ceremonial bow. He came and shook Born's hand and said "Carl Heimat called and spoke to Rusty Loman. Rusty said your closing argument was 'phenomenal'."

When Born finally got to his own office and checked his computer electronic mail, he found it flooded with congratulatory messages. He and Dave Thompson had become instantaneous folk heroes within the firm. The word spread throughout the state that the impossible had been done. Unfortunately for Born and Thompson, the case was far from over.

CHAPTER THIRTY-FOUR

WEIRDED OUT

About three weeks after the end of the trial, defense counsel received strange motions in the mail filed by plaintiffs' counsel. The motions requested Judge Andrews to appoint guardians ad litem to represent the interests of the minor plaintiffs, with no explanation for the request. Obviously, such guardians would formally represent the minors' interests in lieu of their parents who were now informally representing them as "next friend." Unnoticed at first by the defense was another strange feature of the motion: The "style" or caption of the case omitted any reference to Bess Johnson and Doretta Anchrum in their individual capacities, but continued to list adults only in their present informal capacities as representatives of their respective children. Normally, the caption would list all parties even if the motion was on behalf of only one or two of them, unless an abbreviated caption was used, which this one did not purport to be. Strange.

Was this possibly a preliminary step to terminating the case? Did plaintiffs' counsel possibly feel they needed an independent guardian ad litem to evaluate the prospects for a new trial or appeal before taking action which could prejudice the interests of the minors, in effect a buffer to insulate them from a malpractice claim for dropping the case? If so, the strange motions would be a good sign for a defense, suggesting a preliminary move preparatory to letting the case expire without an appeal. Or was there some other purpose?

More days passed. It had now been twenty-seven days since the verdict had been rendered and judgment entered for the defendants. Ted Born had been in contact with other defense counsel, and they had been speculating as to whether plaintiffs would move for a new trial within the allotted thirty days. It was the consensus that the plaintiffs' lawyers might feel compelled to do so on account of pressure from their clients, but there seemed no strong grounds for such a motion. There were no er-rors in jury instructions - a popular ground for new trials or appeals - because plaintiffs' lawyers had essentially consented to the instructions. It was possible plaintiffs could contest the Court's disposition of the *Batson* challenges, but the defendants felt any errors were in favor of the plaintiffs rather than against them, and Judge Andrews in any event was not likely to change his mind on a new trial motion. Other grounds for a new trial could be imagined, but all of them seemed like long shots. The more the defendants thought about it, the more they thought an appeal or new trial might be difficult and just possibly might not occur. Anyway, the time was drawing near when plaintiffs would have to show their hand or fold.

Since Trip Gillespy was located in Columbia, like Fred Bates and Jack Ripps, and knew them best, he was assigned the job of finding out what was on their minds and, if they were contemplating a motion for new trial, to try to persuade against it.

The telephone rang in Ted Born's office. "Ted, this is Trip Gillespy. I've got Chet Bernhardt on the line also. I've just been weirded out."

"Weirded out" was a new verb for Born, but he thought he understood the general meaning. "How's that?" Born asked.

"I've just been talking to Jack Ripps, and he tells me the plaintiffs are going to ask for a new trial based on *bribery*," Gillespy related.

"Bribery? *We* certainly didn't do any bribing, and I know good and well you didn't either," Born said in astonishment.

"No, of course not," Gillespy continued. "If I understood him correctly, he was saying his own plaintiffs committed the bribery."

"Now, wait a minute, Trip," Born said. "My mind's not so nimble anymore. Let me get this straight: The plaintiffs want a new trial because of their own bribery. Am I hearing you right? You're pulling my leg."

"I'm dead serious," said Gillespy. "That's the way I understand it."

"I'm weirded out, too, whatever that means," said Born. "Know anything else?"

"No, quite frankly, I was so taken aback, I couldn't think what to say or ask him. I would have been prepared for *anything* but bribery. Of course, it doesn't surprise me that there might have been bribery, given the track record of Phoenix County litigation, but it did surprise me to hear about bribery from Jack, lawyer for the plaintiffs. I don't know who or what or how."

"I think I'll call Jack and see what he'll tell me," Born said.

"Let us know," Bernhardt requested. "Damnedest thing I ever heard of."

Born called Jack Ripps who was very guarded in what he would say. However, it came out that one or more of the adult plaintiffs had been quoted in jury deliberations as having attempted a bribe. Ripps was planning to argue that this bribery suggestion poisoned jury deliberations and caused the jurors to "sanction" all the plaintiffs by voting against them. "We've explained it all to the State Bar and they've approved what we're doing."

Born called the State Bar after talking with Ripps and reached someone who knew all about the situation. "Mr. Bates came in to see me about it. He said that, in interviewing jurors after the trial, they learned that possibly a bribery attempt had been made by one of their own clients, a woman, I believe. They then confronted her and she at first denied it. Then they got her to agree to a polygraph test and she flunked it. At that point, she broke down and admitted it. Mr. Bates was concerned about the effect this adult's bribery might have on the cases of the minor children. I told them I thought they could no longer continue to represent both the adults - or any guilty adults - and the children, because of the conflict of interest. I think they were tending to drop the representation of the adults and to have guardians ad litem appointed for the children, in lieu of the parents' continuing to represent the children's interests as next friends."

Born shared this information with Dave Thompson and with Tergano's lawyers. They continued to be puzzled but took a wait-and-see attitude until they received the motion for new trial which presumably would throw more light on the matter.

They did not have to wait long. On the very next day Rusty Loman faxed Born a copy of plaintiffs' motion for new trial supported by three affidavits. The motion carefully avoided any acknowledgment that bribery had actually taken place. It merely alleged that one of the jurors, Estrata McNemar, had told the other jurors of an attempted bribe by Bess Johnson of fifty thousand dollars per juror. This was alleged to be an "extraneous circumstance" which tainted jury deliberations. Furthermore, it was misconduct on the part of juror McNemar not to tell the Judge about any such alleged bribery. Had she done so, the Judge surely would have declared a mistrial. Since the Judge had no opportunity to declare a mistrial because the juror's misconduct concealed it, he should do the equivalent now and grant a new trial. In any case, minor children cannot be held responsible and should not be penalized for any misconduct on the part of the adults. So the motion contended.

The affidavits were from three male jurors saying in each case that the juror had originally intended to vote for the plaintiffs but, when he heard about the bribery, changed his mind and voted for the defendants. There was no affidavit from Bess Johnson or from Estrata McNemar.

Thompson came into Born's office shaking his head. "These are bad affidavits," he said. "The first thing I want to do is to find out if it's true, if there really was bribery. I want to leave right now, drive down there, locate Estrata McNemar and find out what happened."

"That's fine, Dave, except we're having a firm meeting today at five o'clock, remember, where you and I are supposed to tell the firm about this case. I'd like for you to be there and get the credit you deserve," Born told him.

"Oh, I don't care about that - I've already had plenty of credit. I can't get out into the hall without somebody congratulating me, and on the streets, too. I just don't want to have to retry the case. I need to be in Phoenix County," said Thompson.

"That's what makes you such a fine lawyer, Dave. You do the job first, and you never rest until it's done, and done well. I can't argue with the fact we need to dive into this as quickly as possible. We have fifteen days to file our response, and we'll need to make use of every bit of that time. Good luck!" Born gave a salute-type send-off to Thompson who quickly left the office.

When the firm meeting had originally been set up and Born and Thompson had been asked to talk about the case, the assumption was that the case was over, except for possibly a perfunctory appeal. As lawyers convened for the meeting that evening, few had heard of the bribery development and of the unusual motion for a new trial. The lawyers could hardly believe what they were hearing as the tale unfolded. "I am in the peculiar position," Born told them, "that I was originally convinced a corporation could not get a fair trial in Phoenix County, then I decided maybe - if you tried hard enough - maybe you could. And now I've been proven wrong, and I'm again doubtful a fair trial can be had in Phoenix. The sad truth appears to be that, even if by some miracle you win in Phoenix County, you have to walk through unseen minefields to do it, and sometimes those hidden mines blow up on you after the fact, even after you've successfully walked through them. The fact is, if the bribery had succeeded, we would have never known about it. People would have just said, 'Well, Ted and Dave lost. We have to respect the verdict of the jury. Maybe they didn't do a good job on the trial.'

"No, if we'd lost, the bribe would never have come to light because the giver and receiver of the bribe would have stayed mum. We know about this one only because it didn't work, and the juror who was offered the bribe told the other jurors about it. And now, the plaintiffs are trying to get a new trial because of the bribery. It's a no-lose situation for them. If the bribe works, they take home millions of dollars and nobody ever knows. If it doesn't work, then they claim they should get a new trial and take another shot at it. Somehow it looks like there's some force out there determined to keep any corporate defendant from winning in Phoenix County,"

That night after the firm meeting, Thompson called Born from Rusty Loman's office to report on the meeting with Estrata McNemar.

"We've confirmed it *did* happen," Thompson said. "Rusty went with me, and Estrata told us she got a telephone call Tuesday night after the closing arguments from Bess Johnson offering fifty thousand dollars per juror if they would render a plaintiff's verdict. Said Bess made out like she had known Estrata from high school, but Estrata didn't remember her. Estrata told us there wasn't any amount of money in the whole world that would cause her to vote against the way she believed was right. Bess apparently didn't come right out and say it, but she implied she knew there were a couple of others who were going to vote for plaintiffs. Maybe some others also got offers and haven't revealed it. Estrata told the rest of the jurors the next morning, and they all agreed it didn't make any difference to their vote, so they just decided not to mention it to the Judge. I guess they didn't want to get Bess into any trouble," Dave Thompson reported.

"Did you get a signed statement from her? I actually hope you didn't," Born inquired.

"No, we didn't. We thought about it but didn't want to push the point because she really wasn't too comfortable talking about it anyway," Thompson said.

"That's fine. We can go back if we decide we should. I got to thinking about it after you left, and we might be just as well off without a statement from Estrata McNemar. I've been doing some preliminary research. You know, normally, you can't use a juror's testimony to impeach a jury verdict. But there's an exception: if an "extraneous event" improperly influences a jury verdict, then a juror's testimony can be used to impeach it.

"Now bribery might be an extraneous event - probably is - but only two persons have direct knowledge of it, the briber and the bribee. Up to now, the plaintiffs' lawyers haven't submitted any direct evidence of bribery, no affidavit's been submitted by Estrata McNemar or Bess Johnson. The only affidavits submitted so far are by *other* jurors who say they *heard* Estrata say there was bribery. That's just hearsay, and it should not be admissible under general rules of evidence.

"I don't think Bates and company will be filing an affidavit by their client Bess Johnson confessing to the bribery nor by Estrata confirming the bribery. They would be directly implicating their client in criminal bribery if they did. If we don't submit affidavits from either of those two, there will be no direct and admissible evidence of any extraneous event," Born thought aloud.

"Yeah, but suppose there wasn't any real bribery, but Estrata told the jury there had been. Wouldn't that be something the other jurors could testify to, that the statement was at least made in deliberations?" asked Thompson.

"I'm not sure," said Born. "Maybe so, maybe not. In one sense, without admissible proof of an extraneous event, it all just becomes a part of deliberations, you know, things jurors *say* to each other. If you can impeach jury deliberations just because a juror says something that's not true, does that destroy the sanctity of the deliberations? I doubt there've been many jury sessions where some juror hasn't brought up some incident from his or her past and tossed it into the jury brew. Should the loser be able to set aside the verdict if it can be proved the incident never happened or was not accurately described? I'm not sure yet. We're still researching. The only point I'm making right now is, I'm just as glad you didn't get an affidavit from Mrs. McNemar. There could be some technical reasons under the law of evidence why we would not want it."

"Okay. I'm heading back for right now, and I'll see you tomorrow," Thompson said.

Born and Thompson did some intensive research in the days ahead and met to evaluate it and decide on the next step. Born began by sharing his research results. "I thought I might get some comfort that the children are bound by what the parents do, that when a parent who sues on behalf of children is implicated in wrong-doing, it taints the case of the children as well as the adults.

Unfortunately, the law is all to the opposite effect. The Courts are very solicitous for the welfare of children and will protect them from the misconduct of adults who represent them. So I have totally struck out on that line of research."

Thompson then volunteered, "My research is a mixed bag, but it also is basically not too encouraging. On the positive side, the law liberally admits into evidence affidavits of jurors supporting the jury verdict but will not admit any juror affidavit impeaching the verdict except as to "extraneous events" which materially influence it. There are a couple of precedents about extraneous events. In one case, a juror brought a dictionary into the jury room and the jury used it to look up the meaning of legal terms - instead of using the instructions on the law which the judge had given them."

Born interrupted, "But our case is different from that. In the dictionary case, all the jurors actually personally saw the dictionary; it wasn't hearsay. In our case, the affidavits on file thus far do not provide any direct evidence of bribery, just inadmissible hearsay."

"Yeah, but there's this other case," Thompson responded, "where a woman juror said her son had had a bad experience with the defendant company which she related to the jurors. None of the other jurors saw the bad experience, they just heard about it, but that was deemed to be an 'extraneous event' tainting the verdict."

"That's a hard one to get around," acknowledged Born. "I think that is analytically the wrong result, but wc have to recognize it's a precedent which we'll have a hard time dealing with. It looks like here's where we stand, as I see it. I think we have to accept that the plaintiffs might be able to get into evidence the fact bribery was discussed during jury deliberations. It's also pretty clear a losing party can't get a new trial on the basis of his own wrongdoing. That leaves us, though, with the possibility of a new trial for the children, because they aren't accountable for their parents' wrongdoing. I think we can assume Doretta Anchrum was in on the bribery, because the lawyers have dropped both Doretta and Bess from the case. Maybe the Millers were also involved in it, but they've been left in the case by their lawyers. In any event, Bess and Doretta are out, but on a new trial, it doesn't help us much because practically all of the damages claimed by the other side were for the children, living and dead - I think eighteen or nineteen million of the twenty million claimed.

"Now I see only two things we can do that might help us," Born continued. "First, we can try to show the bribery did not affect the result. I think, to get a new trial, they would have to show the mention of the bribery affected the result or at least should be presumed under the circumstances to have affected the result."

"I can't see anything but a brick wall there," said Thompson. "It's obvious from the three affidavits that the bribery discussion did affect the results. Here are three jurors who have sworn they were planning to vote for the plaintiffs and then changed their minds and voted for the defendants when the bribery came up."

"Exactly," said Born. "That brings me to the second point. We need to check the accuracy of those affidavits."

"I wouldn't think any of those who signed the affidavits are likely to say, `I confess I didn't tell the truth,'" Thompson observed logically.

"I know, Dave," Born answered. "It's a long shot. But it's all we have. We're in trouble and it's the only way out I can see. We can make policy arguments, but they're just arguments and we don't have any good authoritative law to back them up. I think we first go to the jurors who have *not* given affidavits yet and see what they have to say. If we get good information, we'll take it and confront the three who've already signed."

"I've thought about taking Bess Johnson's deposition," Thompson mused. "But I know she'll take the Fifth Amendment and refuse to testify. Besides, the deposition would make a record of the bribery, and that wouldn't necessarily be good. I'd also like to see this whole mess investigated, see what all is behind it."

"That would take longer than the fifteen days we have for our reply," said Born. "Plus, it might even benefit the plaintiffs. I can hear them now. They'd be sure to argue they were unable properly to prosecute this civil action because they were so involved in defending themselves in the criminal investigation. Tempting as it is, we'd better leave it alone."

"Okay. What do you suggest?" asked Thompson.

"Start with the jury list. Get together with Rusty Loman and get him to show you where the jurors live. You probably should get Rusty to go with you. This is sensitive stuff, and we want to be sure you have a witness in case a juror accuses you of intimidation or improper conduct," Born suggested.

"Sounds good. I'll get in touch with Rusty and we'll jump on it with both feet," Thompson said.

CHAPTER THIRTY-FIVE

BRINGING IN THE SHEAVES

"I got an affidavit, Ted, our first one," Thompson told Born by telephone. "It's from Jamie Acton. You remember her, she's the juror we thought was sleeping a lot of the time. We tried to get some others first but missed them and will go back by and try to get them this afternoon. But Jamie Acton will surprise you. She's very alert and is a fine woman, very religious. She said she prayed to God not to make her have to serve on the jury but since God didn't take her off, she decided she would do the best she could. She was praying and thinking all the time we thought she was sleeping. She didn't miss a thing."

"What'd she say?" Ted Born asked. "I mean, about the deliberations."

"She said she didn't think the bribery affected

anybody's vote," Thompson said. "She said she was always for the defendants because she didn't see any evidence we did anything wrong. Said the vote on the jury was already at least ten-to-two in our favor on Tuesday before the jury recessed for the night..."

"Wait. Tell me that again, Dave. She says the vote was *ten-to-two* and that was as early as *Tuesday*, before the recess?" Born asked excitedly.

"That's right. Actually, she said *at least* ten-to-two, and that's how her affidavit was worded," Thompson said.

"Could help a lot," Born said. "It could show the trend was overwhelmingly in our favor. Of course, I guess the holdouts were among those who signed the affidavits, and they could theoretically have held out forever, and even converted some of the pro-defense jurors but for the introduction of the bribery into the discussion. Of course, that's bull, but you have to indulge that possibility as a matter of legal theory. At least it's hopeful, really more so than I had let myself think possible. Anything else?"

"Not really. She's convinced it didn't affect the vote, and I think she's reliable. But we'll just have to see. We hope to see a couple more this afternoon. Let you know as soon as I have anything else," Thompson said.

Born sat at his desk, thinking. Suddenly, he realized something didn't fit. If the vote had been ten-to-two - indeed, at least ten-to-two - on Tuesday before the evening recess, how could there be *three* jurors who on Wednesday morning were planning to vote for the plaintiffs and changed their minds at the mention of bribery?

Of course, Jamie Acton could be mistaken, or maybe one of the Tuesday pro-defense jurors became a Wednesday pro-plaintiff juror before the bribery subject came up. More affidavits would help clarify the situation.

At the end of the day, Thompson and Loman telephoned Born. They had in hand two more affidavits, one from the foreperson Denise Jones. Jones confirmed in her affidavit the vote had been at least ten-to-two on Tuesday, and she said she had consistently been for the defendants throughout the deliberations. Strangely, she claimed not to remember reference being made to a bribery attempt at any time the jury was out but said certainly nothing of that nature ever affected the result.

The other affidavit was from Eston Gilliland, the juror whose "second thoughts" after the initial verdict caused the jury to deliberate further. Born held his breath while Thompson told about Gilliland's affidavit, but it was all positive. Surprisingly, Gilliland said he had consistently voted for the defendants and identified the two holdouts as Larry Heath and Jimmy Washington. He testified the bribery did not affect his decision. He said his decision was based on the evidence, and while he was not sure what effect the absence of a stabilizer bar had, he felt the plaintiffs had not proved it would have prevented the accident. "After we returned our verdict the first time, I wanted to go back and discuss the stabilizer bar some more. After we rediscussed it, I again decided that I should vote for the defendants, and that is how we voted."

"Just to show that the bribery didn't affect the verdict,

I've been thinking about what Gilliland told us. Should have asked him to include this in his affidavit. When they went back for more deliberations, the jury talked only about the stabilizer bar; the bribery never was even mentioned. To me, this shows it was not a big issue with the jurors. They heard about it and then they put it aside," Thompson said.

"Another thing, it all just doesn't add up," Thompson said. "The vote was ten-to-two for us on Tuesday, and it seems that was as bad as it ever got for us. So, there were never more than *two* jurors who favored the plaintiffs; yet plaintiffs have filed *three* affidavits from jurors who said they originally were planning to vote for plaintiffs. And to make it even stranger, the three whose affidavits were filed with plaintiffs' motion don't match up at all with the two holdouts. Something is funny here."

"I'll tell you what I think," said Born. "I think we've got to interview the two holdouts and the three who signed the plaintiffs' affidavit. But let's do the three affidavit-signers last. First, let's interview the two holdouts. They're the only ones whose vote could have been switched when the fact of bribery was brought out in deliberations. Let's see what they have to say about it."

"Whatever you say, Ted, but Rusty has some thoughts about that," replied Thompson. "I'm going to put him on the phone."

"Hi, Rusty, looks like you and Dave have done a great day's work," Born congratulated Rusty Loman.

"Ted, thanks, but that's just it. We've been successful

with these first three and I wonder if we shouldn't stop there. The plaintiffs have filed three affidavits and we could now file three contradicting them. I'm afraid as we go further, interviewing the holdouts and the ones who gave affidavits for the other side, we're going to have rough going. I can't imagine any of the plaintiffs' affidavit-givers confessing they signed false affidavits."

"I hear what you're saying Rusty, but I'm afraid we'll lose if we stop where we are," Born answered. "Just look at it: There are three affidavits of jurors saying the bribery revelation changed their minds. Despite our three affidavits which indirectly call all that into question, a judge is pretty much going to presume a bribery exposé would have an effect on voting.. I think we have to go forward, one affidavit at the time. If we learn something that changes our minds, we can stop and re-evaluate. I'm emboldened to do this by the math of the situation. As Dave said, it just doesn't add up. Rusty, what's the chance you could get an interview and an affidavit from John Salmon in the next couple of days?"

"I can probably get that one. It should be fairly low risk... . Hold on... . Dave is saying he has something else to do tomorrow and maybe the next day," Loman passed on to Born.

"Well, I'd say you go ahead and get the Salmon affidavit as soon as you can, Rusty. You probably can handle that one on your own, and Dave and I will work out something on the two holdouts, Heath and Washington. One more thing. Let's keep quiet about this with Tergano.

This is a very delicate, one-step-at-a-time kind of thing, and we can't run the risk they'll come in and mess things up. As far as I can tell, Tergano is not really doing anything. Maybe it's resigned to a new trial, or maybe it's just planning to make general legal arguments, which would be a losing approach as far as I can tell. Obviously, we should be even more careful not to let the plaintiffs know what we're up to."

Late the following afternoon Rusty Loman called Born with the news that he had an affidavit from John Salmon. "John was with us all the way," Loman said. "He's in accord with the others on the ten-to-two vote Tuesday, but he is also emphatic that the vote went to eleven-to-one early Wednesday morning, he thinks before the bribery issue ever came up. The jurors talked briefly about the bribery, but they all decided it did not affect anyone's vote, so they didn't mention it to the Judge. They just didn't want to get Bess into any trouble, really felt sorry for her. When they went back for the second round of deliberations, the bribery never came up at all, and that's in his affidavit."

"So now, Rusty, we have four affidavits, totally consistent with each other, which do not jibe with the affidavits of the plaintiffs. I think we are ready to tackle the two holdouts," Born said.

"Ted, you're a riverboat gambler," Rusty Loman laughed. "I'm not sure I'd have the guts, but you're call-ing the shots. Okay, here's what we know. We tried to make contact with those two in the beginning, before beginning, before we knew they had been holdouts. I got the definite im-pression—I think Dave did, too—that Larry Heath is avoiding us. His father told us he's working at Whitesell Packing, where Bess Johnson used to work. Best I can tell, he never overlapped with Bess, he's only been there six or eight months. His father volunteered, though, that Sheriff Sam has been trying to see him, hasn't made contact yet, apparently. Maybe Heath's trying to avoid both sides. Anyway, I think we might have to interview him at Whitesell to have any hope of getting this job done before our fifteen-day deadline hits us in the face."

"I'll take that as my challenge," Born said, "to try to get permission from Whitesell's management to interview him on the job. I know somebody whose son has an investment stake in Whitesell. Maybe I can get the arrangements made through him. Know anything about the other guy?"

"Yeah. Same story, in a way," Loman explained. "We tried to contact Washington in the beginning also, as I said, before we knew he had been a holdout. We've been getting the runaround, but we haven't tried in a few days. He seems to work part time, odd jobs or something."

"Okay, I'll get in touch with Dave as soon as he gets back in the office - he's out of pocket, not sure where - and try to get this done. We'll be in touch," promised Born.

Born broke the telephone connection, then called Tom Byrd. "Tom, don't you have some connection with Whitesell Packing Company?... Your son is personnel manager?... Is your son interested in being a a good citizen and striking a blow for justice in tort litigation? All we need is a few minutes, thirty minutes at the most, with one of the Whitesell employees who served on the jury in a case we won... Yeah, impossible case, but we won, and now there've been some allegations of bribery, brib-ery by the *plaintiffs*, and how that impacted the jurors in reaching their verdict. We'll need an affidavit. No, I'm just explaining the background. Don't mention anything to the employee, just let us have a few minutes with him and a place to interview him. We'll try to accommodate your convenience, not interfere with the operations, if you'd just give us some acceptable dates and times of day. That'd be great. Thanks a lot, Tom."

The arrangements were made, and Rusty Loman met Dave Thompson at Whitesell, located on a backroad in the rural countryside near Columbia. It was a large whitewashed block building with outside livestock ramps and holding areas, the air filled with the unmistakable aromas of a slaughterhouse and the mournful sounds of fearful animals who somehow sense the mission of the place. Men with black rubber aprons and rubber boots were in evidence inside and out. Thompson and Loman were ushered into a small conference room and offered coffee while someone went for Larry Heath. When Heath came, the three needed no introductions. Heath was reasonably friendly and seemed glad to see Thompson and Loman, somewhat to the surprise of both of them who had assumed Heath was trying to be evasive.

"Mr. Heath, do you recall a vote being taken in the

jury room the first day you started your deliberations, Tuesday, I believe?" asked Thompson.

"Yes, I do."

"Do you remember what the vote was?"

"I think everybody was for the defendants except me and Jimmy Washington. 'Course, I knew the case was real weak against the tire company and pretty weak against the van company, but I felt sorry for those families and 'specially those children and really wanted to find some way to get them some money, so I wasn't ready to vote for the defendants right off the bat, like most of the rest were ready to do. So, I wanted to think about it overnight," Heath explained.

"What happened the next morning?" Thompson continued.

"Well, I'd pretty well decided overnight there just wasn't no evidence the tire or the van was defective. I was ready to go on and vote for the defendants, which I did on the first vote Wednesday morning," Heath related.

"Do you remember any mention of bribery?" Thompson asked.

"Yeah, I do. Seems like it was Estrata McNemar said she'd got a call from Miss Johnson offering fifty thousand apiece if we'd vote for the plaintiffs. We all thought it was kind of silly," said Heath.

"Did it - talk about the bribery - have any effect on how you ended up voting?" Thompson pressed.

"None at all. Like I say, I'd already pretty much made up my mind and, in fact, I'd already voted for the defendants first thing that morning, Wednesday morning, I think. It didn't have no influence at all on me. My vote was based on the evidence," Heath affirmed.

"Would you sign an affidavit saying just that?" Loman asked.

"Sure. It's the truth," Heath said. Then, while Thompson was writing out the affidavit, Heath added, "You fellows did a good job laying it all out. But it was tough on me. I know y'all all worked hard, but I worked hard too, with my conscience. You might think working around a slaughterhouse would toughen and harden me. But every time I thought about those kids in the van, I couldn't help picturing the slaughter line here at Whitesell. Those poor kids didn't know what happened to 'em. Somewhere, somehow, if justice means anything, there ought to be some amends, some atonement. You know what I mean? There we were, about to set the defendants free, say to the world they weren't guilty, but who *is* guilty? Who's going to pay? If Universal and Tergano don't pay, nobody's gon' pay. Is that justice? That's the kind of thing I was wrestling with. It wasn't easy, let me tell you."

"How did you finally work that out?" Thompson asked, handing Heath the affidavit.

"How'd I work it out?" Heath repeated the question aloud with a distant look in his eye. "Well, I guess I said to myself, 'We the jury aren't here to decide whether *somebody, somewhere* has done something horrible to Sarena and Jimason. The question is whether Universal and Tergano did something wrong.' I just couldn't honestly say they did. I decided I wasn't going to do an injustice in the name of justice. No, I was going to do justice by Universal and Tergano. Someday, maybe there can be justice for the plaintiffs. But at least a little justice is better than no justice." He handed the signed affidavit back to Thompson.

"Thanks, Mr. Heath," Thompson said. "You did the right thing. You never can help an injured party by hurting an innocent party. We share your frustration over Jimason and Sarena. But it's a complicated question which involves parents and uncles and seatbelt habits and road conditions and a lot of other things. Believe me, I had to work through a lot of the same questions you dealt with. In fact, I almost refused to get involved with this case in the beginning. I think - I know - we both worked those questions out right. We appreciate your taking the time to see us."

When Thompson and Loman left Whitesell, they went straight to the residence of Jimmy Washington on the chance they might find him home, delighted at the results of the just finished Heath interview. It meant Universal now had five affidavits, including one of the two hold-outs, who had sworn the bribery revelation affected no one's votes. However, they realized that a single affidavit to the contrary would likely be decisive against Universal. Loman's conservative instincts told him Universal should stop while it was ahead. After all, Universal already had two more affidavits than the plaintiffs, and the strength of the affidavits would require the plaintiffs to do some explaining. Nonetheless, the decision had already been made to try to interview Washington on this trip, and by now Loman and Thompson knew that Ted Born would not back down.

Washington's residence was not easy to find, but Loman and Thompson were aided by their earlier attempted visits. He lived on a road which did not even appear on the County map. After driving down a narrow one-lane road which looked more like a rustic driveway, the twosome sighted a rusting, faded '50's style trailer which did not measure up to "mobile home" or "modular housing" standards. Some rough fencing kept in the chickens which had pecked away every blade of grass, every weed, leaving the yard in front of the trailer a brownish-red dirt expanse. A pit bull had roused from a sunny spot to bark loudly at their approach. There appeared to be a vegetable garden behind a length of fence, out of the reach of the chickens. The car was so old it bore an antique license plate, but it had received none of the care one generally associates with antique cars. Thompson looked at the tires on Washington's car and noticed that they had plenty of tread.

As they were parking, Washington came out of the trailer. "What brings you attorneys out this way? Somethin' about the case, I guess?"

"That's right, Mr. Washington. Can you talk for a few minutes?"

"Yeah, I guess so," Washington answered, seeming to look around for a suitable place to talk, obviously not inclined to invite them into his trailer. "I'll come out there so you don't have to come inside the fence with this dog." He opened the gate and walked to meet Thompson and Loman. The three men shook hands.

"Mr. Washington, we just have a few questions... ," Thompson began. Washington told them he had been the last holdout, but really hadn't held out all that long. Like Heath, he had felt sorry for the families.

"I finally decided," Washington said, "I'd never convince the other ten - then, eventually, the other eleven - to vote for the plaintiffs, and I knew in my mind already the defendants weren't guilty. It was just my heart, that's all. My heart went out to 'em, but there was no way. Those companies really didn't do anything wrong, and I knew it and all of us knew it, and I'd think about the evidence and Judge's what-do-you-call-'em directions... ."

"Instructions," Thompson prompted.

"Yeah, his instructions. I'd think about 'em, and I just realized there was no way," Washington said.

"Do you remember any mention of a bribery attempt?" Thompson asked.

"Yeah, sure do. But we all agreed that didn't matter, didn't affect us at all. Damn, I could use fifty thousand dollars, but I'm not gonna get it that way. Even if I'd been willing, which I wasn't, that was kind of amateurish, if you ask me. Didn't make no difference at all to me."

Bells rang and fireworks were exploding in the minds of Loman and Thompson as they tried to control their elation over Washington's welcome statements long enough to write them into one of their hand-written affidavits. Washington signed the affidavit, and Thompson and Loman headed back to Loman's office, where they telephoned Ted Born.

"Ted, we did it! We've gotten affidavits from both of the two holdouts saying the bribery had no effect on them - and they're the only ones who really could have been affected! Then we already had the other four affidavits, so that makes a total of six - fully one-half of the jurors - verifying that the jury was overwhelmingly in our favor and the bribery had no effect," Thompson said excitedly.

Loman was on the line also and added, "Ted, you've been right so far, I admit, and so I will make this recommendation with due humility" - laughing - "but I hope you won't press on to the affidavits of the three who signed for the plaintiffs. I'm afraid we're going to meet our Waterloo there."

"Let's talk about that," Born said. "If we believe what six members of the jury have told us, then we have to believe that every one of those jurors who signed the plaintiffs' affidavits were staunchly in our camp the whole time, voting consistently with us. If that's so, their affidavits are downright false. Now why would three jurors file false affidavits?"

"Could be they were bribed," Thompson said.

"Yeah, but these are jurors who turned down a fifty-thousand-dollar bribe at the trial. Why would they turn down one bribe and take another?" Loman thought aloud.

"So, if the bribe possibility doesn't make sense, what

does?" asked Thompson.

"I can think of only a few explanations," Born reasoned. "Either they were hoodwinked into signing it, or they thought it didn't matter at this point and signed it just to get rid of the plaintiffs' pressure. Now I've been thinking about their three affidavits. One of them was signed by Tom Ferris. Remember him? He's the one who can hardly read or write. The Judge had to help him fill out his questionnaire before we struck the jury. I wonder - "

"You wonder if he knew what he was signing!" Thompson said.

"Exactly," Born answered. "Dave, can you stay overnight and see if you can talk to him tomorrow? We're beginning to run out of time."

"Yeah, I can stay," Thompson said. "This is the most important thing on my plate. I don't want to have to try this case again. I think Rusty has a conflict tomorrow, though."

"At this point, I'd say, Dave, the time being so short to our deadline, you should go alone," Born advised.

The next day Dave got his directions to Tom Ferris' home. Thompson remembered Ferris as an older and rather dapper looking man, a bit frail, but apparently alert and serious. Loman had voiced some reservations about Ferris at one point, based on the close friendship of one of Ferris' daughters with the Clerk of the Circuit Court, Fred Bates' protégé. However, Ferris had a large family and, all things considered, he was deemed preferable to many of the other jurors.

Thompson found Ferris in a modest one-story brick home, with a flower garden in front by a rotting picket fence. A large satellite television dish graced his side yard. Young children, possibly grandchildren, played in the front yard. The house, like most in Phoenix County, was fairly isolated with plenty of elbow room.

Ferris was cordial. He acknowledged signing the plaintiffs' affidavit, said an "investigator" for the plaintiffs read it to him - or read something to him. He did not remember exactly what the earlier affidavit had said, but he was firm in stating he had at all times been in favor of the defendants and that the bribery had not affected him in the least. It was pretty clear Ferris had not understood what he signed, but he never explained why he signed something he did not understand. He just said he thought it was something he was legally supposed to do. He was unwilling to say in his new affidavit for Thompson that he had been misled on the first one, undoubtedly did not want to be accusatory. Still, his new affidavit was powerful and effectively disclaimed the first one.

Thompson went to Loman's office and made a photocopy for Loman's files, then headed back to Greenville.

"Ted, I think we've done it this time. Tom Ferris has retracted his original affidavit, and we have seven consistent affidavits showing the other two must be false as well. That should about do it, don't you think?" Dave Thompson led.

"Look, Dave, I know you're tired of making trips back and forth to Phoenix County," Born said sympathetically.

"You've done so much traveling and you've done such a magnificent job with these affidavits, I hate to ask you to do anything more. But let's don't die on third base, let's go for home. We've got two other plaintiffs' affidavits staring us in the face. I'm more convinced than ever that they're false. I think we should go after them, find out what happened and correct it."

"I was afraid you were going to say that," Thompson smiled. "Well, at least we're getting closer. There can't be more than five left," he laughed. "I've got the telephone numbers of the other two right here. First, I'm going to call Satch Doolin. If I can use your telephone, I'll call from here. Here goes." Thompson called the number and asked to speak to Doolin. "Oh, he's in Greenville... . Can you tell me how to reach him?... Construction project on Jefferson Avenue?... What's that phone number, please? Thanks a lot." He hung up and said, "That might be one trip I don't have to make to Phoenix County. He's here in Greenville working on a construction project. I have a number where I can reach him tonight."

"The other juror is John Baxter. Here's his number, let me call him." He dialed the number and punched the speakerphone button on the telephone so he and Born could both hear. "Mr. Baxter, this is Dave Thompson, remember me from the trial?"

"Sure do. You did a good job, you and that white lawyer both," Baxter said.

Thompson smiled, "He's here in the room with me and we're talking to you on the speakerphone,"

Thompson said.

"Hello, Mr. Baxter, this is Ted Born."

"Hello, Mr. Born," Baxter responded.

"Mr. Baxter," Thompson continued, "When you served on that jury, do you remember taking a vote Tuesday night?"

"Yes, I voted for both defendants," Baxter answered.

"And did that continue to be your position the whole time, you never changed your mind?" Thompson asked.

"That's right. I never changed my mind. Of course, I felt sorry for the plaintiffs, but I just couldn't blame Universal and Tergano based on the evidence I heard," Baxter answered.

"The plaintiffs have filed an affidavit, which they say you signed, to the effect you planned to vote for the plaintiffs and changed your mind when you heard about the bribery attempt. Did you sign that?" Thompson asked.

"I'll have to tell you how that was," Baxter explained. "I was in a hospital in Columbia where my father was about to be taken to the operating room for open-heart surgery. An investigator for plaintiffs found me there and asked me to sign this affidavit they had already prepared for me. I read it, and I told them it wasn't right. Then he said to me, 'Oh, go ahead and sign it anyway. It'd take us an hour to re-write it. It won't make any difference. Just go ahead and sign it.' I tell you, Mr. Thompson and Mr. Born, I was so stressed out at the time I would have signed anything just to get rid of that guy. I know I shouldn't have signed something wrong, but I just wanted to get rid of him."

Born and Thompson looked at each other wide-eyed. "And you really never changed your mind at the time?" Thompson asked.

"No," Baxter answered.

"What effect did it have on you when you heard there had been a bribe attempt?" Thompson asked.

"Nothing. Didn't affect me a bit. I always was going to vote for the defendants," Baxter said.

"Will you sign a corrective affidavit saying just what you've told us?" Thompson asked.

"Sure. It's the truth," Baxter said.

"Can I meet you at your house tomorrow?" Thompson asked.

Born had long since jumped from his chair and was clasping his hands over his head in celebration. As Thompson disconnected the call, both men whistled out loud. Then they slapped hands together and shook hands. "We shall come rejoicing!" exclaimed Thompson.

"Dave, I think you've just brought in the sheaves!" Born said to the younger lawyer. "It may be a little sacrilegious, but now let's sing it together -"

"We shall come rejoicing, bringing in the sheaves," the two lawyers harmonized, as passersby paused by Born's open office door and shook their heads.

CHAPTER THIRTY-SIX

JUST A LAWSUIT

Bess Johnson and Louis Goodlett were sitting on Johnson's front porch, talking with Doretta Anchrum.

"It could've been," said Bess Johnson. "It could've been. Yeah, could've been a whole lot different. I always dreamed of gettin' out of this shack, gettin' me a real fine house. But I was born poor and I was born black, and I guess it was never meant for me to do anything but work and get nowhere - that is, if I don't go to jail. Is this what it's all about, Doretta, just gettin' by? Is that all there is here on this earth?"

"Reckon so," said Anchrum. "'Course, Mrs. Driscoll got hers."

"No, I'm serious," Johnson insisted. "Is it just meant that we're born and work - or run on a treadmill - and then die? Is that it?"

"What you want it to be, Bess?" asked Goodlett. "Cain't everybody live in Hollywood houses. I know rich folks, rich white folks, who don't do anything but just what you say. They're born, they work hard, they die. Sure, they drive new Jaguars while I drive beat-up Chevys, they drink imported wines and I drink Red Dagger, they go to Colorado skiing and I go down here to the creek bank with my fishin' pole. But they haven't really got any kind of life. They don't have time to spend with their wives, nor with their children. They're all the time worrying about payin' their bills and keepin' good credit and keepin' the Jaguar repaired and the appliances running. They've never lived five minutes - that's right - if you add it up, they've never lived five minutes all together, their whole lives."

"No, Louis, you're wrong," Johnson said. "Well, you're right, and you're wrong. I agree lots of folks with money don't enjoy living, the way they could. But they've got one thing that's important about living. They've got their self-respect. People are nice to them, people look up to them. They feel like they've got a place. Me? I ain't got no place. I ain't got no respect. I'm just somebody who gets tolerated, by the hardest. I'm dirt under the feet of 'responsible' people."

"I still say you're rich if you've got your health, and you can enjoy the seasons, and you can sit on this porch in autumn and relax and breathe in that good fresh air," Goodlett offered. "Go on now, Bess, take a deep breath and draw it in. How's that?"

"Louis, you makin' fun of me when I'm trying' to be serious. I'm upset. We lost the case, and I'm in trouble, and all you can do is tell me to take a deep breath. *You* take a deep breath for you and for me.

"Those lawyers. I knew our case wasn't goin' good. I could feel it, that jury wasn't for us. And I didn't know what to do. My whole life unfolded, or maybe it unraveled, right there in front of me, and I knew I had to do somethin', and that's when I first called you, Doretta, and I couldn't get Ben and Agnes, but I went ahead and called Estrata anyway. It was the only thing I could do. I fig-ured, if it worked, it'd make me rich. If it didn't, life in a jail cell's not much worse than what I've got now. Maybe they'll have mercy on me, with the children, and all."

"What's this thing the lawyers've been sayin', about this new trial?" Doretta asked.

"Ha!" Bess Johnson said. "I'll believe that when I see it. They're making out to us like, if we'll be patient, they'll get us a new trial. And here's what I cain't believe. First, those lawyers preach at me and tell me I did wrong, shouldn't have offered a bribe. Then they turn around and tell me we might get a new trial 'cause of what I done wrong I oughtn't to've done. Beats all I ever heard. We're never gon' see no new trial. You know that: It's over. It's over. Don't you worry about it. Far as I'm concerned, we deserved that money, and you just tried to help," Doretta said.

In Columbia, Jack Ripps was in Fred Bates' office as the latter put books and personal files into boxes. "It's best, Jack. We had what you might call a detente, we nev-er really had a partnership. Sure, we made some money, but I knew it wasn't going to work much longer. And I really didn't care. I'm tired, I've had enough, and I want to retire and enjoy the good life while I can. My father died young; I don't know how much time I've got. I can make it if I never hit another lick of work, but I'm talking with a fellow about buying out his law practice over near the coast. It'd keep me from going bananas, just enough to piddle around a little bit but not enough to interfere in any serious way with my basic retirement."

"Well, our deal is, you've still got an interest in this case if we can pull it out." Ripps said. "I think we got a darn good shot at it, from what I can tell. I just don't see how Judge Andrews could deny us a new trial when three jurors have said in sworn affidavits they had planned to vote for us before the bribery bit came out, then sanctioned our side by agreeing to a defense verdict. Of course, it would only preserve the children's case, but that's where all the money is, anyway, so who cares? I'll say one thing, if we do get a new trial, we're gon' do some things differ-ent the next time around. Things have been pretty quiet with the defendants. I guess our motion and affidavits put a damper on their celebrations. Wish I could've seen 'em when they first read our affidavits. That should've told 'em something. Yes, sir, this case ain't over. We're in it to win, and we aren't gon' take 'no' for an answer."

Ripps' secretary came to the door, "Mr. Ripps, you told me to let you know if an envelope came from the defense lawyers in the *Johnson v. Tergano* case. Here's a fairly thick manila envelope from Ted Born's law firm." She handed him the envelope.

Ripps opened the envelope and frowned. He shuffled through the papers. Fred Bates quit packing and came to look over Ripps' shoulder. "Damn," said Ripps. "That Ted Born is playing hardball. He's filed *nine* affidavits, to our three, and he says our three affiants have repudiated the affidavits they gave us. Says we filed false affidavits. Says the vote was ten-to-two in their favor Tuesday night, then eleven-to-one the next morning early. Damn! This is serious. Those guys don't like to lose."

"What's this motion?" asked Bates, looking over Ripps' shoulder but addressing mostly himself. "It's a motion to preclude further communication with the *Johnson* case jurors. Born claims we got 'false' affidavits from the jurors, claims the order precluding contact is needed to preserve - listen to this - 'the integrity of the jury testimony'."

"They're pretty hard on Bess," Ripps observed. "Say Bess lied several times and defrauded the insurance company. Claim Bess had already demonstrated she was untrustworthy, and we should have declined further representation before the trial even started. That's nice and patronizing of 'em," sneered Ripps with disgust.

"Unfortunately, for Mr. Born's information, we don't have the luxury of choosing our clients and being sure they're all saints. You take what you can get. Hasn't anyone told Born that even bad guys are entitled to their day in Court and a right to competent legal representation? If we were in one of those big rich defense firms, we could afford to be a little more high-minded. That's what gripes me about those holier-than-thou 'ethical' defense lawyers. They're insulated from these things. We're literally out on the streets trying to make a living, just coping, hop-ing to survive. Yeah, let me swap places, and I could be high-minded. It's easy when there's no pressure."

The telephone rang. "Yes, Judge. This is Fred Bates. Jack Ripps is in here with me. Can I put you on the speakerphone?"

Bates punched a button on the telephone and the Judge's voice came in loud and clear: "Hello, gentlemen. Rusty Loman is here in my office and has presented me with an emergency motion to preclude plaintiffs from further contacting any members of the *Johnson* case jury. It is plain to me that we have some conflicting affidavits from jurors and that someone, or someones, are not tell-ing the truth. I don't want to see both sides descending on the jurors or harassing them into signing affidavits in this affidavits war. My inclination is to enter an order enjoining *all parties* from further contact with the jurors pending further order of the Court. But I'll be glad to hear from you if you oppose it."

"Judge, all we did was to send an investigator out to interview the jurors, find out what caused them to reach their verdict and get affidavits," Bates said. "Frankly, we were taken aback by what he reported to us, but when we thought about it, it all seemed logical. This was a very rep-utable investigator with good credentials, and we didn't have any reason to think he harassed anyone - and still don't think he did. We just got the motion ourselves and haven't even had time to talk with the investigator. Hard to believe that the bribery accusation didn't adversely affect the plaintiffs in the jury deliberations."

"Of course, you can talk to your investigator. I'm not forbidding that," the Judge made clear. "But I'm inclined not to make table tennis balls of the jurors, so I'm going to enter this order enjoining juror contact - and that will include direct and indirect contact - and my order will apply to all parties. I'll notify Tergano's lawyers. Let me make clear the lawyers are responsible for notifying your clients, and in your case that means your former client Sam Johnson, to make sure they don't attempt to contact the jurors."

"That's fine, Judge," answered Bates, "as long as it applies to all parties, we won't oppose it."

"Thank you, gentlemen. I'll get you a copy of the or-der as soon as possible. Good-bye," said Judge Andrews.

"Damn, I hate that!" said Ripps. "He cuts us off so we can't defend ourselves."

"Hold on, Jack. Listen to me," Bates instructed. "The

order may be a good thing. What if the jurors stick where they are, and we can't dislodge them? Then we've got noexcuse. As it is now, with Andrews' order, we can simply say on appeal, 'We possibly could have clarified the situ-ation but were prevented from doing so; we never had a fair chance to rebut the Universal affidavits."

"I dunno," Ripps pondered aloud. "Right now, it looks like we or our investigator was dishonest. I doubt we'll get a lot of sympathy on appeal."

"You've got to roll with the punches, Jack," said Bates as he resumed his packing. "Hell, I wish it hadn't happened, I mean, the Universal affidavits. I wish they hadn't come up with 'em, and I'm surprised they did. Took some guts to go out and find those jurors and get their signatures on affidavits. But they're here. We've got to face it. So, what do we do? Do we crawl under a rug and just tell ourselves over and over we wish they'd give up and surrender? Hell, no! We fight back. Keep the thing in perspective, Jack boy, here's the situation: A juror drops a bombshell in deliberations, saying a plaintiff tried to bribe her. She does this while deliberations are still going on, before everybody's unanimous. It's bound to have had a devastating effect. Anybody can see that."

"So far so good, Fred," replied Ripps. "But how do you deal with the jury being ten-to-two against us, maybe eleven-to-one against us, before the bribery was even mentioned?"

"The answer, my dear Watson, lies in the theory of jury deliberations. Think back to juror Eston Gilliland.

What did he do?" Bates asked pedagologically, resuming his packing.

"He changed his mind, or almost did," Ripps answered, nodding his head as he understood Bates' point.

"Ah ha! He changed his mind! Wht does a juror always have the right to do before discharge? Why, he can change his mind. So, there you have it. The ten jurors - or even the eleven jurors - who were against us might have changed their minds. We have to assume that was a possibility. But what did the bribery accusation do? It destroyed any possibility of a change of mind. It solidified feelings against the plaintiffs even if there were no conversions one way or the other. The upshot is, you simply have to presume prejudice when a major bombshell like bribery explodes in the jury room. There's no way around it."

"Another thing, Jack," Bates said. "Don't lose sight of the fact that Estrata McNemar was guilty of juror misconduct when she failed to report the bribery. Then when she told the other jurors about the bribery and they also failed to report it, they too were guilty of miscon-duct. Had the Judge known, then and there, that bribery was being talked about in the jury room, would he have allowed them simply to continue their deliberations? Of course not. He would have declared a mistrial and sent them home. Obviously in this case, he didn't have that opportunity because of juror misconduct in failing to report this 'extraneous event.' Now that he's found out about it, he should do the next best thing and grant a new trial. So all is not lost. Don't be so gloomy."

"I've gotta' say, you're giving me some hope," Ripps affirmed. "When you said something about rolling with the punches, I was telling myself I was reeling from them. I feel like a damn punching bag for Born to hit again and again. But you might just have the right approach. This was a big one to lose. We're in hot water with Sheriff Sam, and the publicity of losing is going to hurt. Our competition, especially Jeff Tokers, is going to have a field day telling clients we lost it. So far, Tokers hasn't lost one, at least not in Phoenix County. It's going to hurt, and we need to turn it around."

"*You've* got to turn it around, Jack," Bates corrected him. "I'm retiring, remember? I'll come back in and re-try it if you get us a new trial, but that's gonna' be your baby. I've pounded the trail to the Courthouse long enough, and I'm tired of that routine. I don't necessarily find the client contact stimulating. I need white, sandy beaches. Don't let it get to you, Jack. It's just a case, a pretty good one, we thought, but just one more case."

"Yeah, you always said, 'Don't let yourself get personally involved.' In dealing with Bess on this case, I think I know what you mean. As for the kids, well, what's done is done. No use crying over the past, though you did a pretty good job crying at the trial," Ripps said.

"It's just a lawsuit, Jack. It's a way to make a living, nothing more. It's just a lawsuit."

CHAPTER THIRTY-SEVEN

TO FALL ON THE SWORD

Neither side was conceding anything. Jack Ripps on behalf of the plaintiffs claimed the children did not get a fair trial because the jury in effect punished them for their parents' misdeeds, or alleged misdeeds. Ted Born was equally strong that the bribery accusation made no difference, that in fact there was no proof bribery ever really took place.

It was a strange confrontation between plaintiffs and defendants. The central event had been the attempted bribery, yet plaintiffs had deliberately avoided submitting any direct evidence of that offence to avoid fingering their adult clients with a criminal act. Defendants for their own and entirely different reasons - mainly to avoid supplying evidence of an "extraneous event" - also refrained from submitting direct evidence of bribery. Thus, it came about that the motion for a new trial did not technically focus on the bribery itself, but on the jurors' *discussion* of bribery.

A new round of briefs made their way to Judge Andrew's desk. The days passed, and no ruling was issued on the motion. The time would soon expire when the motion, if not acted on, would be deemed denied by the passage of time. This was not a result that Born or Thompson wanted because they felt such a denial by default would leave the case more vulnerable to attack on appeal. A good, strong order from the trial Judge showing he had considered and rejected the motion would be much better in fending off an appeal. Jack Ripps did not want the deadline to pass without Court action, either, because it would be, after all, an automatic denial of his motion.

As the deadline drew near, the motion was set for oral argument on the next to last day before time would expire.

Born wanted to let Dave Thompson argue the motion on Universal's behalf, feeling Thompson had earned that right by his success in garnering most of the nine critical affidavits. In the end, he decided against it because there would be too much second-guessing if Universal lost the motion. Some would ask, "Why did you risk letting that miracle win slip through your fingers by letting a young lawyer of Dave Thompson's tenure handle this crucial motion?" Thompson would feel terrible, too, if the Court ruled against him. It was like a replay of Born's internal debate as to whether Thompson should participate in the closing argument. Born did not ask Thompson, knowing what the answer would be: "I'll do anything you want me to do." Thompson would do it well, too. Of that, Born had no doubt at all. Unfortunately, motions can be lost even when lawyers perform flawlessly.

What if Born argued the motion and lost it? Of course, Born would take responsibility for the loss. But at least no one would say it was lost due to youth and inexperience. Born suddenly realized something else, something he had not thought of before. If Born lost, he would have lost more than victory in a gigantic lawsuit. He would lose something else which had come to be important to him, the ability to share with Dave Thompson a message Dave needed to hear, deserved to hear.

Sure, Ted Born had congratulated Dave Thompson. Sure, he had complimented Thompson, bragged effusively on Thompson every chance he got. But really, he had never said it to Thompson quite right, nor had he said it in writing, so it would have some little permanence and not vanish in air.

If Born lost and *then* wrote Thompson such a letter, it would fall with a thud, it would come across as a condo-lence. No, to be sure he said what he wanted to say and so that Thompson could hear what he ought to hear, Born needed to write it - now. He picked up a pen and began scratching on a legal pad, saying to himself as he did so, "I may be one of the last lawyers to write anything out in cursive, other than my signature. I could type on the computer, but for this letter, I want to feel the pen in my hand, I want to see each letter and each word being born as I create it. I want Dave to know exactly how I feel.

Dear Dave,

I have been writing this letter on the easel of my mind since we got the jury verdict and won the case. Regardless the outcome of the motion for a new trial, we did win this case. You and I know we won it, we won it on its merits because jurors listened to the evidence and were inspired to do justice. No one can take that away from us. We looked into their eyes and we know now that we won and would have won, bribery or not.

We are about to have a hearing on the new trial motion which I believe we should win, yet we might lose. But Dave, even if we lose, no one can ever take away from you or me the sure knowledge of our accomplishment. God forbid we should ever have to try it again, but if it must be, I'm willing to take my stand with you and win again.

We have not chosen this lawsuit as a testing ground. We rather found ourselves catapulted onto it. You responded with ability and effectiveness far beyond your years. Never will I forget your splendid opening statement, nor the manner in which you handled witnesses, researched and argued motions, and otherwise participated as a full equal in the trial of the case. It was a moment of definition of which you should take pride.

I am proud and privileged to have been in Groveton in person to witness your extraordinary achievements. You did not simply help to win a lawsuit, you helped to do justice. So, it was a defining moment for you and a reassuring moment for a world skeptical of elusive justice, a confluence of great moments.

With my personal thanks and deep respect, I am

Yours Sincerely,

Ted Born

He looked at it and shook his head. "Doesn't quite do it. I saw Dave transformed. I saw myself transformed. I saw a white man and a black man, an older man and a younger man, become brothers and work seamlessly together. Not lawyer to lawyer, not father to son, but brother to brother. We shared the brotherhood of suffering, the brotherhood of joy."

Born thought of tearing up the letter and writing something different, something more along the line of brotherhood, but he shook his head. "It's one of those things that can never be said, only felt. It would sound cheap and tinny. It would embarrass Dave. It would seem melodramatic. No, it just wouldn't work." He sealed the letter, marked the envelope confidential and sent it to Dave Thompson in the interoffice mail.

Born turned back to the preparation of his argument on the motion for new trial. In the back of his mind, he wondered how Thompson would take the letter. He resisted asking on the occasions when he saw Thompson afterward, and Thompson did not mention the letter. Maybe the letter did not strike Dave Thompson quite right. Or maybe Thompson could respond to almost anything but effusive praise.

The day for the argument came, and the plaintiffs' and defense lawyers once again converged on Groveton. The Judge was still deep in a hearing, and running behind time, dealing with the testimony of several live witnesses, when the lawyers in the *Johnson* case arrived. Born waited in the courtroom for a while, remembering all that had taken place in that very place a few months earlier. He looked at the jury box and imagined the faces he had seen peering from seats in the box. The lawyers waiting to be heard were largely the same lawyers who had been at the trial, except Fred Bates did not appear. There were no boxes of documents, no posters, no ruptured tires, and the briefcases were much slimmer than before. Secretaries and paralegals and company representatives were absent this session.

Born walked out on the bridge to the Annex and studied the Courthouse, seeing some things he had seen before, some things he had not. The shutters of the downstairs windows still displayed peeled and mildewed paint, one of them hanging loosely at an odd angle. A window would not close in its casing. The elegant cornice work near the base of the cupola was rotting in places, entirely missing in others. The sickly green of algae was insidiously overcoming once spotless white paint. Rust red colored the visible metal. Despite the degradation, the old structure retained an aura of grandeur, albeit faded, neglected grandeur, crowning the highest point in Groveton.

Jack Ripps came out of the courtroom onto the bridge. "Are they still going strong on the other case?" Born asked him.

"Still going," Ripps answered laconically.

"Jack, I've been looking at this Courthouse. It needs a lot of work," Born remarked.

"Yeah, this is a poor county," Ripps answered. "They can't afford anything but the bare essentials."

"I've got an idea," Born said half seriously, half-jokingly. "Why don't you rich plaintiff lawyers, who've taken so many millions home from that Courthouse, pitch in a few thousand dollars to spruce it up? It wouldn't take that much money to do it. They might be willing to display a 'Jack Ripps Appreciation Plaque' on the side of the Courthouse, something like that."

Ripps did not crack a smile. "People already say I'm guilty of bribing. They'd say it even louder if I did something like that. Anyway, you've been telling me in all your pleadings what a dog of a case I've got here. Maybe you rich defense lawyers should do it."

"We defense lawyers are paid by the hour, just like an hourly-rated factory worker. We can't make millions that way. You folks are the legal entrepreneurs, putting your capital to work, financing litigation, getting some big hits. Speaking of entrepreneurial strategy, why don't you let Universal out of the case, Jack, dismiss us? I tried to convince Alton months ago y'all would be better off without us in it. You should think about that," Born suggested.

"Don't you think Tergano might get lonesome in there all by itself? Now, you wouldn't want that, would you?" Ripps teased.

"I'd try to keep Tergano company from the sidelines. Just give me a chance to see how that would work out," Born invited.

Ripps smiled but said nothing. They turned and ambled back into the courtroom. The earlier hearing was winding down, and the lawyers in the *Johnson* case readied themselves to move up front to argue their motion.

Judge Andrews wanted to know whether the parties would agree to extend the deadline for a ruling. Ripps indicated he was not willing to do so. The Judge next verified with the parties that tomorrow was the deadline. He then asked Ripps to proceed with his argument in support of the new trial. Ripps' argument was surprisingly brief.

Ripps said, "Judge, we've argued some of the points at earlier stages in the trial, and we believe the Court is aware of our positions. The main thing new is the juror misconduct in failing to advise the Court - as the Court had instructed the jury - to bring any indication of bribery or improper outside communications to the Court's attention at the time. Had the jury done so, the Court would surely have ordered a mistrial, sent everybody home and scheduled a new trial. That's all we're asking, that the Court do *now* what it would have done *then*, if the Court had known then what it knows now."

"Do you agree that there was a bribery attempt by at least some of your clients?" asked the Judge.

"No, Your Honor," answered Ripps, "and even if we knew the answer, the attorney-client privilege would preclude us from answering. We do contend that even if there was misconduct by any of the adult plaintiffs, it would not be chargeable to the minor plaintiffs on whose behalf this motion has been filed. On the other hand, whether or not there was any real bribery, the jury should have reported the bribery allegations, as Your Honor had directed them. It was misconduct on the part of the jury to decide the case with this explosive bribery issue coloring the deliberations and keeping that fact away from the Court."

"Anything further?" asked Judge Andrews.

"No, Your Honor," replied Jack Ripps. "You have our briefs citing the case where the jurors used a dictionary and didn't tell anybody. The Supreme Court ordered a new trial. This is a lot worse, a lot more prejudicial, than consulting a dictionary."

"What say the defendants?" asked the Judge.

Born responded. "It is important to bear in mind, Your Honor, that the defendants have not been accused of any misconduct. We did nothing more than try a good clean case and win it. As between the parties, the only misconduct suggested is misconduct on the part of the plaintiffs.

"With that in mind, we remind Your Honor that new trials require proof of an 'extraneous event' - which we don't have in this case. In the dictionary case, all the jurors saw the dictionary being used. They gave affidavits to that effect, and this was direct and admissible evidence of misconduct by the jury to which none of the parties contributed.

"In the present case, there is no admissible evidence of any 'extraneous event', only inadmissible hearsay evidence by certain jurors that they *heard* another juror say there had been bribery. Without proof of the extraneous event, we are left merely with jury deliberations, and juror affidavits cannot impeach the integrity of jury deliberations. Plaintiffs would like to be able to have their cake and eat it too, by getting a new trial without admitting their own misconduct. They should not be permitted to get away with that."

"Aren't you cutting it a little thin, Mr. Born?" asked Judge Andrews.

The Judge obviously doesn't like that argument, Born thought. The fact I find it persuasive is not very important, because *he's* the Judge. "Your Honor, we have other arguments and I think they should be looked at together. The plaintiffs have the burden of proving that any alleged misconduct adversely affected them in the jury verdict. They can't sustain that burden, first, because their supporting affidavits have all been repudiated by those who signed them and, second, because it is clear the jury was overwhelmingly in favor of the defendants before any jury bribery was mentioned in deliberations. The vote was ten-to-two Tuesday afternoon, before the alleged bribery is said to have taken place, and then eleven-to-one the next morning before the bribery was mentioned in deliberations. Both of the two original holdouts have testified by affidavit that the reference to bribery did not have any effect on their eventual vote for the defendants. There simply is no evidence the bribery accusation in any way affected the final verdict, much less a preponderance of the evidence as the law requires."

"Mr. Ripps says prejudice should be presumed where something as dramatic as bribery takes place," the Judge pointed out.

"That's what Mr. Ripps says, but that's not what the legal precedents say. The law requires the party attempting to set aside a jury verdict to sustain its burden of proving by a preponderance of the evidence that there was an adverse effect on the verdict. The plaintiffs haven't come close to sustaining that burden."

"Finally, there are strong policy reasons why no new trial should be granted when the new trial motion is ultimately based on the losing party's attempt to bribe the jury. Granted, the law is solicitous for the welfare of minors. But should the law allow - really, encourage - a mother, who sees a trial going badly, to attempt a bribe knowing that: (1) if it is successful, she and her children can go home with millions of dollars and no one will ever know about the bribery or; (2) if it is unsuccessful, she gets a new trial, maybe not for herself but at least for her child.

You might say, `She wouldn't do that for fear of criminal prosecution.' My response is, where is the jury who will convict a sacrificial mother, willing to throw herself on the sword to help her badly injured child? I submit few juries would ever convict, almost certainly not a jury of her friends here in Phoenix County where she would be tried. So, there is effectively no downside to attempting bribery. If the bribe succeeds, you will get millions. If the bribe doesn't succeed, at least your child gets a new trial and the briber is unlikely to be punished.

"The choice of this Court is to reward bribers, on the one hand, by giving them the new trial they want even though they were going to lose this case before the jury, or to sustain a just jury verdict in favor of innocent parties who did no wrong. Our system of law cannot survive under the first of these alternatives." Born had finished, and Judge Andrews nodded toward Tergano's lawyers to make their arguments.

"We won't take more of the Court's time, Your Honor," said Brad Mansfield. "Mr. Born has stated the essential arguments in which we join. We ask the Court to consider carefully what we have stated in our briefs."

"Any response?" the Judge asked Ripps and Fox.

Fox responded, "Briefly, Your Honor. Every individual is entitled under the law to a fair trial. These children, those permanently injured children and the dead child, are entitled to a fair trial regardless of what their parents might or might not have done. If a mother does something wrong, she should be prosecuted. The child should not suffer for it. Mr. Born says a mother won't be convicted if her bribe fails. But we have to assume under our system that the innocent will be protected and that the guilty will be punished. You just can't assume the guilty will get off Scot-free, as Mr. Born presumes. We want justice for the children. The children are entitled to that.

"We also remind the Court that our motions for the appointment of guardians ad litem are also pending," Fox concluded.

"Thank you for your arguments. I will take these motions under advisement and will render a decision by the end of the day tomorrow," said the Judge.

As they stepped outside the courtroom and waved a courteous good-bye to Ripps and Fox, the defense counsel paused for a brief conference. "What do you think?" asked Born. "Any impressions of what he's thinking?"

"Of course, it all seems so surreal. Here we are fighting to win this case a *second* time after already winning it before the jury once. It boggles the mind to think that, after all our hard work and success, we might have do it all over again - or try to do it all over again - because the other side, or some of them, were damn, good-for-nothing trashy bribers," Mansfield complained. "I do think you made headway with him when you started talking about Bess' falling on the sword. I hope that swung him over if he was on the fence."

CHAPTER THIRTY-EIGHT

THEN THERE WAS ONE

The next day was a long one for the lawyers in the *Johnson* case. The plaintiffs periodically checked with the Clerk's office in Phoenix County to see if the Judge had filed an order. Born and Thompson kept checking with Rusty Loman who in turn kept crossing the Square to the Courthouse to check the file in the case. Brad Mansfield and Chet Bernhardt alternately checked with Trip Gillespy and Ted Born.

At noon, no order had been entered. At three o'clock there was still no order. At four-thirty, the normal closing hour, Rusty Loman was in the Clerk's office waiting for something to arrive from Judge Andrews. The telephone rang and the Clerk answered it. The Clerk's office was so small and so crowded Loman could easily hear every word on the Clerk's end of the line. It was obvious she was talking to Judge Andrews. "Yes, sir, Judge. Sure will, Judge. I'll be here."

The Clerk hung up the telephone and looked at Rusty Loman. "You could probably tell. That was Judge Andrews. He wants me to hold the Clerk's Office open 'til he gets here. Said it could be six o'clock or even a little later."

Loman left the Courthouse to return to his own office where he immediately called and reported to Born. "Looks like we might not find out anything until six o'clock or later. He'll have to drive a good twenty-five or thirty miles to get here from his home base of Garfield. He knows he has to actually file the order in the Clerk's Office for it to be effective today. It won't do him any good to make his order and sign it unless it gets filed today. He's driving it over himself."

"Gee, I'm not sure I can take this, Rusty," Born said. "This is my night to teach my class at the law school and it starts at six o'clock. In fact, I have to leave the office here at about five o'clock to get to my class on time. I'm not sure I could keep my mind on my lecture, wondering about that order. I'll have to think what to do. Thanks for giving me the update."

Born hung up the telephone and stared blankly at the opposite wall in his office. Just then, Dave Thompson entered. "Dave, we might not know until six o'clock tonight how we came out on the motion. Judge Andrews is going to drive it over from his home and has asked the Clerk to keep her office open for him. We've had to wait to the last minute and we still don't know where we stand. To make it worse, I have to teach a class tonight and need to leave in a few minutes."

"Do you think we dare call the Judge's office and ask his secretary to read us the order?" asked Thompson.

"Hey, maybe we could. I hate like the Dickens to call and bother the Judge if he's racing to get the Order typed and filed, but there's a chance he already has the Order and is on his way to Groveton," Born thought out loud. "Let's wait five minutes and call. Then, regardless what we find out, I have to leave to teach my class."

The minutes dragged by. Born made sure he was packed up and ready to race out to his class. Then, as the five minutes finally ran their course, he picked up the telephone and rang Judge Andrews' secretary. There were five rings with no answer, and Born was about to hang up the telephone, convinced the Judge had left for Groveton and his secretary had gone home. Then a familiar voice answered the call, "Hello?"

Born was flustered. He had connected with the Judge himself, to whom he definitely had not wanted to speak. "Judge, this is Ted Born. Sorry to bother you. I thought I'd reach your secretary. I have this class I have to teach tonight..."

"I was walking out the door to drive the order to Groveton when I heard the 'phone ringing," Judge Andrews said. "I started not to answer but then decided I would. The order will be on file within the hour."

Born felt a lump in his throat. The Judge was not volunteering what the order said. Could this be bad news for the defense? "Judge, I'm leaving, too, to teach my class. Would you mind telling how it came out?"

"Well, I guess I will, since it's all signed. I denied the motion for a new trial and denied the motions for guardians ad litem. I did not strike the plaintiffs' original affidavits. You'll see it all in the order."

Born glowed and raised his free hand high in the air as he tried to appear calm on the telephone. "Thank you, Judge. I won't hold you up any longer. I would have gone crazy if I had had to go to my class not knowing how it came out."

"WE WON, DAVE! WE WON AGAIN! You deserve most of the credit for gathering those super affidavits, and Rusty Loman, too, for his help," Born said.

Dave Thompson was at least as excited as Born, "I didn't want to try that case again! I didn't want to do it." They slapped hands and told Marta Shelby who had heard the commotion and had come in.

It was a three-way release of pent-up emotional energy packed into about two minutes before Born had to leave for his class. "Dave, give Rusty and Brad and Trip a call to clue them in. We'll talk some more tomorrow,"

The law school class was taught, by the hardest. It was antitrust, not products liability, and somehow Ted Born resisted the temptation to change the subject for this evening class. Somehow, he resisted the temptation even

582

to mention what he had learned minutes earlier, large as it loomed in his life.

The next day, Born and Thompson looked at Judge Andrews' order which Rusty Loman had faxed to them. It was a simple, one-page order in which the Judge had simply said there was "ample authority and strong policy considerations" for denying the motion for new trial.

"All that sweat, all that emotional cost, for so few words," Born commented, "but I'll take them. No complaints. Let's call Bert Sayre."

"Bert, Ted Born and Dave Thompson. We have Judge Andrews' order in our hands. It wasn't filed until about six o'clock last night, too late to call you. But you won again, thanks largely to Dave, and next, to Rusty Loman," Born said.

"Ted was a good mentor, Bert. He made us keep getting affidavits when we wanted to stop, when we were afraid the next one would undo everything we had done up to then, and he was right," Thompson said.

"You guys don't have to kill each other with compliments. You all did a great job as a team. You've also kept my perfect record intact. I've never lost a case," Sayre said.

"Bert, I personally appreciate your confidence in us when some of your bosses doubted whether we were up to such a huge case."

"I knew you had it," Sayre said. "You've preserved your win, but now I guess we're looking at an appeal."

"I would think so, but I'm sure the plaintiffs will be looking at the psychology of the appeal. It'll be different from the psychology of trial," Born advised.

"In what way?" asked Sayre.

"An appellate court is going to look at a record where summary judgments possibly should have been granted, a case which really should not have even gone to trial. But plaintiffs got their day in Court, more than they deserved, with the most favorable hometown jury, and yet still lost with that jury," Born explained. "The county's notorious for huge plaintiff verdicts. This one went for the defense despite a plaintiff bribe attempt. With all the pressure for tort reform, an appellate court is going to be very reluctant to give a new trial to a side which has been guilty of bribery. In fact, neither the plaintiffs' side nor an appellate court is going to be happy publicizing the fact of bribery. It was different when the case was still in Judge Andrews' Court. If the plaintiffs could have quietly gotten a new trial in Judge Andrews' Court, then there would have been little or no publicity, but on appeal, the whole state's watching. It's going to be hard to get the case reversed."

"Especially with you guys in there, rolling boulders down the hill at them. Anyway, the ball's in the plaintiffs' court now, I take it," Sayre asked for confirmation.

"The ball's in their court," Thompson said.

In a few days the plaintiffs' counsel met, their numbers now down to two active members, Jack Ripps and Alton Fox. Fred Bates would be waiting in the wings for a re-trial, if that should materialize, but in the meanwhile he would be in retirement or semi-retirement mode and Ripps and Fox would have to handle the appeal work.

"We've got two basic issues," Ripps said to Fox, "the first is to identify what went wrong and the second is to settle on appeal strategy, if we think an appeal is worthwhile. I still think it's a good case and a sympathetic case with a huge potential for damages against big, rich out-of-state corporations. What went wrong, Alton?"

"How much time do you want to give me?" Fox asked rhetorically. "I could fill your ears for quite a while. Our side was in disarray, disorganized, lacked a real game plan. We seemed to assume a win was automatic if we just got the case to the jury, and we were wrong about that. We never expected that unseasoned black lawyer Thompson to be effective, but he was. We never gave Born credit for being the trial lawyer that he was, for making a closing argument that mesmerized the jury. We never realized how helpful Rusty Loman would be in terms of jury selection, and apparently he and his family have generated some goodwill that helped a lot. We did not do enough to stress the injuries, just sort of thought Jimason's presence in the ourtroom would carry the day; it didn't. We screwed up - and I take responsibility for this - in not doing a better job with the deposition of Al Gifford, Universal's quality control man, and we consequently didn't have enough foundation to prove excessive human touching of tire components to pave the way for Wrack Kelly's testimony. Wrack himself was a disaster, he's written too much that hems him in, and he's got income tax problems and frankly he's getting old and has lost a lot of his sharpness. He took Universal by surprise in that Houston case and got away with it, so I hired him in this one. But Born was ready for him, and Kelly bombed.

"We put too much into the tire part of the case, which ended up being a dud, and probably didn't put enough into the van part of the case. If I had realized in the beginning that the tire was so worn it was illegal, and if I had realized it had not just one, but *two* leaking holes in it, I would have tried the case differently. Hell, it just tried perfect from their point of view, and was a botched affair from the beginning from our standpoint."

"So, if we get a new trial, what do we do different?" Ripps asked.

"We've got to get more focus. We've got to present the jury with a simple, straightforward case on the damages issues, trim the rest of the case down considerably. Then day after day we have to serve up a heaping plate of blood and gore and medical horrors to that jury, through live witnesses as much as possible. We've got to do better on jury selection." Then Fox added, "And one more thing, if I participate further I've got to be lead counsel. I'm too busy and can't afford to spend the kind of time needed for a new trial unless I'm in control."

"You've got it, Alton," Ripps said. "I was going to ask you to do that anyway."

CHAPTER THIRTY-EIGHT

"Of course, I'll expect an adjustment on my percentage take," Fox made clear.

"Understood, Alton, just don't get greedy," Ripps answered. "I've made some pretty good money with my partnership with Fred. Of course, he always took the lion's share, but I can't complain. I'm doing well enough I can give you the lead position on this case and give you a bigger cut, especially if you can take some of the responsibility off my hands. Just don't get greedy."

"Shift twelve per cent more of the total to me," Fox said.

"Let me talk with Fred about that. You know he still has his interest, but I'll stand with you on that, Alton. Now, how do we get the new trial? How do we handle the appeal?"

"Frankly, Jack, I don't see a whole lot of reversible error - except the jury misconduct. I know it's a little awkward, with our own clients committing bribery, but we're not asking the Court to give us any money, we're just asking for a new and fair trial for innocent kids. Not for the bribers, but for the kids. Then we correct our mistakes on the retrial," Fox explained.

"How do we do that, Alton? How do we avoid the conflict of interest when we've been representing both the children and the adult bribers? If we appeal for the kids and drop the adults, haven't we gotten ourselves in a conflicting position between two sets of clients, the adults and the children?"

"First, we get everybody's consent. Should be easy enough because it's a choice of not appealing at all or appealing only for the children. There's no way we or anyone else can appeal for both groups. That would *really* be a conflict of interest. In addition, I think the commission of a crime gives us a good deal of latitude to drop the adults. Anyway, I think it's all a moot question. Who's going to complain? The adult bribers wouldn't dare complain. I've got that all figured out," Fox strategized.

* * *

About ten days after Judge Andrews denied the motion for new trial, Ted Born found a curious message on his office voice mail. It was from Alton Fox and his message was: "Sorry I missed you, Ted. I'm about to head out of town for a few days, but I'd like to come talk with you about the case, if you're in, say, next Wednesday. I'll be in touch."

Born shared the message with the other Universal team members. Could it be a settlement proposal of some kind? Most likely so, because a straight appeal would not call for any particular discussions among the parties, just file and serve the appeal briefs. If a settlement proposal, what kind of proposal? Alton Fox knew full well the Universal policy that it would never voluntarily pay money on a tire it felt had been well manufactured. Born was at a loss to imagine what there was to talk about.

It was agreed Born should check with the Tergano lawyers to see if they had received a similar call. Perhaps Fox had actually made contact with the Tergano lawyers and they could shed some light on the matter. Born reached Trip Gillespy and Chet Bernhardt and inquired about calls from Fox or from any of the Tergano lawyers, but they had received no calls and knew nothing. Of course, Born told himself, it would not be unusual for Fox to call the Universal lawyers and not call the Tergano lawyers, because Fox's part of the case had revolved around the Universal tire and had concerned the Tergano van hardly at all.

Promptly on the next Wednesday, Fox called Born and asked if he could come for a conference. An appointment was made for later that day in Born's office. Ted Born and Dave Thompson both greeted Alton Fox in the office reception area, and the three retired to Born's office to talk.

"First, I should let you know that I am now lead counsel in charge of the whole case for the plaintiffs," Fox began. "I've come today to make a proposal to you. There is going to be an appeal, in case you've been wondering. What I propose is that - on two conditions - we will prosecute the appeal only against Tergano, leaving Universal out of it. The two conditions are that you not pursue the collection of costs against my clients, and that Rusty Loman agree not to work for Tergano in the remainder of the case."

Born and Thompson could scarcely believe their ears but resisted any immediate celebration. "The costs are not a big problem. I think we asked for about twenty thousand dollars, but I would assume it would be impossible in the foreseeable future to collect that much," Born said.

"That's right," said Fox. "I don't think it's collectible, but I feel I owe it to my clients to remove any risk you might try to collect."

"Of course, Alton, I'd have to clear all of this with the client Universal, you understand. But I see the point about Rusty Loman as being a problem... ." Born said.

Fox politely interrupted, "If that's a problem with Rusty, I mean his loss of income by not being employable by Tergano, we'd be glad to employ him for the rest of the case."

"I think there would be pretty severe ethical problems with your employing him to work against Tergano," Born quickly observed. "After all, Rusty has participated actively in joint defense strategy sessions involving Universal and Tergano. I don't see any possible way he could begin working against Tergano since he has been privy to their innermost thoughts and strategy considerations."

"I hadn't really thought about that," said Fox. "The most important thing is that he not work for Tergano. I don't know that Tergano wants him, but we thought we should cover that base, just to be sure."

"I'd have to think that through, Alton, and of course Rusty would ultimately have to make that call," Born answered. "Seems to me there are ethical problems to our agreeing to such a thing. By the same token, there might be ethical problems to Rusty's working for Tergano, too. For example, suppose Tergano decided it would be in Tergano's interest to blame the accident on the tire. If Rusty had switched over to Tergano, you would be able to point to Rusty and say, `Mr. Loman has been defending that tire and says it is a perfectly good tire and did not cause the accident.' In other words, my instincts tell me Rusty really could not work with either Tergano or the plaintiffs. I might have jumped over something."

"Well, check it out and get back to me. While I think we made out a respectable case on the tire, we found in talking to the jury they weren't impressed and thought the tire was just worn out. They seemed to have a lot more doubt about the design of the van, and we thought we would just concentrate our guns in a new trial on the van part of the case. By the way, I think we're going to win the appeal. We think we're covered by the precedents," Fox expounded.

"I don't know about winning the appeal, but as to the jurors' impressions, we got the same thing when we talked to them," Thompson said. "They all thought the tire had been fine when it was manufactured and just wore out. Alton, did you or your side have any inkling of what that jury was going to do? I mean, could you read them?"

"No, we didn't have the foggiest idea. Couldn't read them at all," Fox replied.

"Did Bates and Ripps break up over the case?" Born wanted to know.

"I don't think they broke up especially about this case," Fox opined. "I think there were problems between them which had been heating up for a long time. I just think for a lot of reasons they couldn't hold it together after this case was finished. I was just amazed at the amount of disarray and in-fighting on our side. I never met the plaintiffs until the first time the case was set for trial, last February. The weekend before the trial started in June I couldn't reach Fred or Jack. And there were constant problems while the trial was going on. Someday, we'll have to sit down over a couple of bottles of beer and I'd like to share some things with you."

"Well, I'll talk with Universal about it and with Rusty, and we'll be back in touch soon," Born said, sensing the meeting had gone about as far as would be productive.

"I know we've had a few rough edges between us, and I'm sorry about that and would like to have a better relationship in the future. You tried a fine case. I'd just like the chance to tee it up with you again sometimes in the future," Fox said, smiling warmly, to both Born and Thompson.

"I appreciate what you say, and I feel the same way. I'm sorry about the past friction. As for 'teeing it up again,' that's fine, but I hope it's not in Phoenix County," Born laughed.

They shook hands and Alton Fox left to return to his office.

"This time we've really won!" Thompson exclaimed gleefully.

"Yeah, I'm sure we have!" Born agreed, "A few details to clear up, but shouldn't be a big problem. Let's call Bert Sayre."

Just then Marta Shelby came in with a telephone note to call Rusty Loman. "Mrs. Shelby, you won't believe it, but I think the plaintiffs are about to drop us from the case and appeal just as to Tergano!" Born said.

"You're kidding! You mean it's all over?" Shelby asked.

"Not quite. There are some things we have to clear and some ethical questions we have to look into, but I'm expecting they can all be handled," Born answered.

"Aren't you happy? I'm so happy!" said Shelby, elated.

Born's face turned serious, "I'd never really asked myself that question. I'm on the verge of losing a constant companion, a terrifying, sleep-killing companion, but still an intimate companion. I won't have any shortage of work, but this case was special, one of the few cases in a lifetime that grips you and holds you."

"But you and Dave won." Shelby pointed out. "That's why you got into the case, to win, and you've done it."

"We all did it, the whole team. You and Nita and Rusty... That reminds me, I'd better call Rusty," Born said.

"Well, congratulations again," said Shelby as she returned to her desk.

"Dave, let's call Rusty on the speakerphone," Born suggested as he punched in the telephone number.

When Born and Thompson were connected with Loman, the latter skipped all pleasantries and said, "You'll never believe what happened to me this morning."

"What?" asked Born, suppressing the desire to tell Loman what had just happened to him and Thompson. "No. Wait a minute, the plaintiffs have offered to hire you?"

There was a moment of obviously dumbfounded silence at the other end of the line. Then Loman said,

"How the hell did you know that?"

Born and Thompson looked at each other and laughed. "Just a hunch," Thompson said. "Tell us what happened."

"You know today's the first Wednesday in the month," Loman explained. "It was Judge Andrews' motion docket, and I was over at the Courthouse on a couple of cases. As I was waiting in there for my cases to come up on the docket, Jack Ripps sidled up to me and said, 'If we drop Universal from the lawsuit, would you work on our side?' I'll tell you, I was floored. It hit me like a ton of bricks. I didn't know what to say to him. But I was saying to myself, there's no way I'm going to work with *you*.' He said to me, 'Just think about it, and remember we asked you first.'"

"It all ties in, Rusty," Born said. "You certainly made quite a hit with the plaintiffs. We've just had a visit from Alton Fox who says he's running the plaintiffs' show now. And he offered to drop Universal if we wouldn't collect court costs and if you wouldn't work with Tergano. I can see now they had it all worked out to cut you in just as they were dropping us out. How do you feel about it, Rusty? You're apparently a hot item."

"I'm certainly not going to work with those guys, that's for sure," Rusty said emphatically. "I don't know about Tergano, I'd need to think about that. Of course, I don't know if Tergano would even want me, since they've got Trip Gillespy as their local counsel."

"Check out the ethical questions, Rusty. We have to leave it to you to make the call. Off the top of my head, it looks pretty clear there'd be ethical problems with your representing the plaintiffs, possibly also if you represented Tergano - at least if Tergano tried to blame the tire."

"I'll look at it, but I'm sure you and I won't have any problem with it. Gee! I thought you were psychic when you guessed they'd asked me to come aboard. Damn! It's a strange world. Have you talked with Bert Sayre yet?" Loman asked.

"No, but I will." Born started to suggest that he patch in Sayre, but he thought better of it. He and Thompson would need to talk frankly with Sayre about the Rusty Loman factor in the deal, a conversation necessarily to be had without Loman's participation.

"Think it over, Rusty. I'll be in touch with you in a few days and see where we stand," Born concluded the call.

Born and Thompson then called Bert Sayre, and Sayre was ecstatic. "Bert, my first impulse was to say to Rusty, 'Look, you've *got* to go along. You're committed to do what is in Universal's interest since that's who you represent. If it takes it to get Universal out of this case to opt out of a possible Tergano representation, that's what you've got to do.' But Bert, I didn't do it, partly because I thought it unnecessary, and partly because he'd been too good to us and he deserved the courtesy of a few days to let him come to this conclusion," Born suggested.

"So, it looks like, subject to solving the Rusty Loman part, that we're out and Tergano remains in," Sayre summarized.

"Right, Bert," answered Thompson. "It might seem

like we're bragging, but this is a complete turnaround from the mock trial. You remember the mock jurors thought Tergano had a stronger case than Universal. We worked on that, and it paid off, so at the trial the jurors thought we had a much better defense than Tergano. That's why we'll be out and Tergano will be left holding the bag."

"That's right," agreed Born. "The irony is that Tergano's strategy was to differentiate itself from us as much as possible, hoping it might escape even if Universal got hit for a big verdict. It's sort of poetic justice that the reverse occurred."

"You obviously did a fine job, as I've told you many times, even put in my reports, as you kept prodding me to do. This result is just another validation of your good work. Are you going to call the Tergano lawyers?" asked Sayre.

"Not yet. We've still got the loose ends with Rusty Loman. I'd like to get that settled first. However, they knew Fox was trying to see me, they just didn't know when. I could be getting a call from them soon. I'm not quite sure how I'll handle it if it comes before I'm really ready for it.

"Let's push forward and try to get this deal wrapped up," Sayre directed. "If we've won a jury trial and post-trial motions, and then the other side is willing to drop us without payment of any money, I call that a victory in any litigation. But when you can do it in Phoenix County, and in the very teeth of a bribe attempt, I'd say it's... it's galactic!"

Ted Born called Rusty Loman in a few days and Loman said he had no problem staying out of the litigation henceforth, representing neither plaintiffs nor Tergano.

"Let me make this suggestion, Rusty," Born offered. "Suppose I tell them we cannot ethically give them assurance you will not represent Tergano but, because of your own concerns about the ethics of representing Tergano under the circumstances, you have no present intention of helping Tergano, nor have you been asked."

"Sounds good to me. I'll leave it up to you," Loman said agreeably.

Born called Alton Fox and told him all had been approved, expressing Loman's position as he and Loman had agreed.

"I can understand that," Fox said. "I can see it would be unethical to settle one case on the condition you not do work for someone else in the future. I really hadn't focused on that problem. I think that'll be satisfactory. Let me talk to the others."

"You understand, Alton, even though we cannot ethically promise anything, I am telling you, one lawyer to another, that Rusty does not have any present intention to work for Tergano. He realizes he could be biting off his own brand of ethical problems if he did so," Born explained.

"Okay, we'll be doing the paperwork soon, and I'll be in touch," Fox said.

Born hung up the telephone. "Paperwork?" he thought. "Does he want us to sign something? Or is Alton just talking about the paperwork on the appeal? Wish I'd thought to ask him."

The telephone rang. It was Marta Shelby. "Mr. Born, I have Chet Bernhardt and Trip Gillespy on the other line. Can you talk with them now?"

Born swallowed hard. He really did not want to talk with the Tergano lawyers yet, not until all the "i's" were dotted and all the "t's" crossed. But Tergano had been his ally, Chet and Trip his friends. "Yes, I'll take the call."

"Ted, we were wondering whether you ever heard from Alton Fox. The countdown toward appeal deadline is pretty far advanced, and we're totally in the dark. We don't know whether they're going to appeal or what. Do you know anything?" asked Gillespy.

"Yes, Alton came to see me, and we've talked a couple of times. The reason I haven't called you is, it hasn't been tied down yet, and I'm nervous it could come apart," Born stumbled along.

"What hasn't been tied down?" asked Bernhardt.

"Okay, here goes," said Born. "I've been straight with you from the beginning, and I'm not going to be any different now. Looks like Universal may be getting out of the lawsuit, dropped. And no, we're not paying them a red cent, not a one. The only thing we've promised is we won't pursue court costs. That's not much of a concession, because the Judge is not likely to award any big court costs, and if he did, we probably couldn't collect them from mostly poor plaintiffs."

"What about us? What about Tergano?" asked Gillespy.

"I understand the plaintiffs plan to keep you in the case," Born answered. "Look, this was Alton's idea. He came to me and offered us out, and of course I'd be a fool not to take it. Alton says in interviewing the jurors, he and Ripps - by the way, Alton says he is now the leader of the pack - anyway, he says they became convinced the jurors thought the case against Universal was lousy but the case against Tergano was, well, close. Reading between the lines, I think Alton believes our presence is a drag on the whole case, detracting from what might otherwise come across as a good claim against Tergano. After all, they don't need two defendants. Tergano has deep enough pockets to pay any favorable money judgment the plaintiffs might get on a new trial. So why keep Universal in the case if its main effect is to hurt the plaintiffs in their assault on Tergano? Alton isn't in the habit of being benevolent. He's doing this out of his perception of his own best interest."

There was stunned silence on the other end for what seemed an interminable period, as the reality of Born's statement sank in. No doubt Bernhardt and Gillespy reflected, at least momentarily on Tergano's strategy in the beginning to distance itself from Universal, then later seeming to cling to Universal.

"Well, I guess we'll see what happens," Bernhardt finally said. "We'll miss you."

"It's been a pleasure working with the two of you and, of course, Brad," Born said. "And you can bet I'm not going to ignore developments in this case after what it's done to me. I'll be watching, and I hope you'll call me if you want a sounding board, since I do have a little background about the case. You should win on appeal. Good luck!"

"Thanks," said Bernhardt, hollowly.

CHAPTER THIRTY-NINE

EPILOGUE

"Ready?" asked Dave Thompson.

"Ready," Ted Born answered.

"Your car or mine?"

"My car. That's the way we used to do it."

It was a gray March day as they headed out. Thompson noticed Born was making a detour, and shortly they pulled into a strip shopping center. "Wait here. I'll be right back," said Born. Thompson watched as the older lawyer disappeared. A few minutes later, Born returned with an opaque plastic bag, about eighteen inches square, which Born carefully placed in the back. He got in the driver's seat, cranked the engine, and they drove on.

"Have you ever asked yourself, Ted, if this is a guilt trip?"

"Many times," Born answered.

"Is it? I've asked myself that, too, Thompson asked."

"Maybe, partly. Would that make it wrong?"

"Maybe, partly," Thompson repeated Born's last answer. "Then, again, at least we're better than the priest and the Levite."

"But not as good as the Samaritan? Agreed. No one has time for compassion anymore. No one has the resources for compassion. It's possible we are so numbed and so battered by the world we no longer can feel, or empathize, or do anything except mutter 'too bad' and go on our way," Born opined.

"It's too hard just to survive. You spend all your time trying somehow to deal with what you have to deal with, and it's all-consuming. All we care about is money because the truth is, everything has a price, a monetary price. To cope, you've got to have money, and the ethics of coping, the god of materialism, has replaced the satisfaction of the Good Samaritan," Thompson offered.

"True, that's the way we seem to see it. But picture a group of people, say lawyers in our firm. They've just come out of a service. They'll greet each other, shake hands, and go to lunch together. Someone will say, `Too bad, about old Ted Born, wasn't it?' Someone else will say, `It was a nice service.' Another will say, `You know, he was a pretty good fellow.' Then they'll go back to the office and pick up where they left off and they'll take phone calls, and Ted Born will be far from their minds. Ted's spirit will look down and say, `Ted, was it worth it?

Was it worth the frenzied existence you led, day after day? Were the battles you fought so important?' It's a question that goes unanswered. You spend your life, trying to find your way, and the unanswered question is, 'Was it worth it, Ted?'"

Dave Thompson looked at Born, nodded his head. "At least you met your responsibilities, Ted. Some people don't, you know. People respect you. You've done a lot of good. We're all like the boy at the dike, thrusting a hand in to keep the floods out. You and people like you have helped hold the system together."

"Something is missing, Dave. The personal touch? The Samaritan gathered up the beaten, half-dead man in his arms and bound his wounds, pouring on oil and wine. Then he set the poor wretch on his own donkey and took him to the inn to be cared for. He paid for that man's care and he showed mercy to him and came back to check on him, see how he was. I've been told by the highest Authority to go and do likewise, and I look at myself and know I haven't quite 'gone and done likewise.'

"Making this trip is possibly a cheap way of doffing our hats at compassion and mercy, a feel-good sort of thing," Born mused.

"At least we wanted to do it. We could have gone on and put a notch in our guns and forgotten the whole thing. You don't feel guilty about winning the lawsuit, do you?" Thompson asked.

"Do you?" Born countered.

"Not a bit. Universal wasn't guilty of doing anything

wrong. It shouldn't have had to bear a senseless multi-million-dollar penalty for something it didn't do, much of which would go to a bunch of lawyers anyway. Still, you have to feel sorry for Jimason and for the Millers," Thompson answered.

"It's strange," Born said thoughtfully, "I've never talked to Jimason or to the Millers. That's a regrettable side effect of the ethics ban on direct communication with clients of your opposing counsel. But I did, sort of, talk with Bess Johnson and Doretta Anchrum and Sam Johnson in their depositions. They're not 'bad' people, in a way. They're just basically like you and me. They had a situation and they got caught up in it, didn't have the strength to resist."

"Just trying. They're unhappy with their situation, want to escape. They know money will help, and they know, the way things are, nobody asks you where or how you got your money. They just kowtow to you if you've got it. Otherwise, the world has no time for you. You're scum," Thompson ventured.

Born passed over a small bridge, pulled off the straight, two-laned road, and he and Thompson got out at the familiar and terrible place. It was a place where men had made measurements and taken photographs, just within sight of the big house at the top of the hill. Born started to cross the road with Thompson, then he remembered the plastic bag in the back seat and took it out. They walked over to a large mock orange tree, already budding for spring. There at the base they noticed something new from their last trip. It was a small highway cross, like the crosses and stars one sometimes sees marking highway fatalities. On the cross someone had scrawled a name in black, apparently with a small paintbrush. It read, "Sarena Miller."

Their eyes rose from the ground, where the small cross was, to a scar on the tree, not as deep as one would have expected, and saw the scar was healing. Oh, that Sarena could heal! Born reached in the plastic bag and pulled out his purchase. He offered it to Dave Thompson, who shook his head. "You take one side and I'll take one side, and we'll both lay it down," Thompson suggested. The two men leaned over, then knelt as the greenery was carefully placed at the base of the mock orange, just behind the cross. They knelt there silently. Tears came to Thompson's eyes, "I know you don't cry, Ted, but I cried before, when I first saw Sarena's picture, and I can't help it. She was such a small girl." They rose to their feet.

Born and Thompson became aware that another car had stopped on the opposite side of the road, just behind Born's car. A man and a woman with a bouquet of spring flowers crossed the road to the place where the two lawyers were standing. Born and Thompson were embarrassed. They had wanted to do this act of remembrance privately and then move on. They had not wanted to see the Millers, and certainly they had not wanted to invade the privacy of the Millers. The four of them stood looking at each other. Ben Miller extended his hand to Born. "You remembered," he said, "this was the day." Born took his hand and grasped it firmly, looking at Miller with watery eyes. Agnes Miller and Dave Thompson embraced, as tears again ran down Thompson's face and Mrs. Miller sobbed.

"I'm sorry, Mr. Miller. I don't want to intrude. We were just leaving," Born said.

"No, stay a little, it's lonely. You two cared. I knew you did, even in the courtroom. The jury knew it too," Ben Miller said.

"You're not angry with us?" Thompson asked.

"No use being angry. Nothing will bring her back." Mr. Miller answered.

"Attorneys, we're the ones who feel guilty. We were all torn up when she died, and we prayed and prayed. Then it got to be more of a legal thing, and everybody was talking about money, and we got caught up in all that. But money ain't everything. We didn't really feel human again - or right - until we lost that case, and we finally discovered our memories. You know what I mean. We'd blotted all that out, and it was a sin to do that. We needed to remember, it's the only way to heal." Agnes Miller said.

"Of course, we're still in that lawsuit against Tergano," Ben Miller said. "But it's not the end-all for us anymore. We can take it or leave it. The important thing is, we've got our feelings back. We didn't want to lose, of course, but when I heard the evidence I could see your point of view. I had my own doubts. No way can I fault you."

"We're just gon' put these flowers here. Sarena loved

flowers, and she used to ask me to make up little nosegays for her. She would smell them and smile and look at how pretty they were. I'm just gon' lean over and put these here, lay 'em on your wreath. And we're gon' kneel here a minute. Would you kneel with us?" asked Mrs. Miller.

The four knelt, and Ben Miller said, "Dear God, bless little Sarena. She's with you, I know, somewhere up there pickin' flowers on the crest of the rainbow. She's yours now, God, but we remember her, and we're reconciled to it. We just gon' have to keep on keepin' on down here. And bless these lawyers, God. Amen."

"Amen," came a voice behind them. They looked up to see a man in uniform standing over them. It was Sheriff Sam Johnson.

Ben Miller was the first to speak, "Sam, these lawyers made this trip here today to remember Sarena."

"Mostly Sarena," said Dave Thompson, "but Jimason, too, and the others. We can't do much but remember."

"It's nice of you, I guess. But why? You didn't know Sarena, you hardly know Jimason, we're just characters in another lawsuit," Johnson said.

"They came into our lives. We never exactly pick and choose the people who affect us. We just all come into each other's lives and we take a part of each other's pain and suffering, and also the joy, with us. It becomes a part of us, a part of our lives. You see, Dave and I have - in a way - also encountered that terrible tree on our personal journey, and we'll never be the same. Did it change us in any fundamental way? I guess the answer is, 'not fundamentally.' But it did impact us. We didn't see or hear that crash, but we experienced it over and over. And we care," Born said.

"We'd like to come down here and do something that would help, you know. If we had it and we thought it'd really help, we'd like to throw dollar bills on the street. We'd like to be sure all the people of Phoenix had everything they need to be comfortable, inside and out. But we can't do that, and it wouldn't solve Groveton's problems anyway. We just want you to know, and believe, we feel for you because we hurt, too. That's what brought Ted and me down here," Thompson said.

"So, you come down and bring a wreath, and you pat yourselves on the back and go home and tell your-selves that makes it all okay, is that it?" the Sheriff asked sarcastically.

"We remembered, and we came. We did what we were supposed to do, and the jury did what it was supposed to do. That's all we can say," Born answered. "I guess we'd better go, Dave,"

"Wait, I'm sorry. I should have asked, 'Where are the others? Where are the hundreds of people who covered the hills and pastures and roadsides the afternoon it happened? Where are Attorneys Bates and Ripps and Fox?' It don't make you no angels, you understand. But ain't many of us angels. Bess proved that, and Doretta too. I hand it to you, you never said anything untrue. Oh, how I hated you, Mr. Born, in that closing argument, and you, too, Mr. Thompson, in your opening. I couldn't make myself listen to what you were saying, but I knew that jury was listening, and I knew we - and our case - were hurtin'. I admired you, you did a good job, but I hated you. I said to myself, 'To them, it's just another case, to us, it's our whole lives.' I'm mad because you proved me wrong when you came down here and showed you really did care, and it hurts for the 'law of Phoenix County' to be wrong." Johnson held out his hand.

Born and Thompson both grasped it. "God bless you. Be a good Sheriff," Thompson said. The lawyers turned to leave.

"You be careful crossing the road," Johnson cautioned.

The lawyers continued on to Groveton, past the church with the tall spire, to Courthouse square. They went into Rusty Loman's office. Loman and his staff had been expecting them, without knowing the purpose of the visit. It was a fine reunion, with warm greetings and handshakes.

"Rusty, Dave and I are concerned about Jimason. We think he may need some help with his eyesight. We never were sure about the eye they claimed was blind or going blind. We've contributed something. It's in this envelope. We have to be careful how we do it because, even though we're out of the lawsuit, we could be accused of trying to influence the case on Tergano's behalf, or out of spite, something like that. I thought maybe you could give this to his minister to apply it for whatever he needs. Could be the eyes are okay, and he could use the money for tutoring or something. Of course, we need to bypass

Doretta, make sure Jimason gets the benefit. Nobody needs to know where the funds came from. Could you see this gets to the minister?" Born asked.

"Sure. I think I know his church, or I'll find out which one his family belongs to. That's nice of you." Loman said.

The three lawyers were standing in front of the big window of the storefront space where Loman had his office, looking toward the Courthouse. "Any developments you know of, Rusty?"

"There're rumors the Judge has instructed the District Attorney to investigate the bribery. If the D.A.'s done much, I'm not aware of it. I think it would be hard to get a conviction, regardless of the evidence," Loman said.

"If not a conviction for the sake of deterrence, what else could be done to keep this thing from happening again?" Thompson asked.

"There's something I'd like to see done that can't be done now and, truthfully, probably never will be done. I'd like to see a monument there on the Courthouse grounds to Estrata McNemar. She had the chance to dip her hands into those riches and take them home. She turned her back on them, said there wasn't enough money in the whole world to buy her vote. With people out there like Mrs. McNemar, the system will work, justice will be done. She deserves a monument," Born said.

Born added, "Her conduct was a profile in integrity."

Just then, they saw Judge Andrews descending the staircase from the Courthouse. Born remembered that this was the first Wednesday in the month, and Judge Andrews had just finished his motion docket.

Born looked thoughtful as he said, "I'm betting on people like Judge Andrews and Estrata McNemar. We'll come through all right,"